Free to Be Insane

by

Kathie Rodkey

DORRANCE PUBLISHING CO., INC.
PITTSBURGH, PENNSYLVANIA 15222

ISBN: 978-0-8059-7897-1
Library of Congress Control Number: 2008923430

Printed in the United States of America

First Printing

For more information or to order additional books, please contact:
Dorrance Publishing Co., Inc.
701 Smithfield Street
Third Floor
Pittsburgh, Pennsylvania 15222
U.S.A.
1-800-788-7654
www.dorrancebookstore.com

This book is dedicated to the surviving siblings of children who are killed by a parent and then subjected to a lifetime of suffering because they must return to the care of a parent who is free to be insane.

Contents

Introduction

In 1989, a three-week old infant was thrown out a window of the family's third floor apartment. In 1999, a mother drowned five of her children in a bathtub. In 2000, a mother drove two of her children into a lake, where they drowned. In 2005, a-six-year-old boy was bound and gagged and drowned in a bathtub; his mother was later charged with his murder. In 2005, a twenty three year old mother drowned three of her children by throwing them into the San Francisco Bay. These are just a few of the thousands of cases of child abuse meted out to children at the hands of their parents each year.

In 1953, my mother threw two of my baby brothers out a window to their deaths. Her intent was to kill all of her five children. To this day there are times when I still wonder if I could have done anything to prevent what she did, even though I was only six years old at the time.

Chapter One: The Day It Began: April 20, 1953

"Katie, shouldn't we go see what she is doing?" Five-year-old Jonathan's inquiry was repeated for the second time in a voice that reflected fear. His beautiful face had lost its serene look as he gravely waited for her answer.

"Damn it, Jonathan, stay behind the couch!" Katie deliberately tried to make her voice sound authoritative and threatening, hoping that for once he would listen to her. The fact that she had used a curse word would normally have sent her brother scurrying to their mother to tattle. Today, however, his innate sense of self-preservation warned him that to do so would not be in his best interest.

Never in her six years had Katie experienced such strange feelings. Her mouth was unbearably dry, it was hard for her to swallow, her legs were shaking, and her stomach hurt. Both children were startled when they heard the bloodcurdling scream that came from somewhere close. At that point, Jonathan reached the peak of his tolerance and began to cry. Katie's arms and legs were drenched with perspiration as she fought to control the lightheadedness that overcame her. The floor seemed to be getting closer and closer as she grasped the back of the sofa. She thought it was strange that she could see through her arms, they were so white.

As the sound of the sirens approached, Katie instinctively put her hands up to her ears to block out the piercing noise. She kept repeating to herself over and over again, "Please don't let her come in here, please don't let her come in here."

The sound of the fire trucks peaked Jonathan's curiosity and, without warning, he left his hiding place behind the couch, running quickly to the nearest window. It took every ounce of effort that Katie had to join him there. When she saw all the ambulances, fire trucks, and police cars on the street, she thought her eyes would pop right out of her head and she had to lean her body against the window and grab onto the windowsill so she wouldn't collapse.

She knew they should still be hiding and she kept looking behind her, sure her mother was going to grab them at any moment. Every time she took a breath, a knife-like pain stabbed at her chest.

Suddenly, she heard a far away pounding sound and, shortly after that, a strange voice asking if anybody was home. Then more strange voices reached her ear, and they were all shouting at once: "Hold her down." "Don't take any chances." "She's dangerous." Then another frantic voice shouting: "Get someone down to the alley. It looks like she threw something out the window."

Now the gruff voices were coming toward Katie and Jonathan, one announcing to the other that he had found a couple of kids in the living room. Katie saw the big black boots first, then the shiny yellow coat and, finally, the biggest man she had ever seen in her whole life loomed before her.

She couldn't hear the questions he was asking her, she couldn't resist when he wrapped her up in a blanket and cradled her in his arms, and she couldn't lift her head to see what was happening to Jonathan. She was dazed.

Katie opened her eyes when the fireman carried her out of the apartment, only to see wall-to-wall people crowding the entire street, pushing at her to catch a glimpse of the victims of the tragedy. A flashbulb went off in her face and it was at that point that she slipped into blessed unconsciousness.

Katie didn't recognize where she was until she caught a glimpse of her grandmother sitting in her rocking chair, her rosary beads held in her hands as her huge fingers passed quickly over each individual bead. Her long black hair was in its usual severe braid, and her facial expression was grim. Katie was deathly afraid of this grandmother, and she couldn't remember a time when she smiled or when her house wasn't dark. She couldn't bring herself to talk to her even though her mind was filled with a thousand questions, so she feigned sleep until she heard the old lady leave the room.

Katie was surprised at her inability to get up from the couch. Her head was pounding and her throat was sore, and the room began to spin around when she attempted to rise. After about five minutes of failed attempts, she was finally able to stand and began walking unsteadily toward the kitchen. She felt parched and needed a drink of water badly. When she reached her destination, however, she saw something that made her forget how rotten she was feeling, something that she would remember with great clarity for the rest of her life.

The evening newspaper was lying on the table and on the front cover was a picture of her brother Kevin, with his blonde hair, blue eyes, and impish grin. He was three years old, and spent most of his day lining books from one end of the apartment to the other and driving his small cars along the pretend roadway. She loved this quiet little brother who didn't cause her any trouble.

Katie felt the hand across her face before she saw it coming. The grandmother's slap was delivered quickly and viciously enough to knock her to the floor; however, it didn't help to get rid of the words that kept flashing across her mind: WIFE DROPS TWO BABIES FOUR FLOORS TO THEIR DEATHS....WIFE DROPS TWO BABIES FOUR FLOORS TO THEIR DEATHS. The words kept flashing before her eyes until Katie began to sob hysterically.

Anna O'Maley, Katie's maternal grandmother who was born in 1883, immigrated to the United States from Ireland. She and her husband, Joseph, who was also born in the Emerald Isle in 1887, struggled to raise a family of nine children. Anna lived her life preparing to die in God's good graces; unfortunately, that meant spending more time saying rosaries and novenas than enjoying her children and her life.

Nan O'Maley, Katie's mom, was the youngest of the nine children born to Joseph and Anna in January of 1926. Joseph was thirty-nine and Anna was forty-three when Nan was born. Even though times were financially easier for the O'Maley family by the time Nan came along, she had to contend with eight older siblings, including several alcoholic brothers and domineering sisters, all of whom were equally enthusiastic about telling her what she could and couldn't do.

The shining light of Nan's life was her father, Joseph, a big, burly, hardworking Irishman, who spent his life with just one shot of liquor too many in his rotund stomach. He adored Nan with a passion; she was all of the things his wife was not—beautiful and full of life.

By the time his youngest daughter came along, Joseph had mellowed so Nan didn't know about all the times her mother and sisters hid from him in the closet until he fell asleep in a drunken stupor. On some days, they found themselves back in the closet again when one of the older brothers arrived home inebriated and ready for a fight.

The attention her father showered on Nan more than made up for the indifference of her mother. Because she was the baby in the family, she was rather self-centered and enjoyed having fun more than anything.

Nan was a devastated fifteen-year-old when her sixty-nine-year-old father passed away in his sleep in 1942 from a sudden heart attack. After the initial shock, Nan resumed her fun loving ways, but something deep in her psyche had been disturbed at the quickness with which she lost her beloved father. She never got to say goodbye and this thought weighed heavily on what would prove to be her very fragile psyche.

There is a certain air of pride that emits from Catholics who truly believe they are following the teachings of the church with total dedication, and this conceit reeked from Anna O'Maley. She was sure she would be welcomed with open arms at the pearly gates when her time came. After all, no one could have lived more in the service of the Almighty than she had.

When the commotion began on that fateful day, starting with the stranger who knocked on her door with Katie in his arms, it marked the beginning of a humiliating experience for Anna, an experience that shattered her biblically protected world and caused her to spend the rest of her life, which would be two short years, searching for answers that would clear her of any blame for what happened. Anna had always felt her youngest child was different and her husband's indulgence of his favorite child's every whim had helped to make her the spoiled person she was.

Bo, Anna's youngest son, reached his mother's apartment just as she delivered the blow to Katie that carried with it all of the frustrations of a life shattered by so devastating an experience. He couldn't believe his mother could act so violently, and she even appeared ready to strike the child again before he quickly intervened.

Through her tears, Katie saw a pair of big hands with red hair and freckles coming toward her. Whoever the hands belonged to lifted her gently from the cold brown tiles and carried her up the stairs. His chest was big and warm and she leaned her aching head against it, succumbing to unconsciousness for the second time in less than twelve hours. When he placed her on his bed he could see that the right side of her face had begun to swell.

Katie's uncle Bo lived with his family in an apartment above his mother's. He was the most successful of the O'Maley boys and had worked hard to make a decent life for himself. He was unlike his brother Shane, who had perished from a head injury when, in a drunken stupor, he pulled too hard on the flush chain of a toilet in a bar, bringing the whole contraption slamming down on his head.

He was unlike his brother Jessie, who was constantly going through the DTs, severe flu-like symptoms, and shaking from lengthy alcohol abuse and the inability to find more liquor to appease his body.

Jessie's wife was an alcoholic also and during one of their joint DT experiences, they abandoned their beautiful children in an apartment for weeks. When the children were finally discovered, they were relegated to the nightmare of foster homes and group homes, where they were abused both physically and mentally.

He was unlike his brother Erin, who had mysteriously disappeared one day from a local bar, never to be seen or heard from again.

Although Bo had escaped the tendency toward dependence on alcohol that his father had unfortunately passed on to his male offspring, he was not untouched by the religious zeal that plagued his mother or the sternness she displayed in her dealings with those around her. All of Bo's strict beliefs made him appear hard, but the real severity of his nature was mainly a surface characteristic. Deep down inside, he was as sensitive and passionate as his father, whom he despised, so he fought to conceal any feelings which reminded him of his old man. But now, looking at little Katie lying on his bed, he couldn't help but let the tears of a compassionate man flow.

Bo was very cocky about his ability to handle any situation that came his way, but the events of the last day had thrown him into a panic. He had spent many hours since the tragedy agonizing over why it happened.

Bo's reaction to the incident was strikingly similar to that of his mother. Their religious beliefs assured them that rapes, robberies, murders, and all of the other assorted crimes they read about in the newspaper were only committed by others, and that Catholics were put on this earth to pray for such lowly people. Both Bo and his mother suffered not so much from grief over the loss of two human lives or from concern over the fate of the relative who had done away with these two lives, but from the blow to their pride that such a despicable act could occur in their family. Murder, they were calling it—the most serious sin that one could commit.

Bo was furious as he paced the kitchen floor of his apartment like an expectant father, venting to his very attentive wife, Midge. "How could this have happened? She seemed fine when we saw her last week, as well as anyone can look after having five kids in five years. Or is it six? I lost track. Those two are like a pair of rabbits. I just knew she couldn't handle all those kids."

"Look, Midge, I don't want anyone I work with knowing about this. It doesn't sound good. I have a lot going for me at the company and I don't want it messed up by something like this." It was pride that made Bo thankful that Nan's maiden name had not found its way into the papers, and that his business associates would probably not connect him with the event.

"And now we're saddled with Katie! What are we going to tell her?" As usual, Midge remained quiet, knowing full well her suggestions would not really be welcomed anyway. True to form, Bo didn't wait for an answer from his wife before he decided on a course of action by himself.

"We can't tell her anything." Bo believed kids should be seen and not heard and that, under any circumstances, they didn't need to know much about what was going on. However, he realized this was not an everyday family crisis...it wasn't as simple as the loss of a job, an impending move, or the death of a pet or a distant relative.

What did I do to deserve this burden? Bo asked himself as he scratched his head. There was perspiration running down his forehead. It is doubtful the arrogant Bo would have accepted professional help for the situation he found himself in even if it had been offered. Unfortunately, in 1953, the medical profession had not given much serious thought to counseling for the surviving children of parents who had murdered one or more of their siblings. For Katie and the rest of her family, any impact this event had on them would have to be worked out by themselves. Bo decided to play it by ear and answer as vaguely as he could only those questions that Katie asked.

When she finally regained consciousness, Katie was relieved to see that she was not in her grandmother's house anymore. She ran her hand along the right side of her face, remembering the sting of the awful blow as if it had just happened.

"I hate that old witch," she said quietly to herself. Very slowly, like a time bomb ticking toward its destructive end, Katie's mind awakened to the nightmare from which her unconscious state could only provide temporary relief. The newspaper headline appeared vividly in front of Katie's eyes. MOTHER KILLS. Did they mean her mom? Did she do it? TWO CHIL-DREN. Did she kill two of them? Which two? There were five of them and she was still alive. Was Kevin's picture in the paper because he was one of them?

Katie was in a pitiful state by the time Bo entered the room to see how she was doing. Her whole body was rigid.

"Hi, Kate, how do you feel?" Uncle Bo asked as Katie stared blankly at him.

"Who is dead?" Katie asked. She felt like it wasn't really her who was talking.

Bo experienced a sudden quickening of his pulse and his voice cracked as he replied, "Kevin and the baby, Marty."

Deep within her Katie felt something lacerate from her insides, taking with it the real emotion she was feeling. Bo stared in amazement at the little girl who didn't move a muscle when he told her that her brothers were dead.

"How did it happen?" Katie asked without looking at her uncle. Bo felt his temper rising at her questions. He thought she really didn't need to know; there were things in life that children just had to accept. He mumbled that there had been a bad accident. Again, Katie felt the unmerciful pain attack her, starting in her chest and working its way down to her toes. Outwardly, no one would have guessed that she was experiencing any kind of turmoil.

"Where is my mom?"

"Right now, she is on her way to a hospital."

"Where is everybody else?" Katie inquired in a voice totally devoid of emotion.

"If you mean your dad, he is staying at his parents' house. Jonathan is there also."

"Where is Barbara?" Katie said in a small voice, still lacking emotion.

"I don't really know where your sister is right now, Katie, but I know that wherever she is, she is safe." For five minutes, Bo sat staring at the pathetic child; five minutes of silence after which he realized with great relief that she wasn't going to ask him any more questions.

"Aunt Midge is making you some soup, Katie; be sure to eat it." After making his command, Bo left the room, congratulating himself on how well the situation had gone.

From the day she was born in January of 1926, Katie's mom Nan turned heads and made hearts beat faster. Her crystal blue eyes, which became more luminous with each passing year, were perfectly placed in a heart-shaped face that featured flawless skin, straight pearly-white teeth, and a radiant smile. Her picture-perfect face was framed with naturally curly strawberry blonde hair.

Short at five-foot-three-inches, Nan managed a much taller appearance by wearing high heels all of the time. She was not heavy, but neither did she look like she was starving, as she was big-boned with well-endowed breasts. She was cursed with a hearty Irish appetite which she liked to indulge. She was full of life, very talkative, friendly, and outgoing, but she had a tendency to be self-centered and stubborn.

Being the ninth child born to her very tired parents, Anna and Joseph, Nan was practically raised by her two older sisters, Wilma and Madge. Anna O'Malley, Nan's mom, was not a particularly affectionate woman and that, combined with her religious zeal, prevented her from establishing a close relationship with any of her children. She was the matriarch, however, and worked hard to keep her dysfunctional family together. She was more revered than she was loved.

Nan was born with an independent spirit which did not cope well with the demands of her older siblings, and so she sought refuge wherever she could get it. Her father became her greatest ally.

Joe O'Malley enjoyed the antics of his youngest daughter; he thought she was the most beautiful child ever born, and he expected nothing of her but to see her smile and give him a bear hug at the end of the day. As far as he was concerned, Nan couldn't say or do anything wrong.

Wilma and Madge were protective and indulgent of Nan but also very concerned about her ability to remain so carefree and disconnected, when they did everything they could to instill in her a sense of responsibility and an understanding of the realities of life. Most of her older siblings had serious addictive issues with alcohol, cigarettes, and food, so it wasn't as if she was raised in a bubble environment where everything was perfect—she just chose not to recognize any of it. It seemed that, even as a teenager, she was still stuck in the imaginative world of a very young child, separating herself from reality and entering into a place of her own choosing.

It was also evident that no matter what anyone said, did, or thought, Nan would say it, think it, or do it differently. She had always been able to get her daddy to agree to any scheme or idea that she came up with, and when he died suddenly when she was only fifteen, it was as if she lost the only person in the world who gave her unconditional love.

After her father's death, Nan had a hard time accepting the fact that people might not see things her way. She was still completely absorbed in her own life, which was harder to do without her dad supporting her tendency toward self-absorption. She always seemed to find impersonal issues to obsess over, as if focusing on distant, less personal matters would take her mind off of her own problems.

She very often scared her conservative siblings by pursuing new interests with reckless abandon or fanaticism. All of her siblings smoked, so Nan started the habit when her father died. At the time, it was the popular thing to do and, more importantly, smoking made her feel calm.

Nan and Jack Ramie, her future husband, lived in the same neighborhood, but didn't meet until her sister Wilma's boyfriend, Jake Field, brought his best buddy Jack with him to the local ice cream parlor to meet Wilma. Jack was one year and three months older than Nan; he was in eleventh grade and she was in ninth grade.

The minute Jack walked into the parlor, Nan was instantly attracted to him. She felt secure and comfortable with his quiet, easy going, agreeable manner, which coincidentally was just the opposite of her brothers' aggressive personalities. No matter what she said, Jack would nod in agreement and, at last, she felt she was experiencing something close to the relationship she had enjoyed with her adored late father. She dominated the union in every way and was deliriously content.

Within months after they met, World War II broke out. It was obvious that it would be a long war and, even though he was still a junior in high school, Jack made the decision to join the navy. There were a lot of reasons behind his choice, the most critical being that he knew he would eventually be drafted into the army and he didn't want to fight in the trenches if he didn't have to. He liked fishing with his dad and being on the water appealed to him. He was sure life in the Navy would most likely be easier than life as a general issue (G.I.).

Nan couldn't understand any of this and was devastated by what she perceived to be Jack's abandonment of her. On the other hand, Jack's parents were thrilled as it meant their oldest son would be in a position to contribute to the household coffers.

Instead of openly expressing her fear and grief at Jack's departure, Nan exhausted herself by dwelling on efforts to end the war, hoping that by doing so he wouldn't leave. She wrote letters to government officials, annoyed friends by trying to get them on board with her obsession with peace, and eventually became very depressed when her opinions were disregarded. She experienced feelings of dejection and her activity level was markedly reduced. She had difficulty thinking and concentrating, and everyone close to her thought she was crazy to invest so much time on issues that she had no chance of changing. What they didn't realize was that she was experiencing feelings of misplaced grief; it was not the rejection of her ideas that caused such psychological problems, but the worry and concern over Jack leaving her that was at the core of her depression.

Because she was only fifteen at the time and still free of any major responsibilities, her bouts of depression did not seriously impact anyone else.

Her behavior was ignored and even indulged by her well-meaning sisters. Nan was a visionary, incapable of dealing sensibly or prudently with practical matters. She was unrealistic in setting goals for herself and was convinced that she was going to be the most wonderful wife anyone ever had. She would have hordes of kids that she would adore and who would adore her. She would be patient, never screaming or shouting, and everything would be just perfect.

So far, Nan was surrounded by people who tolerated her for her impractical thoughts rather than cause conflict, and this kept her in a dream world in which she thought everything would go her way no matter what. She was confident that she would eventually marry Jack and that Jack would let her do whatever she wanted to do.

Jack did indeed join the Navy in November of 1941, and after a hellish few months in a rain-soaked boot camp in Maryland, the seventeen-year-old disembarked for four long years of battle as a radioman aboard a light cruiser. He survived a kamikaze attack in which he dove for cover on the gun deck, ending up stacked on top of three of his buddies, all of whom escaped death from the suicidal Japanese pilot bent on killing Americans. He endured several torpedo near-misses and many bombing attacks on the cruiser. He saw Japanese fighters bobble in the water as light dawned after all-night battles, and watched in sorrow as they refused to surrender and were shot by the Marines on board, whose job it was to protect their fellow Navy buddies from the enemy. The Marines also shot at sharks that got too close to the sailors as they swam in the Mediterranean, Pacific, and Atlantic oceans to escape the incessant and oppressive heat that permeated all arenas of the war.

Jack met General MacArthur, who spent time on the light cruiser he was on, and personally dispatched a telegram for him to the crew of the cruiser, thanking them for their valor in fighting the war.

He did not see his family for three long years. After the war was over and his floating home finally arrived in the harbor in New York, orders were waiting for most of the crew, including Jack, their valuable radioman, to turn right around and head back to Europe with a contingent of middle-aged, married men with children, drafted to replace the war-weary troops awaiting them in France. The mission was called "The Magic Carpet Ride," which was a joke—what it was actually dubbed by the sailors is unprintable. Jack watched helplessly as countless inexperienced men washed overboard, trying to seek relief on deck from seasickness.

On the way back, despite constant vigilance, they still lost many of the war-weary GIs to seasickness and drowning. When they arrived in New York harbor, several of them told Jack that the trip back home was worse than anything they had experienced in the war.

Again, when Jack arrived home and thought his part in the war was finally over, he was met with the same orders to turn around and do it again. It was a repeat of the same miserable journey as the first, only worse.

By the time they were making their voyage home with a second batch of World War II warriors, the gales of November were blowing and the trip, which normally would have taken only two weeks, took a month because of the violent seas spawning 100-foot waves. This time, the light cruiser remained in port and Jack finally mustered out of the Navy in November of 1945, four years after he enlisted.

While Jack was maturing rapidly from the rigors of war, Nan continued to be indulged by her well-meaning family. She and Jack exchanged letters and their long-distance relationship flourished. She graduated from high school in 1943 and, even though both Wilma and Madge were working full time and jobs were plentiful for women during the war, Nan did not make any effort to get a job despite pleas from her family to do so.

Nan and Jack were married in a hurriedly put together ceremony in the rectory of the Catholic church to which the O'Malley's belonged. John only had one week of leave before he had to report back to his ship to participate in the rescue operation, The Magic Carpet Ride, which would take him away from home until January of 1946.

Within three months after they were married, they were expecting their first child, Katie. When Katie was five months old, Nan conceived their second child, Jonathan. When Jonathan was barely a month old, Nan was already pregnant with their third child, Kevin. When Kevin was sixteen months old, Nan was carrying their fourth child, Barbara. When Barbara was eight months old, Nan was pregnant with their fifth child, Martin.

Jack was a machinist, making enough money to comfortably support a family of four, but not a family of seven. Even with overtime, which he worked more of as each new family member arrived, money was a problem.

Jack did not like conflict of any type, so he kept quiet on issues rather than express his own opinion—whatever went on in the mind of Jack Ramie was a mystery to those around him. There were some who thought Jack really didn't have any views on anything or was just taking the easy way out by remaining silent. Occasionally, he attempted to relay his mounting concerns regarding the way in which his family was multiplying, but it was done in such a feeble way and lacking in determination, that his fears were ignored by his stronger-willed and more determined wife.

While Jack dwelt on the serious aspects of life, Nan was more carefree—so he masked his anxieties about the future and went along with the irresponsible day-to-day existence that was the norm in their marriage. More importantly, however well-meaning his intentions were to limit his family, he abandoned all of them when he and Nan were in bed. Now, in a little over six years of marriage, Jack was the worried father of five children, and it seemed there was no end in sight; after all, Nan was only twenty-four and he was just twenty-five years old.

Jack and others were vaguely aware that Nan was acting more strangely since their fifth child, Martin, was born, but she had gone through similar periods after the births of the other children, so they shrugged it off with the belief that it would pass. Jack was so busy trying to make a living for his expanding brood, he didn't notice that since Martin's birth Nan was getting more nervous as each day passed. There was no apprehension as he left for work that day in April, a day that would leave him a lonely and broken man before darkness fell.

By the time Martin was born, Nan was both physically and mentally exhausted. Although some people detected the change in her, they thought it was just a normal reaction to the pressures of such a big family. They had their own lives to live and were too busy taking care of their families to see that Nan was in trouble.

At times, Nan was completely uncommunicative and aloof, while at other times she became pointlessly and annoyingly talkative. She began to show an uncharacteristically obvious lack of concern for the children and, at some point after the birth of their fifth child, Nan Ramie decided the children were responsible for all of her problems.

Nan's blue eyes were dulled by a white film that caused them to appear almost indistinguishable from the iris. She was staring beyond reality into a world she had created for herself. There could be no doubt in looking at the hauntingly corpse-like face of this poor disembodied soul that there was a demon lurking within; a devil getting ready to kill. Every nerve fiber in her body was impaired and her brain was no longer capable of providing her with the endurance and control so vital to a normal human being. The depression, the headaches, the fatigue, the feelings of inadequacy, the impaired functioning of interpersonal relationships, the sensitivity to sensory stimulation—all that had been occurring for weeks. Now, she had stepped into a world beyond that of a person suffering with neurasthenia. Overpowered, she no longer existed as she once had; she was a demoniac. Fiendishness and cruelty reeked from every pore of her body as she rose from the bed that ironically had served as both a place for the conception of the Ramie children as well as a place to plan their demise. She was now a hunter searching for its prey.

"Mommy, do you want me to stay home today?" With eyes widened in fright, six-year old Katie watched her mother slink into the kitchen. Nan was a mess; she hadn't showered in days and her hair was dull and dirty looking. Her body was flaccid and out of shape from the frequent pregnancies. More than that, however, there was something about the strange glassy look in Nan's eyes that made Katie afraid.

"No, you brat, get yourself ready for school and don't try to convince me to let you stay home anymore." Katie flinched at Nan's reply to her question because the voice didn't even sound like her mommy's. Katie quickly departed the kitchen and recoiled at the words her mother had spoken; she was very confused about her statement. She thought to herself that she wasn't trying to miss school and that her mother was wrong about that; it was her mother who didn't wake up lots of times, and the baby was crying and the other kids were hungry, so she couldn't leave them to go to school.

Katie clutched her stomach, doubling over with the pain that was now a frequent part of her life. She didn't like her mother very much since the last two babies were born. She was always smoking and staring at nothing, and yelling for Katie to pick up, feed, or change a crying baby. Then at night she would hear Nan fighting with her dad about money and the kids.

"Are you gone yet?" With a heavy heart at the viciousness of Nan's parting words, Katie hurriedly dressed and left the house, despite Jonathan's pleas that she stay at home because he was afraid to be alone with his mother.

As she walked to school, Katie realized she was relieved to be away from the mother who had recently become so strange. Little did she know that on this fateful day her life would be changed forever.

The house was unusually quiet when Katie returned home from school. Tiptoeing into the kitchen, she laid her books on the table and continued walking stealthily through the railroad flat. This was a very common style of apartment in the city, basically similar to a railroad car in that all the rooms were lined up in a row and the occupants walked from the first room, which was usually the kitchen, through the bedrooms to get to the living room.

As she passed from the kitchen through the first bedroom, Katie could see Barbara sleeping in her crib, Martin sleeping in his bassinette, and Kevin, also sound asleep, sucking his thumb in the twin bed that he had just started sleeping in. He was so proud and happy to finally be in a big boy's bed.

Katie moved on tiptoes, passing the tiny bedroom she shared with Jonathan and then through her parents' equally small bedroom, where her mother appeared to be sleeping in her bed. She was on her side, facing the wall, so Katie could not see her face. When she reached the living room, she saw Jonathan huddled on the couch as pale as a ghost, his lips quivering. He seemed relieved to see her.

"Katie, mommy's real sick," he whispered in a low voice. "She's been yelling at us all day and she hit Kevin really hard this morning. I had to give Martin a bottle and he choked a lot. I gave Barbara a bottle and tried to feed her some cereal. She messed her pants, too. Oh, Katie, I tried to change her but she kept wiggling. All mommy does is walk around saying silly things and looking out the window." Jonathan caught his breath and continued. "I'm scared, Katie, I'm really, really scared!"

And then it began.

Nan lifted herself from the bed. It was time to proceed with her plan. Kevin, the three-year-old, would be first; he had always given her the most trouble. She moved into the children's room and frantically opened up the window. She wanted it to be over with quickly. She lifted the sleeping four-year-old from his bed. She was no longer fatigued and felt as if she had the strength of Goliath. She easily lifted him over the black safety rails protecting the window. As she let him go, she felt instantly relieved and less burdened.

She thought she saw someone in front of her, but she turned quickly to snatch the infant from his bassinette. She found it much easier to release his tiny little body from her arms to the hard concrete below; he was only a month old. Still, she was sweating profusely, and this time she thought she heard someone scream.

As she reached for Barbara, the toddler was awake and backed away from her. She began to cry, realizing even in her childishness that her mother meant to do her harm. But Nan captured her in a tight squeeze and lifted her up to the window. It was much harder to get her over the safety bars because she was struggling so much, but she was intent on completing the job she had set out to do. She could hear someone talking behind her now, but she couldn't make out what they were saying as she pushed Barbara over the top of the bars. Considering her work more than half done, she turned to find the other two, but three strangers tackled her. In a very calm tone, she responded to being restrained by repeating over and over, "Please, let me go; I haven't finished yet. I wasn't raised like this!"

In the apartment across the alley from Nan and Jack's apartment, Barbara was being held tightly by the straps of her overalls while she dangled precariously. Dorothy didn't know how long she could continue to hold onto the hysterical child. She couldn't lift the baby up above the safety bars, because her arm had pierced the sharp tip of one of them when she had frantically reached for the child. It was stuck and bleeding profusely and some of her blood was flowing onto the child. Dorothy refused to acknowledge the pain, although she was becoming more light headed as the seconds passed. Just as she thought she had only minutes of strength left to hold onto the child, the police arrived at her door.

It had been such a beautiful day and normally Dorothy would have been at the park with her son, but he had a cold and so she was confined to the apartment that afternoon. As she entered her son's room to check on him, she noticed that the window to Nan's apartment was wide open. Even though there was a safety bar across all of their windows, it was an unwritten rule that no windows were to be left open, especially if there were little children in the home. Dorothy was somewhat familiar with the Ramie family, having spent numerous afternoons chatting with Nan in the park or through their apartment windows, which were cattycorner from each other and from which she now perched precariously.

She opened her window intending to yell to Nan, when she was forced to watch in horror as her neighbor lifted something above the guardrail and threw it out the window. At first she thought it was a doll, but as her eyes followed the descent of the object, she saw its arms and legs flailing wildly in the air until its body hit the ground. It was a child. Forcing her eyes to move upward toward the window again, she screamed at the sight of the wild-eyed Nan lifting a small bundle high in her arms and, with a wicked smile, letting it fall from her hands.

Everything in front of Dorothy seemed cloudy and she thought for sure this was a nightmare from which she would soon awaken. Instead it got worse as she saw another child in Nan's arms. Dorothy screamed, "What are you doing, Nan, what are you doing? Put the baby down, please!"

Her plea went unheard and Nan proceeded to lift the screaming child over the safety bars. As if the 15-month-old youngster knew her life was in danger, she entwined her small fingers around the metal on the guard rail, giving Dorothy the time she needed to climb up on the sill and extend her arms as far as she could toward the child. Just as Nan let go of Barbara, Dorothy was able to grab hold of the back of the baby's overalls. With strength she didn't know she possessed, Dorothy was able to continue her grip on the terrified child; but it was only a few seconds before the pain of her injury began to impact her ability to continue to hold onto her.

Katie was not the only one to hear Dorothy's agonizing screams. Immediately after Nan threw Kevin out the window, the police received dozens of calls from people frantically reporting that someone was throwing people out of a window. By the time Nan threw the second child out the window, the police, both in squad cars and on foot, were outside of the apartment. By the time Nan picked up Barbara, they were already at her front door. Within seconds of breaking down the front door and restraining her, the police broke down Dorothy's door and quickly freed both Dorothy and Barbara from their precarious positions at the window.

Dorothy would never forget those big burly arms and hands in navy blue uniform reaching around her and grabbing the child just as she started slipping from her grasp. The three of them remained entwined together for another few minutes before it was decided that Dorothy's arm could be safely pulled from the spike without further injury. Dorothy's last memory of the incident before she passed out from loss of blood was being pulled under the body and through the legs of the officer holding Barbara. When she finally came around, as she was being loaded on a gurney, her only concern was for the child whose life she had most definitely saved.

"Did she make it?" she said weakly to anyone who could hear her. A smiling medic pointed to the corner and Dorothy followed his finger. She grinned from ear to ear to see Barbara in the arms of a police officer—still hysterical, but alive. Her own toddler son had been placed on the gurney with her, and she couldn't help but give him an extra hard squeeze as she commented, "Well, little fellow, cold or no cold, I guess we are going out today."

Sergeant Miles arrived on the scene approximately three minutes after the call was relayed to all squad cars in the area. Miles happened to be only a couple of blocks away, investigating a lead on a homicide. By the time he pulled up in front of the building, two other police cars had responded. A fire truck was also on the scene, but its equipment was still in place.

As he was entering the building, Miles was almost knocked over by a young rookie he immediately recognized from the training sessions he had given not more than two weeks before. Miles demanded an explanation, and the anxious new recruit lost all of his composure as he relayed to his superior that he was on his way to investigate a possible body or bodies in the alley behind the apartment.

Twenty-five years as a policeman had given Sergeant Miles the distinct ability to sense with incredible accuracy where he was needed most, and right now he knew it was with this boy. Miles began shouting orders to the other arriving police officers to cordon off the alley entrance and, seeing people begin to gather, he asked the firemen on the newly arrived fire trucks to control the crowd. Noticing an ambulance inching its way through the thickening traffic, he shouted to one of his officers to get a couple of medics down to the alley as soon as they could. By this time, Miles and the nervous rookie had reached the entrance to the alley through a basement door.

The novice held the door open for Miles, looking relieved that he didn't have to lead the way. Miles had been through more than his share of first-on-the-scene situations, and some people said he was hardened to seeing dead bodies and people in all stages of life-threatening circumstances. They were partially right. There was one weakness that Miles was unable to conceal from anyone who knew him, and that was his inability to accept those incidents in which the life of a child was involved.

Miles and his wife had tried for years to have their own family without success. Because they had made the mistake of waiting until they were older to start adoption proceedings, they were rejected countless times until they were able to adopt a severely retarded baby girl. There had never been any doubt in Miles' mind that he loved children; he had many nieces and nephews whom he adored and who idolized him as well.

The magnitude of affection he felt for his little girl, however, surprised even him. Just that morning, she had put her arms around his neck and grunted in her pathetically limited vocabulary the almost unrecognizable words, "I love you." For all of her fifteen years, she had bestowed on him more love than he ever thought possible, and he couldn't imagine leaving for work without having her say goodbye to him. As much as he was fond of his emotionally and intellectually normal nieces and nephews, there was a special place in his heart for his baby that no one could fill. He became a crusader for handicapped children and was very outspoken in defense of mistreated youngsters.

As Miles surveyed the alley quickly, he saw what looked like a pile of rags in the far corner of the narrow passageway. He quickly assessed the remainder of the area and heard someone gasp. He turned his eyes in the direction of the sound to see the young rookie breathing spasmodically and vomiting. When he reached the policeman's side, Miles took in the sight of the small, lifeless form lying in a pool of blood, bones protruding from his inanimate body. He immediately took the child's pulse to confirm his sickening suspicion, and then took off his jacket and laid it gently over the broken doll-like figure. At that moment, he remembered the cloth in the corner and like a wild man he weaved toward it.

When he approached the baby blanket, he knew what was probably in it and cursed himself for not investigating it more quickly. He had wasted too much precious time. As he pulled at the blood-stained blanket, he was shocked to find that the infant was still breathing. Dropping to his knees, and without touching the tiny body, Miles began to administer mouth-to-mouth resuscitation with the gentleness he had acquired through years of experience. Thinking back to all of the times he had done this before, Miles remembered specifically the young girl who tried to rid herself of the child she had been carrying for six months and how the baby had still been alive when he reached it but died in his arms as he tried to breathe life back into it.

Returning to the present, Miles pressed the blanket against an open wound on the infant's head to stop the bleeding. He knew enough not to try to do anything but help the child breath. He was totally unaware the medic had arrived, so intent was he with trying to save the baby's life.

As he was pulled away from the infant, Miles began to sob and beat his fists against the brick wall, causing immediate abrasions to his knuckles. Everyone heard him say, "There is no God if he allows this to happen to innocent babies!" He wiped his bloody hands on his suit.

By the time the medics had taken the baby to the nearest hospital, and the body of the other young child was on its way to the city morgue, Miles had resumed his composure, trying to suppress the anger he felt for the person who had done this. Seething at the unfairness of the grievous act committed against the two babies, Miles spoke in a determined but gentle command. "Well, son, let's find out what the hell this is all about." The young rookie, still shaken, remained close at his superior's side, the two of them sharing a unique bond.

"Is this Jack Ramie?" The voice on the other end of the phone sounded anxious. Jack had been summoned to the office of the shop steward where he was told he had an emergency phone call. Jack eventually made it to the small, dark room which served as the office of his boss.

"Yes."

"I'm sorry to have to tell you this over the phone, but there has been a terrible accident involving your family. Can you get home right away?" It took Jack some time to comprehend what the stranger was saying. Enough time elapsed between the question and a response, that the caller asked, "Are you still there, Mr. Ramie?"

"I'm on my way," Jack replied and, with that, left his supervisor in stunned silence as he darted out of the office, down the aisle, and out the exit door.

Jack felt the blood rushing from his head as he ran the mile to his home. He wondered what the emergency was and berated himself for not having asked. Probably one of the kids had hurt themselves; they were lucky to have escaped injuries thus far. He tried to convince himself that maybe Barbara had a relapse from the life-threatening issues she was born with, but he knew from the way the caller had sounded that it was something much more serious, something he didn't have the nerve to tell him on the phone. Jack's actions, the way his body was moving, and the way he felt were not indicative of a man running home to face a hurt child; no, he was moving as if his very life depended on it, as if some force had taken over his entire body.

When he was within sight of the elevated train station, he noticed a crowd of people. At first he thought something had gone wrong with one of the trains. As he came closer, he realized the congregation extended all the way down to the entrance to his apartment building.

He suddenly realized the crowd was probably connected to the phone call and he thought he was going to pass out. *What could have happened that would interest all of these people?* he thought. He had never seen so many ambulances and fire trucks in one place before. The thought of turning around and running in the opposite direction sped quickly through Jack's mind, but he found himself already fighting the crowd to make his way to his apartment. As a jumbled mixture of thoughts occupied his brain, Jack was unaware of what the people around him were saying, for if he had heard them he would have had a good idea of what had happened. Without realizing it, Jack had created a disturbance in his attempt to push his way through the crowd. An alert policeman who had been put in charge of crowd control grabbed Jack by the arm, noticing that the man he was holding seemed dazed.

"I've got to get into my house...I got a call...I've got to get to my family...someone called me and told me to come home....I've got to get over there!" Jack kept repeating himself as the officer tried in vain to get his name. Realizing he was not getting anywhere with the half-crazed man, the policeman decided to take Jack to Sergeant Miles and was in the process of doing that when Jack broke loose and bolted up the stairs and through the open door leading to his apartment.

Leaning heavily against the wall, Jack panted and gasped for air as he focused his eyes on the kitchen table. A blur of people surrounded it. As they came into focus, Jack noticed about six people: a man with a suit on, four or five other men in various uniforms, and a woman, a haunted, pathetic-looking woman with a blanket around her. He quickly stepped away from the wall when he realized the woman was Nan, but he was stopped from advancing any further by Sergeant Miles, who pulled him into the bedroom where just a couple of hours earlier three of his children were sleeping peacefully.

"I assume you are Mr. Ramie?" After Jack nodded in the affirmative, Miles continued. "I have some very bad news for you." As he focused on the stocky man in front of him, Jack recognized the voice as belonging to the person who called him on the phone at work what seemed like an eternity ago.

"Are you okay, sir? Would you like a glass of water?" Defeated-looking, Jack simply shook his head no.

"Mr. Ramie, one of your children, Kevin Patrick Ramie, was pronounced dead a few minutes ago due to a fall from this window." As he pointed to the window in question, Miles saw the shoulders of the young man begin to shake, and thought to himself that he would break down if he did not see an end to this day soon. He was not allowed by law to tell Jack Ramie there had been an eyewitness account indicating that his wife had thrown two of his children to almost certain death from their bedroom window. His duty was to relay the facts without implication and without emotion. What a joke that was—without emotion. The scene at the bottom of the alley window he was facing was too fresh in his mind not to interfere with his feelings.

Now, turning his back away from the alley window, Miles wondered if he had lost his touch. He agonized at the thought of giving the distraught father any more bad news. With the other cases that involved children, he was careful to present all the facts as best he could, waiting until he was alone to vent his emotions, but this time he had let himself slip. Maybe it was time to call it quits. His voice cracked as he continued.

"Mr. Ramie, another child, Martin Ramie, has been taken to the hospital, and it doesn't look good for him."

"The baby, what happened to the baby? How did the baby get hurt? He can't even walk." One thing those close to him knew about Jack Ramie was his love of infants. He could walk a colicky baby for hours, or sit and hold it for long periods of time without moving. On the other hand, as his children reached the toddler stage, he became less attentive.

Miles cleared his throat and tried very hard to fight back the swell of water that was demanding to be released from his eyes. *To hell with it*, he thought. *This guy has to know what we suspect.* In a little while he had to book his wife for murder.

"Mr. Ramie, it appears from an eyewitness account that your wife was responsible for dropping the children from a window." A low, anguished moan erupted from Jack. "We believe your wife is mentally disturbed, but we are going to have to book her for the time being until we can get her examined properly. This means taking her to the police station. I'm so sorry." As Miles moved quickly toward the kitchen before this man could see his tears, he was stopped by a slight tugging on his arm.

"What about the other children?" Jack's inquiry was barely audible, and he turned his head away from Miles as though he didn't want to hear the answer. Miles thought his heart would break, and he had the urge to gather the man in his arms and comfort him. *Christ*, he thought, *I'm getting too soft for this job*. By now, Jack had collapsed on Kevin's big boy bed, so Miles got down on his haunches in front of Jack, and sniffing back the water that threatened to run down his face, reassured him that the other children were okay.

Jack, who was in a stupor, and Nan, who was in another world, were taken to the police station where Jack quietly accepted the news that his youngest son, Martin, had died on the operating table, just one hour after he had been admitted to the hospital. The child's injuries were so severe that it was considered a miracle he lived as long as he did. Jack uttered not a word, nor was there any visible emotional reaction when he identified the bodies of Kevin and the newly arrived infant, Martin, at the morgue. He let himself be guided like a blind man through the painstaking activities which were required by law. Feeling alone, tormented beyond endurance, Jack hid the pain he felt at the thought of Kevin lying on the steel table in that cold room, and Martin, who was there now, too—both of them all broken up. He controlled a desire to scream as he remembered how pathetic Nan looked when she was booked for murder, not understanding any of it as she struggled to free herself from the straightjacket. She was taken to the state mental institution for observation immediately after the paperwork was processed by the police.

This day was a turning point in Jack's life. He had been quiet and unassuming before, but now he was drained of all enthusiasm and left hopeless. He couldn't feel anything...not guilt, hate, or love; he felt absolutely nothing. People do not dwell on the susceptibility of their lives; it is too depressing. Yet, every day someone's life is changed dramatically due to an unforeseen event.

Jack Ramie was going through his own form of hell in his effort to cope with the day's calamitous events; the tall, attractive man had been staring at the brick wall in the police station for three hours making no attempt to communicate, while everyone around him worked frantically to process paperwork. Later, he appeared to be in a trance as his brothers led him like a child to the home of their mother and father.

Jack Ramie Jr. was born in November of 1923 and was the third child of Emma and Jack Ramie Sr., both of whom were born in the United States. The elder Jack was mostly of English descent, and Emma was a full-blooded American. There was evidence that her ancestors had come over on the

Mayflower and that she was part Native American. Emma Ramie was a wonderfully softspoken, gentle lady who emitted warmth and love. She genuinely liked her role as mother and wife, and the entire family, which included her six children and all of their families, adored her.

Jack Ramie Sr. was not as easygoing as his wife. He was obsessively jealous of Emma and would launch into unprovoked attacks on her moral character. On all occasions, she would quietly let him continue his assault, knowing it was caused partly by drinking and partly by a deep-rooted insecurity about his own self-worth, which she had known existed from the day she met him and fell madly in love. Jack Sr. was not above hitting Emma during these violent outbursts, and the other siblings looked to Jack Jr. to intercede and protect his mother. It was not in young Jack's nature, however, to participate in violence of any kind, so he disappointed his younger brothers by not getting involved in his father's unacceptable behavior.

When he was not under the influence of liquor or in one of his self-pitying moods, the older Jack was a charming, funny man, who was obsessed with playing cards. The Ramie Clan were non-practicing Protestants who loved nothing better than to get together as a family and raise hell. Permanent facial laugh lines were their trademarks, as they enjoyed each other's never-ending repertoire of jokes and funny stories.

Jack Jr. was the oldest of the boys in the family and was the most impacted by the behavior of his parents. It seems everyone mellows with age and Jack Sr. ran true to form, rarely ever beating his wife by the time the two youngest children would have been old enough to remember. After each furious eruption on the part of his father, Jack Jr. came away from it a little quieter and more introverted than he was before. He had a revulsion for yelling, screaming and hitting that would send him cringing into a corner, hoping he wouldn't be needed to rescue his mother. By the time Jack Jr. married Nan O'Maley, his relaxed, quiet, and gentle temperament was permanently established.

Nan's decision to marry Jack was met with grave protests by her family because of the religious difference, meaning for one thing that they couldn't be married in the church. It was easy for Nan to convince Jack to do whatever was required by the church to allow them to get married in the rectory. Jack also had to sign a form in which he consented to raise any children which might come of their union as Catholics. On November 1, 1945, Nan and Jack became Mr. and Mrs. Jack Ramie in a somber ceremony, which could only be attended by a handful of Nan's Catholic relatives.

Love is blind, so they say, and in the case of Nan and Jack, no truer words were ever spoken. She was as talkative and accessible as he was quiet and secretive. He was as responsible as she was irresponsible. He was a realist; she a dreamer. He was a saver; she was a spender. All this didn't matter at the time because their physical passion for each other outweighed everything else. When Jack was drafted, the separation served only to increase their infatuation with each other and by the time Jack returned from over-seas, they were both as highly charged as two human beings could be.

Nan and Jack had not thought seriously about discussing their future together. After all, as Catholics it wasn't fashionable to determine how many children one wanted or could afford. God would take care of that! There was no discussion about expectations for personal achievements and how they might impact on the family. They took each day as it came, never stopping for a moment to think ahead with regard to what was best for the quality of their lives.

Proving to be as fertile as she was unrealistic, Nan presented Jack with their firstborn as a combination birthday and anniversary present. Katie came into the world on November 2, the Day of the Dead, or All Soul's Day as it is called in the Catholic religion. She was born just one day before Jack's twenty-second birthday and one day after Nan and Jack's first wedding anniversary. Katie weighed in at a tiny five pounds after a very difficult labor during which Nan was administered too much anesthesia, making her extremely sick for days after the delivery.

The pregnancy itself had been typical except for Nan's abnormal craving for chocolate milk and Yankee Doodle cupcakes, and she was surprised that Katie's complexion was so white it was almost transparent in view of all of the chocolate she had consumed. Nan had inverted nipples and was unable to breastfeed her baby; she reacted very badly to this news and cried for most of the week she and the baby were in the hospital.

Katie was nicknamed Rip van Winkle by the hospital nursery staff because she slept so much they had to wake her up to feed her. When she got home, Katie continued to sleep as much as eight hours at a time, causing her parents to spend a lot of time leaning over her bassinet making sure she was still breathing.

Two weeks after Katie was born, Nan was still experiencing depression and her family assumed it was totally connected to her inability to breastfeed. They knew Katie slept most of the time and Nan's debasement could have nothing to do with being exhausted from the additional burdens of child care. As a matter of fact, Nan bragged that taking care of a baby was the easiest thing she had ever done; however, she continued to struggle with postpartum blues.

Like so many other first-time mothers, Nan's expectations of being a parent had been very high. When the baby finally arrived and life settled back to normal, less attention was focused on her and the baby. This, coupled with her concern about the weight she had gained, her failed attempt at breast-feeding, and the realization that she couldn't be as flexible with her time as she was before Katie came along, caused Nan to sink into a low ebb.

During this time, she had trouble maintaining a normal sleeping pattern and spent the day napping and the night restlessly stalking the apartment.

She was extremely nervous and became agitated at the slightest provocation. She also became irrationally concerned about matters that shouldn't have bothered her at all, like how often her neighbors put out the garbage, or how many young kids were playing in the park across the street. It was fortunate Katie slept so much that she didn't make any demands on her mother's much needed rest periods during the day and night.

The dark cloud over Nan passed slowly with each day. When Katie was five months old, Nan became pregnant again; she was absolutely thrilled and Jack was also happy about the news.

Jonathan came into the world just as Katie was becoming proficient at walking around by herself. She was still taking long naps and when she was awake, would quietly occupy herself with her toys. Jonathan, however, was not a sleeper. Nan was able to hold down the fort without too much difficulty at first, but when the baby blues arrived this time it was a little more serious.

Nan's mother and sisters took shifts helping Nan get through the dark period. They didn't understand it when she talked about wanting to hurt the baby when he cried too much or didn't sleep or eat well. Unlike Katie, Jonathan had lots of problems with his ears and was sick often, which added to the stress of the situation.

Jack spent lots of time holding his new son as he suffered with frequent earaches. Eventually, with constant babysitting help from relatives and friends, Nan gradually became more even-tempered and exhibited less nervousness.

Jonathan was barely a month old when new life began in Nan. True to her unrealistic determination to have lots of children and to be the best mother in the world, Nan totally ignored the concern of family and friends that she and Jack should be more careful about having children so quickly. Actually, it was the closeness with which she was having the children that disturbed the more well-meaning people, not to mention the seriousness of her obvious dark periods after each birth. Nan, however, had no second thoughts about the rapid growth of her family and, in fact, the more discouragement she received on the issue, the more stubborn she became about proving how well she could handle her family. It was with an air of smug satisfaction that she announced there was a new Ramie on the way, with Jack shrugging his shoulders and grinning beside her.

Kevin, Nan and Jack's third child, was so colicky that he wasn't able to make it home from the short hospital trip without vomiting on Nan. He was a very unhappy baby and, to add insult to injury, Jonathan was a rambunctious toddler who was into everything.

Nan was in a constant state of exhaustion, and everyone kept their fingers crossed, but Nan's depression and nervousness increased with each passing day. She stopped spending time outdoors with the children, an activity she enjoyed at all times of the year. The neighbors saw less and less of Nan and the children. Of course, it was difficult to prepare three little children for an outing, but the truth was that Nan had ceased even making an attempt.

Nan gradually increased her cigarette smoking from one pack to two packs a day, as they definitely helped take the edge off. They hired a young neighbor girl, Patsy, to watch the children once a week while Jack took Nan out. Patsy was disabled, having been born with only one hand, but she was fantastic with the kids. They would jump up and down with glee when they saw her coming in the door. As she had after each of the other births, Nan eventually got through the dense fog, although each time she did she was more exhausted, more fragile, more addicted, and less functional than she was before.

There was a twenty-one-month hiatus before Nan was pregnant for the fourth time, but it wasn't a conscious effort to avoid pregnancy as Nan and Jack still acted carelessly in the bedroom. Even with the almost two-year break between pregnancies, during this gestation Nan was totally depleted of strength. The morning sickness, which lasted all day, was far worse than any she experienced before and, again, Nan's sisters, Wilma and Madge, pitched in to help get Nan through the nine months.

Nan and Jack were lucky in that Katie, Jonathan, and Kevin were basically very well-behaved children who played quietly with each other. Jonathan had outgrown his ear problems and was very healthy, and Kevin had the easy-going temperament of his father, even though he ironically got on Nan's nerves.

Nan was sufficiently lucid to hear the scream as her fourth child was pulled from her body. She closed her eyes and drifted back into unconsciousness, realizing if something was wrong she would have to wait to hear about it. The female child was quickly separated from her mother and administered all of the life-saving techniques the hospital had available. She was a very seriously ill child who was born with all of her organs below the waist exposed and displaced, due to the failure of the skin to grow around the umbilical cord.

Later, as Nan and Jack agonized in the recovery room over the fate of their new offspring, specialists from around the country were quickly learning about the ill-fated child. A team of top surgeons worked feverishly into the night placing each tiny organ in its rightful place, and transplanting enough skin from the buttocks of the remarkably plump little girl to cover the once exposed organs. The baby's heart was strong and she weighed in at eight pounds—two factors which were helping to keep her alive.

Barbara was monitored for three months to ensure that each organ was working properly, that breathing and heart activity remained normal, and that no infections were brewing from the skin transplant and organ realignments. The Miracle Baby of St. Francis, as she was called, had survived one of the few operations of that type ever performed. The only telltale sign of the battle this infant had fought at birth would be a rather large and scarred belly button.

Jack and Nan had previously agreed that if the child was a girl they would call her Barbara, and she was given this name during a frantic combination Baptism and Last Rights ceremony by the hospital priest on duty. Ironically, Barbara was the biggest of the Ramie children at birth, weighing in at almost eight pounds.

Barbara thrived in the hospital and was finally sent home. She was three months old when she joined her family, and all was going well until Nan tried to feed her solid food. Actually, the culprit was an extremely watered down version of rice cereal. Barbara became grumpy and obviously uncomfortable after the feeding. Nan was in the process of burping the baby when Barbara projectile-vomited. The foul smell of the vomit permeated the air, and Nan sensed immediately something was very seriously wrong when she realized that what Barbara had vomited was fecal matter. The diagnosis was that the baby had developed a severe intestinal blockage, which is not uncommon in young children who are born with serious digestive abnormalities. Barbara was operated on once again and, within a month, was released from the hospital in what appeared to be perfect health.

The incident, however, left its scars. Nan was reeling from the emotional and physical strain of Barbara's illness, as well as the effort required to take care of four children, all of them under five years of age.

Jack, on the other hand, was staggered by financial strains that were magnified even further due to the hospital bills for Barbara. There were definite changes in Nan's personality; she was very easily agitated, lost her patience more frequently with Jack and the children, started to dwell again on matters that should not have concerned her, and seemed to be obsessed with arranging nights out to get away from the kids.

Not understanding Nan was using diversionary tactics to keep her attention from the real issue—a family she could not cope with—Jack sensed only that Nan was totally beyond reason when it came to discussing the problems they had in their marriage. He also didn't have the communication skills that were necessary to be the aggressor in this serious situation. They did not have the ability to fight their battles together, for their personalities were miles apart. They also did not have the maturity to realize that adding to their family would only seriously complicate an already deteriorating situation. Nan became pregnant with their fifth child, Martin, when Barbara was a mere nine months old.

By the time Martin was born in March of 1953, Nan was a physical and mental wreck. As the oldest child, Katie, who would not turn seven until November of that year, assumed more responsibility for the younger children, especially when Nan began sleeping away the day and roaming the apartment at night, dwelling on the injustices in the world, and how to get rid of them.

One evening, a well-meaning neighbor cornered Jack in the hallway and begged him to take Nan to a doctor, expressing the concerns of several neighbors who had noticed a marked deterioration in Nan's personality. They were very worried about the children. Jack, exhausted from working two shifts, shrugged and quickly forgot the conversation until a few days later.

"Jack, I just don't understand what's wrong with this country!" Nan's high-pitched voice screeched in Jack's tired ears. "There are starving people all over the United States, and now they tell us they are destroying food that our farmer's grow rather than distributing it to the needy. I just can't believe such a thing!" It was two o'clock in the morning and Jack was delirious from listening to Nan rant for three hours.

"Nan, I think you had better try to get some sleep...we're both exhausted. I have to get up early in the morning, and you will probably have to get up with the baby shortly. Please go to sleep." Jack didn't notice the quizzical expression on Nan's face, which indicated that she didn't understand him, and continued on. "Look, you haven't been getting enough sleep, and it's beginning to show. You're not acting right, and it's starting to worry everyone. A neighbor actually said something to me about you. Not only that...." Jack hesitated while he considered whether his next comment was worth saying. "Katie is missing too much school. I don't know if you even realize this, but you're sleeping right through most of the day, and she has to stay home. It's too much for her; she's too young to be taking care of the kids, especially the baby. She shouldn't stay home from school anymore; we could get in trouble if they find out she's really not sick and she is missing school to take care of her brothers and sister. I think some of the neighbors are ready to report us."

Jack's comments got through to Nan as her face contorted in anger, and she shot back. "You have no right to say that. I take good care of the children. You should talk; you're never home anymore."

Bracing himself for an inevitable confrontation with Nan, Jack tried to ease the situation by smiling as he gently tried to justify his absence from the home. "I told you I would have to work a lot more in order to meet the bills; I told you it would be like this. I can't be in two places at one time. I'm working my fingers to the bone to pay our bills. Now please try to get some sleep."

Lying in stunned silence as Jack's words finally penetrated her deeply disturbed mind, the barrier she had built between herself and reality came tumbling down, and there was nothing left for Nan to do but face the real problem; the problem that existed on a day-to-day basis....the one she had avoided with diversionary tactics but which she now realized had to be dealt with. The voices had been telling her for a long time, on many different occasions, that she had to do something about the problem, but she had been trying to ignore them. Now she realized the voices were absolutely right; the children were the problem. There was only one solution—they would have to go. As Jack lay beside her in a sound sleep, Nan went over everything. Tomorrow, she vowed to herself, she would solve their problem.

Chapter Two: The Months of Waiting

She was so afraid. She wondered what was going to happen to her and why she couldn't cry. Katie overheard a conversation between her aunts and found out her father had not talked since the boys died, and had not even been able to make arrangements for their funerals. She listened as the discourse turned to her, and heard them express their concern about the fact they hadn't seen her display any emotion. Feeling alone and nervous, she reflected back on a comment one of her cousins had made to her about her mother being crazy. Katie wondered if she could be crazy also.

On the surface, Katie seemed content with her life as it was, living in Uncle Bo's house. She particularly enjoyed coming home from school and eating butter cookies dunked in soda, a special treat from her uncle's wife, Maggie, while she watched her do her chores in the kitchen. They had a canary that Katie was fond of, even though it frightened her when they let him out of the cage. Uncle Bo's stern behavior scared her, but she looked forward to the different stories he read to her and his two children every night at bedtime.

What was going on in the far reaches of Katie's mind was a different case altogether. Because no one thought it was important that she be told what the situation was with her family, she lived in a constant state of anxiety regarding her future. Her little mind conjured up all sorts of scenarios, all of which left her feeling deeply insecure and frightened. Would she live with Uncle Bo forever? Would she ever see her own family again? No matter how welcome she was made to feel at Uncle Bo's, she still felt like an outsider who didn't really belong anywhere.

This seed of not belonging was sown deeper when, without warning or explanation, she was packed up and sent to the home of her mother's sister, Wilma. She was already extremely confused and hurt when she found out her brother was living with her father and grandparents, wondering why they didn't want her; now, with this latest development, she felt totally rejected.

Katie's Aunt Wilma had five children of her own that she was trying to bring up in a small two-bedroom apartment on the ninth floor of a tenement building in New York City. To make matters worse, her husband was a lifer in the navy and was away most of the time, so her aunt was raising the children by herself. Katie was already quiet and withdrawn as a result of her family situation, but after the move out of Uncle Bo's house she became even more so, and the feelings she was suppressing began to surface.

Deep down inside her, Katie knew her brothers' deaths were no accident, but without the facts, she was content to believe it was nobody's fault. Until, that is, a well-meaning older cousin made some startling revelations to Katie about that day in April, assuming Katie already knew it all. Later, when she was alone, she reflected on the parts of the one-sided conversation she actually remembered.

Nothing she had previously experienced could compare to the desperation she felt at the moment she realized that, indeed, her baby brothers had been thrown from the window by her mother, and Barbara was alive only because a neighbor caught her before she fell. She realized it was true that her life had been in danger, and from her own mother. There seemed to be no hope left for her with this new development and Katie felt despair—the kind of hopelessness that makes a six-year-old hurt from the top of her head to the tips of her toes. How could she face anyone knowing that her mother was a murderer? How could she ever love her mother again after what she did? How could they ever be a family again? Being virtually cut off from her immediate family was a ravaging experience for Katie, and there was no adult in her life who thought it was necessary to talk to her about her future; most of her aunts and uncles weren't sure themselves what the future held for the Ramie family.

She was just a six-year-old after all, and why should she care as long as she had a roof over her head and food in her mouth? She had nothing going for her with a father who found it impossible to communicate and so avoided her; a mother who was being administered shock treatments because she was so out of it; a system that didn't yet realize the surviving children of parents who murder their own children would need psychiatric help; and relatives who also did not understand the sensitivity of the situation.

Lying in the big bed, crowded by two cousins on either side of her, Katie stared at the cracks in the ceiling. She tried hard to remember her life prior to the day Kevin and Marty died, but she couldn't. Biting her lip to hold back the tears that wouldn't come anyway, she thought about how messed up everything was. Confused by her feelings, she bitterly decided that she hated them all for not telling her what was going on.

The little blonde boy was crouched in the corner of the dark room with his hands covering his head so he wouldn't see what was happening.

Suddenly, he was being pulled roughly from the corner and partly lifted and dragged to the open window.

She jumped on the monster's back to help the little boy, but it was too strong for her and it grabbed her long blonde hair and swung her around so that she and the little boy were both in its arms. She held tightly to the little boy's neck as the monster approached the big open window and threw them out. They were spinning around in the air, but she didn't let go of the boy. They hit the ground, but landed on their feet. She looked up at the monster and laughed as she picked up the little boy and ran away.

Katie felt elated when she woke up, but the happiness didn't last long as she realized she had only been dreaming and the little boy was dead. Still, it had been a much better dream than the others. Every day, however, she was remembering more and more about the day the boys died, especially flashes here and there of Kevin struggling in his mother's arms.

Some months passed as Katie went through the motions of living; moody and sullen most of the time and resentful of everyone. Lice infested the heads of all of her cousins and Katie actually felt extremely guilty that she was the cause of it. Actually, it was not clear who got the lice first, but Katie had already begun a self-destructive process in which she believed everything bad that happened was all her fault, from simple things like spilling something to the deaths of her two baby brothers. With every passing day, she was convinced she should have tried to prevent her mother from throwing the boys out the window. After all, she knew something was wrong when she left the house for school. The fact that her father never came to visit or that her grandparents did not want her in their home solidified her feeling she was somehow to blame. This thought haunted Katie's waking and sleeping hours.

Meanwhile, Jack Ramie figured Katie was doing just fine where she was. He had nothing to say to anyone, least of all a child who wouldn't understand what had happened. Yes, she was better off not seeing him at all. Sadly, Jack could have used some psychiatric help also, but there was nothing in place in the mental health system to help him either.

Katie spent most of her time wondering why she was so bad and began eating dirt, picking it off the sides of buildings or from underneath the wheel wells of parked cars. She was sure that consuming this filth could be dangerous and she might even die from it, but it didn't deter her in the least.

Then, history repeated itself. This time she was packing her suitcase and being sent to the home of strangers somewhere far away. Even though they told her it was only for a little while, she was convinced it was a scheme to get rid of her, the cause of all of their problems, and she would never see her family again.

The blocks stretched out for what seemed like miles to Katie, and her heavy suitcase didn't help to make the walk any easier. It was a typical New York City summer morning; already the air was thick and humid, and the day promised to be a scorcher. Katie was having one of her frequent conversations with herself, and the familiar lump in her throat was ever-present as she struggled hard not to let the tears building up in her eyes escape. She had become a master at that. She had no idea where she was going; she heard the name of the place mentioned, but she couldn't even pronounce it. She wished her stomach would stop doing flip flops; it never felt good anymore. The suitcase she was carrying was hurting her fingers. She couldn't feel them anymore, and she wished they would fall off so Aunt Wilma would take her to the hospital and make her miss the train that was taking her to nowhere. She kept reminding herself that she wasn't going to cry; but it was hard not to.

What Katie didn't know was that with the best of intentions, her Aunt Wilma had requested a spot for her in the Fresh Air Kids program run by the local welfare department. She thought it would be a great vacation for her little niece who had been through so much.

Katie made a mad dash for the bathroom as soon as the train pulled out of the station, before she messed herself from the sudden and severe attack of diarrhea that came over her. Running her tongue over her dry, cracked lips, Katie took a few deep breaths to squelch the all too-familiar feeling of uneasiness which seemed to plague her these days.

Somewhere on the train trip, this unhappy, confused little girl built a wall around herself; one meant to protect her from any more hurt. She had come to the conclusion she was totally on her own now and the whole world was her enemy. She viewed life with well-deserved cynicism; the pain and suffering she had experienced made her believe life was harshly contemptible. This six-year old fought her demons the only way she was capable of—by withdrawing from them completely. She despised everything about her existence; it was just too much for her to handle and she couldn't think about it anymore.

At the other end of Katie's trip, someone else was experiencing anxious moments at her impending arrival. June Reynolds, a soft-spoken, lanky brunette who sported heavy-rimmed bifocals on her otherwise pretty face, had not slept at all the previous night. When she first heard of the Welfare Department's program to place needy, troubled children from the city in country homes for a couple of weeks, it didn't really interest her. She was busy enough taking care of her own family having just given birth to her second son, and she also enjoyed helping her husband maintain their farm.

June had been mildly disappointed when her second child turned out to be another boy. She loved her sons, but she was very close to her mother and her sisters, and she thought having a girl would assure her of that same comradeship in the future. She already saw the difference in her relationship with her firstborn, Roger, who was ten years old. He was fun-loving, but he was very independent and resisted her attempts at affection on the grounds that it was too sissy. As each year passed, he had more in common with his dad; they disappeared for hours to practice whatever sport was in season.

It was quite by accident that June and her husband found themselves in the local welfare office signing the papers that would bring Katie to their home for two weeks. A few days prior while returning a borrowed item to Emma, one of her neighbors, June ran into a cheerful looking young man who was about to depart Emma's home.

"Junie, this is my nephew, Jimmy, the social worker." Emma rattled on; she could talk the ear off of a brass monkey. "Jimmy's been assigned the job of getting homes in the area for the city kids for the summer. He certainly knew where to come to first—to his old Aunt Emma. He figured I'd spread the word around quicker than advertising in the local newspaper." Emma laughed heartily at her insight into her own personality.

"I'll let you know, son, if anyone around here is interested. By golly, I must be going senile. Why, Junie here would be perfect for something like that. She and her husband are the kindest two people on the face of the earth, and I can vouch for the fact that they are great parents. I wouldn't let her out of your sight, Jimmy!"

Shifting uncomfortably from one foot to the other, June stared down at the porch to avoid the anxious eyes of the young man. Perceiving instantly that June was not enthusiastic about the idea, Jimmy quickly bid goodbye to the ladies.

"Don't worry about it Mrs.-er. I'm sorry, I didn't get your last name."

"Reynolds, but you can call me June."

"Mrs. Reynolds, it's a big responsibility...taking on someone else's child, even for just a short period of time. No need to feel bad, we will find homes for all of them." As he flashed a warm smile at June, she could tell his reply was totally genuine. In thinking it over afterwards, June had no idea what made her shout to him as he opened the door of his car.

"If you can guarantee me a little girl, I might be interested." Stunned at the words that had just come from her mouth, she thought if she could laugh it would sound as if she meant it as a joke, but she didn't feel like laughing. Jimmy was aware that June was still not sure and he was dead set against pressuring people, so he arranged to meet her family and discuss the whole issue the following evening. When June relayed the incident to her husband Sam, she was thoroughly honest about her feelings. Although he was somewhat surprised she would only consider a girl, Sam took her in his arms.

"If it's a little girl you want, it's a little girl you're going to get; no one deserves it more than you." She couldn't have loved Sam any more than she did at that particular moment, although he made her feel this way about him quite often. By the time Jimmy arrived at the house, June and Sam were completely enthusiastic. What they didn't expect was that they would spend most of their visit with Jimmy in tears as he discussed case after case of children who were available. June wanted them all.

When Jimmy first read the file on Katie Ramie, he made himself a personal vow that he would place her in one of the homes in his area. There were other kids who were so poor they didn't know where their next meal was coming from, but something about Katie's case appealed to Jimmy's intense interest in the psychological aspect of his job. From the bits and pieces the Welfare Department had gathered on the child from her aunt, she was virtually homeless and had become that way in a matter of hours. Her mother was insane and had been committed to an institution with little hope of recovery, two of her brothers had been murdered by her mother, and she had not seen her father or her surviving brother and sister since the tragedy about four months ago.

He couldn't begin to imagine the turmoil the child must be going through. To top it off, she had spent short periods of time in the homes of relatives, one of whom admitted Katie seemed very disturbed and hoped the vacation might help her. It was all of these facts, combined with the affection and understanding he immediately saw in June and Sam, which resulted in his bringing Katie to their attention. He went so far as to obtain the newspaper article on the recent incident, so as not to hide the facts surrounding the child's case in order to dupe the couple into taking her when they might otherwise turn her down. On the contrary, he wanted to communicate every known aspect of Katie's life, leaving no stone unturned, so that his clients would be totally aware of what they were getting themselves into.

Feeling overwhelmed with grief as she read the article, June had secretly favored Katie from the beginning, having had the opportunity to see a picture of the flaxen blonde, blue-eyed, freckle-faced little girl. She wondered now if she could still manage the wide smile her picture showed. Like mother, like daughter...June couldn't help the wild, terrifying thought that flashed through her mind and, as if he had a sixth sense, Jimmy responded to her unspoken concern.

"Mr. and Mrs. Reynolds...excuse me, June and Sam. Katie Ramie has been through hell these past few months. I can't guarantee she will be all there when she arrives, but I can't say that about any of the children you see here. I would like to believe this little girl could and should respond to anyone who shows her love. All I can say to you is if it doesn't work out, we can arrange to have her removed quickly. Of course, that might not make up for the inconvenience you might be caused, but that is the best recourse we can offer." June was liking Jimmy more and more as the evening wore on, and felt reassured by his ability to say the right things at exactly the right time, making her feel good even about her own fears.

Jimmy's lost here in this one horse town, June thought. *He should be out there somewhere on the staff of some big psychiatric hospital saving people from themselves.* As her thoughts turned from Jimmy to the small girl in the picture she was still holding tightly, June looked at Sam. Nodding in unison, they both said at the same time, "We'll take Katie."

Jimmy laughed as he inquired, "Do you do that all the time?"

He laughed harder when they again responded in perfect synchrony, "You bet!"

Standing at the train station with her family, June felt threatened. Had she bit off more than she could chew? She looked at Sam who flashed her a most reassuring grin, and decided this kid was going to get a heck of a lot of love if nothing else.

Katie thought her legs would surely collapse beneath her as she disembarked from the vehicle which had temporarily separated her from her adversaries.

June felt hot wetness on her eyelids as she watched the pathetically skinny child, pale beyond belief and obviously struggling to keep herself upright, slowly and reluctantly plant both her feet on the platform. She felt as if her heart was strangling her in its attempt to reach out with compassion, but a deep maternal instinct warned June immediately that this pitiful child was damaged goods, like a wounded bird clipped of its wings. With a strange feeling of foreboding combined with a strong protective instinct she didn't know she had, June ran toward Katie, arms outstretched in a gesture of welcome. Standing immobile, eyes fixed on the ground as if searching for some valuable possession, Katie uttered not a word as June greeted her. She was equally unresponsive as June introduced her to the rest of the family, except June noticed Katie's eyes widened and her face took on an expression of even deeper pain when Sam lowered the baby so that Katie could get a good look at him.

The sight of the baby, the first infant she had seen since losing her brothers, caused Katie to reflect on a disturbing thought. She didn't really know her brother Marty; he slept most of the time in the few weeks he was home with the family. She reminisced at how she clumsily fed and changed him as well as her other siblings, during the weeks prior to her mother's complete breakdown. She was very upset when she realized she could no longer remember what he looked like, and she hoped he wasn't frightened when he was falling. She convinced herself that he kept right on sleeping and didn't feel a thing. She had no idea he had actually lived for a couple of hours after he plummeted to the ground.

Sam and June were immediately concerned about Katie's extreme remoteness, and wondered if they should take her beautiful empty shell directly to Jimmy's office. They hadn't expected a child so unapproachable; it was as if she was handicapped. June wondered if she had a hearing problem. What on earth would they do with her? Sam was proud of his reputation for seeing things through; he had suffered through some very tough times in his life and never once gave up, no matter what the obstacles were. He handed the baby to June and swept Katie's stiff body up into his arms.

"June, I think Katie is exhausted from the trip. Let's get on home so she can rest up." The decision was made then, there was no backing out; they would cope with all of this somehow.

Because Katie's quietness was calculated, she had to fight the urge to communicate with June as she enthusiastically pointed out the local sights to her. She was consciously striving to maintain an aloofness she felt was necessary in order to be less vulnerable in the future. She knew everyone was nice to her at the beginning, except of course for her grandma O'Malley who was always mean, but then they got sick of her and sent her somewhere else. She figured the same thing was going to happen here also.

Urged on by a combination of pity and a stubborn desire to right the wrongs that had been done to this child and make her happy, Sam and June were tireless in their efforts to shower Katie with attention. They were firm believers that love and affection could cure all ills. June noticed that even her ten-year-old son, Roger, who was the roughest boy in the neighborhood, treated Katie with a gentleness she never thought possible of her boy. Meanwhile, Katie silently enjoyed the attention this family showered on her. She decided maybe she would be a little nicer to them; just a little nicer, though, as she couldn't like them too much.

As the days passed, Katie's quietness became a distinct part of her personality. Soon she didn't have to suppress the desire to speak her mind; she just didn't feel the need to communicate. But even the most hardened creature would have responded to the warmth of June and Sam, and so it was with Katie. Each day found the imaginary barrier she had built around herself chipping away. She secretly adored June, and Sam had worked his way into her heart also. He had introduced her to her first, but not last, butter and sugar sandwich—a delectable delight that more than satisfied Katie's sweet tooth. Although she was still unnervingly quiet, Sam and June could see a tremendous improvement in her ability to convey her feelings, and the personal rapport between them was certainly getting better.

There weren't any girls in the neighborhood who were Katie's age, a fact which had not been taken into consideration by June. She was delighted to have Katie all to herself. Before a week had passed, Katie possessed the biggest paper doll collection any little girl could hope for.

June's sisters competed excitedly over who could do the most to make Katie happy, and Roger would occasionally let Katie participate in some of his activities, even though there wasn't much a girl could do to keep up with a bunch of roughneck boys. June gained a new respect for her son, marveling at his sensitivity to Katie's plight by protecting her from being hurt and taking a back seat while she was showered with attention by his family.

The first Thursday after Katie arrived at her new home was a dismal grey and ugly day with threatening clouds promising heavy downpours. To make matters worse, the baby, Robert, was running a fever and June decided to take him to the pediatrician's office as a precautionary measure. Katie and

Roger rejected the idea of accompanying June, so she gave them a long list of instructions on what not to do and departed with her well-protected bundle into the downpour of rain.

Roger and his other ten-year-old friends had been experimenting with harmless pre-pubescent sexual behavior. When the boys were together, they were inclined to compare each other while they evasively discussed some of the new feelings they were experiencing. On occasion, they played house when there was a neighborhood girl available, and there was always the inevitable trip to the doctor which resulted in perfectly harmless attempts to determine what the difference was between the boys and girls, and to experience the new sensations that seemed to come over them when they were involved in activities of a sexual nature.

Shortly after June left, Roger suggested to Katie that they play house. She immediately remembered how she enjoyed playing house with her little brothers and sister, being the mommy, and ordering everyone around. She felt a pain in her heart as she remembered how much Kevin had liked their games.

Roger didn't notice how unhappy she was when she reluctantly agreed to play with him. After picking up Katie's two new dolls from her bedroom, they went into Roger's room. She was not quite sure what Roger's role would be, but she was pretty sure he would not sit still for being one of her children, as much as she would like that. Feeling awkward at her first experience playing house with a boy who was older than her, Katie kept totally quiet.

"I'm going to be the husband, Katie!" She met Roger's declaration with her usual silence and, as she attended to her babies, Roger rambled on about the house and his work. Like a parrot, he said things he heard his father say on many occasions. When Katie served Roger his imaginary dinner, he suggested that it was time to go to bed. Katie wasn't as frightened by Roger's statement as she was by his aggressiveness. Having slept co-ed on occasion with her brothers and her cousins, Katie thought nothing of it when Roger hopped into the bed beside her, except she moved as far away from him as she could get until her nose was pressed up against the wall.

"I'm not going to hurt you, Katie. That's not the way a married couple is supposed to act, you dummy. You're supposed to kiss me goodnight." Katie thought the whole thing was disgusting; she didn't want to kiss a boy and didn't want to play his game anymore. As Roger persisted, Katie became more fearful.

"See this handkerchief? I'll put it over my mouth and then you won't catch any of my germs." It was a neat trick he had picked up from one of his friends, but Katie grimaced as she reflected on what Roger had said. She figured if he put that thing between them she wouldn't catch any of his stupid germs and wouldn't be able to feel anything either. She knew if she didn't comply, he would get mad and probably chase her.

Inching closer to Roger's prone body, Katie stared wide-eyed as he placed the flimsy cloth between them and planted a quick kiss on her lips. She didn't think it was bad at all, but when he came down on her lips again, this time with a harder and longer version of the first kiss, she pushed him away. She was surprised at the warm and tingly sensation she felt, but as Roger moved closer and pressed his lips against her mouth again, she thought she was going to suffocate. As he clumsily tried to mount her, she shuddered and tugged at him as hard as she could until he rolled awkwardly off her numb right side.

They lay side by side, Katie quietly sucking in air and Roger breathing heavily in a combined state of antagonism and apprehension. He knew that what he had done was wrong; he didn't know why it was wrong, but he was sure that it was. It was discerning for him to think that Katie might tell his mother what he had done, and he dreaded the thought of June's reaction. Since Katie arrived, his mom had commended him on a number of occasions for the way he had embraced her little princess, as she called her.

It hadn't been hard for him to be nice to Katie—she really wasn't much trouble at all. She never talked or demanded that he take her with him everywhere he went like his friend's sisters did. The sweat poured from his brow as he anxiously thought about what the future might bring. If that wasn't bad enough, he couldn't get rid of the extraordinary, splendiferous bodily stimulation he had felt when he kissed Katie. No matter what the consequences, he wanted to do it again.

They both made a reentry into reality at the slamming of the front door. Roger jumped out of the bed as if it were on fire, with Katie at his heels. June was not the least bit suspicious as she opened Roger's bedroom door and found the two children playing house—Katie in a sitting position on the floor pretending to feed her baby doll while Roger busied himself nervously straightening up the mess on his bureau.

"My, my, I see Katie has better luck getting you to clean your room than I do. I hope you two got along well together? Bobby is just fine; it only took Doc Bradley a couple of minutes to determine that he has an ear infection. Come on and get some lunch you two!"

Roger was close to wetting his pants from the tension of it all by the time his mother left the room. Much to his relief, Katie hadn't made any attempt to reveal what had happened and, as he looked at her after his mother departed, he was aware of a bond between them that convinced him she never would. All of his fears diminished as Katie gave him a subdued smile.

They played house again on a few more occasions, but Katie made it clear each time that she was not tired and didn't need to go to bed. She felt guilty about what they had done while June was out of the house; still, she enjoyed the feeling of closeness she felt as a result of their game.

When the first week of Katie's stay came to a close, she was already smiling on an increasing basis and June was ecstatic. One of the happiest milestones had been Katie's ability to look at, touch, hold, kiss, and finally enjoy playing with the baby. June cursed herself at their stupidity in bringing the baby to the train station and practically shoving him down her throat. She was sure that each time Katie looked at Bobby she had relived the nightmare of that awful day her baby brothers were killed. She vowed to herself that she would work to help Katie dwell more on the future than the past, and had picked up the phone a dozen times a day at the beginning of her stay to hear Jimmy's reassuring voice tell her that what she had just said or done was perfectly alright. He seemed to have endless ideas on how to deal with Katie, and June counted on him heavily during that first difficult week. To sit Katie down and discuss the events that had so drastically changed her life was possibly the hardest thing June had ever done.

Sam had taken Roger to a softball game, and Bobby was sleeping blissfully in his room. It was early afternoon and, as she sat in her rocking chair on the porch, June enticed Katie onto her lap with a lollipop. A cool breeze was blowing and they were soon both as comfortable as two peas in a pod, enjoying the back and forth motion of the chair and the beautiful scenery around them. June cleared her throat in nervous anticipation of the upcoming conversation.

"Katie, honey, I'd like to talk to you about your family if it wouldn't upset you too much." Feeling Katie go stiff in her arms, June had the urge to drop the entire discussion. Stroking Katie's back with one hand and her arm with the other in an effort to relax her, she took a deep breath.

"I really think it would be a good idea to talk about how you feel, sweetheart. A lot of people are concerned that you are hiding something inside you and that is really not a good thing." Swallowing hard, June stopped speaking to collect her thoughts for the pulse of the conversation which was about to begin.

"I know exactly what happened to your family, and I think that you possibly know some of what happened. So if you have any questions, I will try my best to answer them for you. Don't be afraid. Please don't be afraid to talk to me." June desperately wondered what she would do if she turned Katie off completely. She couldn't bear that thought. What if she had pushed her too soon? Why hadn't she waited a little longer? But they only had another week, and the first one had flown by so quickly. Hugging Katie closer to her, she wished she had more time and that she could keep Katie safe with her forever. Feeling as if firecrackers were going off inside her head, June pushed these thoughts out of her mind as Katie began to speak.

"I hate my mom and dad!" Katie's blonde head was buried in the cleavage between June's breasts and she could feel her blouse getting wet. June was determined to remain in control of the situation as she bit her lip and blinked away the impending tears. She remembered Jimmy's advice that she must communicate in terms a child Katie's age would understand, and she hoped that some of the answers she had rehearsed would make sense to Katie.

"Oh, sweetheart, it's okay to feel that way. I do think that if you get your thoughts out you will feel better about your mom and dad. I know it has not been possible for you to talk to your daddy and mommy, and I think that has made you hate them. Your mommy is very sick. It is a different kind of sickness than Bobby's earache for instance. It is a sickness in her mind which is much harder to treat and cure. She was not really your mommy when she did what she did." June paused briefly at this statement to give Katie the opportunity to comment, but as silent minutes passed by it seemed she was still content to listen.

"For now your mommy is where she needs to be, and hopefully she will get better and come back to you as good as new. It might take a while, but I'm positive you will all be back together again. As for your daddy, I think he is probably suffering even more than your mommy because his mind is not sick. Your mommy probably doesn't even know she has lost any of her children, but your daddy has had to cope with losing two of his sons. Everybody handles things differently, Katie. Some people want a lot of people around them during a time of tragedy, whereas other people would rather be alone to cope with it. I think your daddy is probably the kind of person who would rather be alone. It doesn't mean he doesn't love you; it is just too painful for him to associate, you know, be with those people who were close to him. After he is finished grieving, I am sure he will want to have you with him again."

June felt a surge of relief pass through her as she came closer to the end of her speech. She hadn't been sure that she would be able to put it all in the right words, but now she felt comfortable with everything she had said.

"I don't want my mommy to come back and live with me. I'm afraid of her. She killed my two brothers and someday she will kill me." June flinched noticeably at the horrible tone in Katie's voice and the cold look in her eyes as she lifted her head to make her statement.

"Oh, honey, remember your mommy wasn't the same person when she did that. You must have seen her; didn't she act differently?" June replied with the only words that came to mind.

June felt Katie shake her head in the affirmative against her now soaked blouse, partly from Katie's tears and partly from her own perspiration. This gave her the incentive to carry on with the delicate conversation.

"If she was your real mommy, you know she never would have hurt her babies. She was under a lot of pressure with such a big family and, instead of becoming sick with a stomach ache, she got sick in her head. I promise you, Katie, the doctors at the hospital will do whatever they can to make her better." Secretly praying that what she had said would come to pass, June wished with all her heart that the conversation did not have to include reference to Katie's eventual departure from her home. June fantasized about how much easier this conversation would be if they could talk about the tragedy in terms of its impact on Katie as a past event and not what it meant for her future. June wanted Katie to stay with her so they could cope with what had happened together. She hated to see this child suffer with anxieties about what was to be.

"I could have stopped her, you know!"

June ceased rocking the chair immediately; she was stunned at Katie's matter of fact comment. It took her some time to respond to Katie. "What do you mean, honey?"

"I know I could have stopped mommy from throwing them out the window if I hadn't hid from her in the living room." Katie's tears now came with such abundance that June was forced to disturb the magic of their closeness to retrieve some much-needed tissues. The break gave June an opportunity to collect her thoughts at Katie's unexpected statement. Hesitantly she reached for the phone to call Jimmy, but decided she didn't have enough time for that. Not in her wildest dreams had June imagined that Katie was suffering from any guilt about what had happened. *Dummy*, she thought, *of course being the oldest child and having been in the house when it was happening, why wouldn't she feel some responsibility? My God, it was probably the heaviest load she was carrying around with her regarding the whole damned incident. Who would have guessed it? Jimmy hadn't even mentioned the possibility.* June rubbed her hands together nervously as she watched Katie wipe away a flood of water from her tiny face with the tissues she had given her. After they both sipped some lemonade in silence, June was ready to speak.

"Listen to me, Katie. You are not to blame for what happened that day." She hoped she sounded convincing, for she was absolutely sure of at least that one thing.

"Katie, you are only six years old, and you could not have prevented your mother from doing anything she wanted to do. By staying out of her way and hiding Jonathan with you, you saved him and yourself from harm. When a person gets as sick as your mommy did, they call it a nervous breakdown. The sick person sometimes gets very strong and can do things they couldn't normally do. You did the right thing by staying out of her way. If you had struggled with her, you might have gotten her more upset and then she might have hurt you and Jonathan. I don't want you to feel one bit guilty ever again about not helping out. You did the right thing by protecting Jonathan and hiding from her." Beads of perspiration were forming on June's forehead; the cool breeze was no match for the heat of the emotionally charged conversation.

Katie was now sitting in the chair opposite June's rocking chair, and she could see from her face that there were more unanswered questions. However, something about the child's almost relieved expression told her the critical inquiries had been made and might even have been answered with some satisfaction.

"Do you know where Barbara is? Is she really alive?" June blessed Jimmy for his insistence on telling them all the details about Katie's family.

"Barbara is in a foster home for children, which is run by the Benedictine nuns. It is a very cheery place with lots of other kids for Barbara to play with."

"Why didn't my grandparents ask me and Barbara to come and live with them, like they did Jonathan?" Knowing she didn't have a good answer to Katie's latest question, June lamely replied.

"In all of the confusion of that day, you ended up where you did and he ended up at your grandparents by coincidence only. No one specifically asked for him over you; it just happened that way. I'm sure they think you are doing just fine living with your aunt." June teased Katie to lighten the conversation.

"Why, just think, if you were living with your grandparents you never would have gotten to go on this vacation and meet me." A sad smile crossed Katie's face as she got up, sat in June's lap, and rested her head once again on June's chest. With that, the conversation between them ended.

Lately June had become obsessed with the notion of keeping Katie for good. She was concerned with the fact that Katie has been shuffled around so much and separated from her surviving siblings. She was not at all pleased about the prospect of her home becoming another in the line of temporary shelters Katie had known. She couldn't justify to herself, let alone to Katie, the insensitivity of people to the needs of this young child. Her biggest fear was that Katie would sustain emotional damage because of her departure from them; not that she thought she was doing such a wonderful job, but because her motherly instincts told her it was despicable to treat a child like a checker piece, to be maneuvered at the will of the player. As she felt Katie become more comfortable, June decided she had to pursue the issue of getting custody of Katie.

Meanwhile Katie kept going over the conversation with June in her head. It was comforting to be told she was not liable for the actions of her mother; she had not thought about her mother becoming so strong that she wouldn't have been able to stop her. She felt some pride that she might have saved Jonathan's life by insisting he hide behind the couch with her. As she regarded the circumstances further, she decided there was little consolation in June's revelation that it was not really her mother who had killed her brothers. Nothing June had said to justify her mother's actions could eliminate the possibility that she would do the same thing again in the future.

She was also bitterly angry with her father for ignoring her since the accident. She had thoroughly convinced herself that he hated her and blamed her for the accident. With June's explanation about her father, she guessed it probably took a long time for a parent to get over the death of a child. Katie had seen the look in June's eyes when Bobby was sick; she couldn't imagine how June would react if Bobby died. Halfheartedly she accepted the fact that her father was suffering and couldn't see her, but she didn't like it one bit.

As Katie relaxed in June's embrace, she felt safe and secure from any threat of danger. One feeling emerged stronger than any Katie had felt in her short life—the feeling that she loved June. They rocked together for a long time, both lost in their private thoughts of each other.

"June, I hate to be so cold but it's just out of the question. You wouldn't have a snowball's chance in hell of gaining custody of Katie. In the first place, her mother has been declared legally insane which makes her incapable of making any kind of decision with regard to her children. And, for goodness sake, have you forgotten she's got a father?" In an acid tone most unbecoming to her, June interrupted Jimmy's speech.

"Why shouldn't I forget she has a father? He's obviously forgotten about her."

"Okay, June, we can argue about this for hours and it still isn't going to change the fact that it would be legally impossible for you to keep Katie. Look at what is happening to you; if I had known this I wouldn't have let you participate in the program. I thought you would be able to handle the fact that it was a temporary arrangement."

"Jimmy, don't you understand what is going to happen to Katie? She will be shifted from one place to another until her mother is discharged from that funny farm, and then what? Oh, I tried to reassure her that her mother would be as good as new, but Katie's no dummy. She is as afraid as I am that her mother is going to do the same thing again. Can you blame her? I can't bear to see her go back to that environment. Please, won't you try? At least give us the rest of the summer with her, just two more weeks, Jimmy. I beg you. I promise I will accept her leaving if I know you at least tried to make an effort to help me keep her."

Jimmy quietly promised to check it out, knowing that June would not accept it if he protested.

Exhausted and drained, June was glad to be going home. She was not accustomed to handling confrontations and two in one day had done her in. Sam had reacted exactly as Jimmy had when she approached him with the idea of keeping Katie, and she had ended the conversation by slamming the front door as she left. She had never done that in the entire eleven years of their marriage. June couldn't wait to get home and apologize to Sam. She hated herself for being so unreasonable and disrupting her relationship with her husband over an issue she knew now was a losing battle. In the back of her mind, she thought that if all this resulted in being able to keep Katie for another two weeks, it would be worth it.

"If they want another child for two weeks, tell them they are lining up by the dozens at train stations all across the country waiting to hear from them." Jimmy's supervisor was red-faced with anger.

"All of these kids have problems, Jimmy, they all deserve a break. You know that two weeks is our policy under any circumstances and we are not an adoption agency!" He could not be moved.

June accepted with devastation the cruel words Jimmy relayed to her during the middle of Katie's second week with them. He had absolutely no success in getting an extension of Katie's stay, nor would anyone to listen to him about the adoption scheme. June was grateful her sister had taken Katie into town to buy her a new paper doll book. June needed the time alone to deal with her own grief before she had to explain to Katie that she would be going home. *Home,* June thought contemptuously. *What a joke!*

It was the next day before June felt capable of telling Katie she would be leaving on schedule. Although she had not made the mistake of building Katie's hopes by telling her she had requested an extension of her visit, June was sure Katie sensed that she was trying to keep her with her for a little while longer. Tears were already streaming down June's face before she got the words out of her mouth.

"Gosh, Katie, these two weeks sure have gone fast." June's body trembled as sobbing noises began to emit from her throat. She was disgusted with herself that she had finally lost control.

"Oh, don't cry, June, please don't cry." Katie had enjoyed her stay tremendously and had never let the fact that she would soon have to depart stray too far from her mind. These people had given her more than she hoped for and she dreamed about the possibility of staying, but she was realistic enough to realize her problems would not be resolved that easily.

"I'll come back and visit you all the time, and when I'm old enough to leave home I'll come back and live with you, I promise!" Frantically, she searched June's face for some ray of hope. June couldn't help but smile at the attempt this precious little child had made to soothe her.

"Oh, yes, darling, I want you to come back as much as you can." June's broken voice was barely audible.

Even though she had succeeded in comforting June, Katie's own distress became apparent as she hugged June closely and began to cry.

"Rock-a-bye baby on the tree top," June's voice rang in Katie's ear, sending warm feelings all through her body. The back and forth motion of the rocking chair made her drowsy as she thought about going home.

Katie felt sick to her stomach as she took her seat on the train, and reeled from the awful goodbye scene that had just taken place with the Reynolds family. She murmured over and over to herself that she shouldn't have let them be so nice to her; she shouldn't have come to this place; they shouldn't have made her like them so much. She wondered why they didn't try to keep her.

All of June's comforting words were now obscured in Katie's distressed mind—so vague and indistinct that they provided no measure of solace. She was unable to console herself by thinking about how much she enjoyed her visit. As she looked out the window of the train that would bring her back to uncertainty, she clutched the box of paper dolls which June had given her to take home. She wasn't even sure where home would be.

Meanwhile in his office, Jimmy wondered if Katie's visit with the Reynolds family had been a tragic mistake; a setback in her attempt to deal with her problems. Was it beneficial in that it provided a necessary respite from the constant emotional trauma she was experiencing at home? Would the reassuring words of June Reynolds surface at times to get Katie through the hard times she was most surely facing? He wished they could have kept Katie; there was no doubt in his mind she would have been better off staying with them in their warm and stable home.

It was Aunt Wilma, pushing a stroller with two of her cousins in it, who met her when she got off the train. During the long walk home she explained to Katie that she was going to live with Mrs. Winkle, who was one of her neighbors. Aunt Wilma said it was for the best and mumbled something about a crowded apartment and another baby on the way. The news of her departure from yet another home served to increase Katie's hostilities; the crushing blow being the fact that she would now be living with someone she didn't even know. Why couldn't she stay with her grandparents like Jonathan did? Why was she going to live with a complete stranger? These questions and more remained unanswered in Katie's mind.

The new lady she was to live with immediately reminded Katie of someone from Hansel and Gretel; the witch who wanted to eat the children. She had an ugly mole on her chin and was hunched over, walking with a big black cane. The whole thing was so creepy that Katie was terrified as she entered Mrs. Winkle's dimly lit apartment. She followed meekly as the stern old lady, who believed that children should be seen but not heard, showed her around her house, prodding Katie along with her cane when she didn't move. Katie reverted back to her sullen, quiet self almost immediately after leaving June, so she fit in quite well with the crone's ideas. The only plus was that she did have her own bed; a small cot in the kitchen of Mrs. Winkle's apartment.

Loneliness haunted Katie's every waking moment; she was sinking even further downhill emotionally. She felt deserted and she didn't care whether she lived or died. She wondered what it was about her that made people want to get rid of her. She yearned to be back at Aunt Wilma's with all of her cousins, for life there was much better than the dungeon she was presently in, and she also cried every night for the lost warmth of June whom she sorely missed.

Just as all hope seemed to slip from Katie's grasp, Mrs. Winkle apprised her of the fact that Jonathan was coming to stay with them. It took just this kind of news to get Katie's motor starting again. She wondered if her grandparents had thrown Jonathan out or if her daddy didn't want him around anymore. She wondered if her father had suffered a nervous breakdown also. The possibilities that loomed in Katie's mind were endless, but she was now sure she and Jonathan were in the same boat; it was comforting to know she would have someone to face all the bad things with.

The promised reunion with Jonathan did not come as quickly as Katie had hoped, but one day shortly after school started in September she came home to find him in Mrs. Winkle's apartment. Katie knew immediately Jonathan was very unhappy being with her; he cried all the time and kept saying he didn't like being away from his dad. Katie's hurt only grew deeper when she came home from school one day and Jonathan was gone. He went back to his grandparents was all Mrs. Winkle said; no mention was made of Katie going to live with them and she knew it was pointless to even ask.

Katie had been able to stay in the same public school in which she started first grade because all of the homes she lived in were within blocks of each other. It was the only constant in her life.

A few weeks after Jonathan's departure, Mrs. Winkle made a sudden announcement that Katie would be spending a day with her parents soon.

"But I thought when you killed someone, they locked you up forever?" Katie's voice was barely audible and it surprised her that she had actually spoken the words that were on her mind.

"Don't be silly, child. Your mother is getting better every day and soon she will be coming home for good. I don't want to hear you talking any more about all this killing nonsense. Watch what you say, young lady, and have some respect for your parents." Katie was bewildered and confused. She had long since given up any hope of a family reunion and had reluctantly accepted the tenacity of her existence. Even though she was extremely unhappy, she was coping. Now she had to deal with this new development.

The happy man and woman ran toward her with their arms outstretched. She waited until they were very close to her and then suddenly she darted out of their path. They were running so fast that they went right through the window she had been standing in front of. Slowly she walked to the broken window and looked out to see their bodies splattered on the pavement below. Her brothers and sisters had joined her and they were all laughing.

Katie was soaking wet when she woke up, rubbing her stomach to try to ease the haunting pain that was always there. In the future and after many years of suffering, Katie would find out she was born with a non-functioning, diseased gallbladder.

Because she was extremely violent when she was discovered by the police at the alley window, Nan was restrained with handcuffs and later with a straightjacket supplied by an ambulance medic. Upset at the fact that she had not accomplished what she set out to do, she screamed repeatedly that she was not done and they had better let her go. As she was leaving the apartment, she also made a statement which didn't make sense to anyone around her. "I wasn't raised this way," she repeated several times.

Either Nan deliberately ignored Jack or she honestly didn't recognize him in her sick state, for not one word of communication was uttered between them from the time Jack entered the apartment on that fateful day until long after Nan was committed to the hospital. When he approached her for the first time after she was admitted to Bellwood, she threw a cup of coffee in his face. Luckily it was tepid by the time it was flung at him.

On April 20, 1953, at nine o'clock at night, Nan Ramie was booked on two charges of homicide, and sent to Bellwood Hospital for observation. The first of a series of shock treatments was administered to her within forty-eight hours after the incident. Within a few days of the episode, a report was sent from Bellwood to the New York City criminal court building containing documented medical information complete with all of the appropriate signatures, which indicated that Mrs. Anna Ramie was insane at the time of the murders of her two sons and the attempted murder of her daughter, Barbara. Days later, a judge dropped the murder charges and declared her not guilty by reason of insanity.

The first doctors assigned to Nan's case at Bellwood decided to administer electroshock therapy immediately because of the violent acts she had committed against her children, making her a threat to herself and to those around her. This treatment of mental disorder uses an electric current to induce a coma-like state in the patient, and is also known as electroconvulsive therapy in that such therapy leads to a convulsive response in the patient. Electroshock was, at the time, a popular and effective treatment for quieting down the eccentric and erratic brain functioning of the mentally-ill patient. Even the side effects of irregular spasms, contractions of the muscles, or uncontrolled fits sometimes resulting from electroshock were preferable to the life threatening deterioration of the patient's brain functioning. It had been medically determined in extensive research that the minimal amount of permanent brain cell damage which this therapy was known to cause was overshadowed by its remedial benefits to disturbed brain functioning over a lengthy period of time.

Nan responded fairly well to two separate electroconvulsive therapy treatments. She did not enter a profound state of unconsciousness much to the relief of her doctors, but instead she became mentally and physically sluggish. This automatically reduced the level of threat she posed to herself and to others and allowed her body to get some much needed rest. For approximately three months she remained in this condition until she was put on psychic energizers to relieve her severe depressive state.

Nan's body was bloated as a result of five pregnancies and, now, psychic drugs. A look of extreme apathy crossed her once lovely face and all her senses were suspended somewhere in time, waiting to come alive again when the turmoil passed. Therapy was impossible at this stage and the psychologists merely watched her for indications of the return of her faculties, or the right psychological breakthrough moment when her mental state would be favorable enough to benefit from therapy.

The prognosis Jack received on Nan was obscure, with constant references to terms he could not comprehend. Through all the ambiguity, however, it was clear no one would commit themselves to a forecast that Nan Ramie would ever be totally lucid again.

Rusty Gladden, Chief of Psychiatric Care at Belwood Hospital, reached for the thick Ramie file and began to read the background material with half-interest. He was an underpaid and overworked state employee whose enthusiasm for his job had long since vanished in the maze of bureaucracy and endless paperwork that seemed to be his lot. Having watched society's defects come and go for years, he couldn't imagine how he ever thought he could make his mark in the psychiatric field. Where did it all go wrong? There was a myriad of reasons of course, all of which he had no interest in psychoanalyzing, just as he had lost interest in treating the emotional disorders of his patients.

Specializing in psychodynamics in school, which is the psychology of mental or emotional forces or processes developing in early childhood and their effects on behavior and mental states, Rusty considered the biggest mistake of his life to be turning down the offer to join a former colleague in private practice and accepting instead an offer to work for the state. As the years passed and he realized the majority of patients he saw were so out of it that memories of their childhood had long since departed from their conscious being, he dwelled on the severity of his mistake. He felt locked into the system, however, because of family responsibilities and the fact that he had given the best years of his life to this particular career choice, and didn't have the energy or inclination to face all of the hassles of establishing himself in private practice. The most critical and frustrating aspect of his job, however, was the fact that he was powerless to determine the fate of his patients; he could only make suggestions on specific treatments, release dates, and length of incarceration. The final and often unsatisfactory decisions were left to an obscure board of directors.

Rusty let out a sadistic laugh as he accused himself of psychological hedonism, for wasn't his own conduct now motivated more by the pursuit of pleasure and the avoidance of pain than it was by the ethics of his vocation? He didn't care; he was simply fed up with psychoanalyzing.

Nan Ramie, the patient, was ready for therapy after three long months recovering from shock treatments He had seen her walking the halls on his daily rounds; just one of the many half-alive people at Bellwood. Only a brief character analysis was contained in her file, a psychograph was as yet impossible to obtain in her present state, and he unhappily supposed that would be his inevitable task when he officially saw her for the first time. He had been the one to prescribe psychic energizers for Nan in an attempt to relieve her depressive syndrome, and he was encouraged to see she appeared less morose.

He believed Nan's mental derangement and lost contact with reality was psychosocial; her inability to adjust to marriage and its responsibilities the underlying reason for the psychosis. *Crap*, he thought, *you have to be psychotic to have five kids in less than seven years. Screw the childhood experiences on this one*, he mused, *this is a clear-cut case of severe baby blues*. Wouldn't people ever realize the pressures involved in raising children? Well if they did, he certainly would be out of a job—and for Rusty, that was a delightful thought.

On many occasions, Rusty also saw Jack, Nan's husband, visiting his wife on the ward. In silence Jack guided Nan down the hall as she shuffled beside him. They sat in the day room and it was sometimes difficult to tell which one was the patient. Jack nodded constantly in answer to Nan's senseless ramblings, stopping only long enough to light one of the endless cigarettes she smoked. He thought them a pathetic pair.

So here he was in the quiet of his small office, rubbing his burly fingers along his creased forehead as he ingested the facts from the Ramie file. Three surviving children; he groaned to himself. Leaning his aching head back against the chair that had served him so well all these years, he wondered what was happening to the kids. At eighteen months of age, the youngest surviving child would probably fare the best. He thought of a highly controversial study he was presently reading about very early childhood trauma and the ability of the very young mind to block it out completely with no negative impact on the personality. He tended to believe along those lines himself, convinced that trauma occurring at the age of reason or slightly before caused the most devastating affects on human personality; more destructive, in fact, than any events occurring in adulthood. He questioned why the youngest child was in a foundling home when he had read in the report that there were many relatives on either side of the family.

Jonathan's disposition at age five remained questionable, depending on how much of the trauma he had seen or been involved with and whether or not he felt secure in his new environment. Interestingly, Rusty noted that the surviving son had been placed with his fraternal grandparents. This was also the place where Jack Ramie, the father, was living. With the other two Ramie boys deceased, Jonathan would become more precious. It was still very much a male-oriented society as far as Rusty was concerned, and he saw evidence of that every day in every way. He could count on his fingers the number of female colleagues he had and none of them were moving on up, that was for sure. School counselors guided girls into business subjects, while boys were encouraged to take college preparatory courses. During World War II women entered the workplace to replace the men in combat, but once the war ended there was still a lot of bias against women who did not stay at home and raise their families. It was highly likely the five-year-old surviving Ramie son would escape this family tragedy without any scars. However, he was absolutely positive that Katie Ramie, the six-year-old, might be in desperate need of help.

He reread the account of the Ramie case as it related to Katie, realizing that from several of the neighbor's comments she had been burdened with the care of the children on an increasing basis during the pre-tragedy days. The police account made it clear she had been present in the house when her mother killed the other children. Even if she felt inviolable in her present environment, he was sure she could not possibly escape without psychological damage unless she was helped. He shook his head and his hands came down hard on his cluttered desk when he read that Katie had been in four homes since the incident, and the last two homes she was sent to were with complete strangers. He couldn't stand his job anymore. Helping this child was what he really wanted to do; Band-aiding her mother and eventually sending her home until she broke down again did not interest him at all.

Later in one of his interviews with Nan's husband Jack, it shocked Rusty when he discovered that the man had not been to see his oldest daughter since the incident. He yearned to talk to the child but, alas, there was no program that would allow him to do this at Bellwood, or for that matter any place else in the state mental health system.

When Nan walked into Rusty's office for her first appointment, he was struck by several things. Her makeup had been painstakingly applied, her lips were perfectly outlined in bright red lipstick, and her nails were well-manicured and painted a bright red that matched her lipstick. He had never seen a patient recovering from such severe mental problems look that good. The last time he saw her in the ward a few days before their meeting, he had thought she looked very put together physically; not disheveled like most of his patients.

"Wow, you look very nice today, Nan. That's some color red you're wearing."

"Thank you."

"You must be feeling a lot better to have gone to all the trouble with your hair, makeup, and nails."

"Yes, I'm feeling great."

"So, Nan, how many children do you have?"

Rusty had caught her off-guard after the pleasantries of the first few minutes and she looked away from him. She remained silent for a few seconds before she replied.

"Three," she said, as she turned her face and stared at him directly.

"Are they the only children you have?"

Again she looked away and stared at nothing for a few seconds.

"Yes," Nan replied, but this time she did not look at Rusty.

In subsequent sessions he tried to get her to discuss her other two children and their deaths, through subtlety at first and finally with outright blunt questions, but she consistently disavowed the very existence of the boys. She also denied there were any problems with her relationship with her children or her feelings about herself. The only thing she did do on a consistent and frequent basis was to complain about her husband and his quietness. She actually told Rusty that it was Jack who should be getting therapy and not her.

Rusty was totally frustrated with Nan's annoying calmness at his attempts to break her down; to find some way of reaching into her mind and pulling out the reasons for her mental instability. It was his professional opinion that Nan was not in any way ready for release, and he vehemently resisted the suggestion by the hospital administrators that she be categorized as an outpatient.

After months of futile efforts to break through the fantasy world of Nan Ramie, Rusty eventually gave up and conceded to the wishes of the members of the hospital board, who were also pressured by overcrowding at the institution, and approved outpatient status for Nan. This meant she was free to leave the hospital for authorized short periods of time and was also considered to be the last step before permanent release from the facility.

Rusty reflected on the Ramie case as he signed the first temporary release paperwork for Nan. He decided Jack would have made a good prisoner of war; if he had tortured him with his penknife, he probably wouldn't have gotten anything out of him. Everything was hunky-dory as far as he was concerned.

Rusty knew Jack and Nan were totally mismatched. Jack was a man with his feet planted firmly on the ground while Nan soared like a bird; he had few words to say, she had too many; he was very serious and aloof, she was extremely social. They did have one thing in common: neither of them had a good handle on reality. The reality was that they could not afford, either physically or mentally, to have any more children. It would be a stretch for them to raise the three children they presently had without problems. The sad thing was that he was sure neither of them felt that way.

He knew it was a mistake to let Nan out. He had abandoned his earlier opinion that Nan's breakdown was based solely on the postpartum syndrome. Rusty was convinced Nan was manic depressive as exhibited by her extreme mood swings from high to low. He was also quite sure she was schizophrenic due to her detachment from reality. From what he had read in research on schizophrenia, Rusty knew enough to know that Nan's delusions about her life were serious enough to fall into the realm of a severe mental illness. If he could have broken through the delusion, he was sure he would have found she suffered from hallucinations also. He was certain that while planning for and killing her children she heard voices. Witnesses had said she was screaming "she hadn't been raised this way," when she was finally restrained. He wondered what else she said; he was sure she had someone else to blame—the devil or God told me to do it were two excuses he heard quite frequently.

Her delusions seemed at times to be grandiose as she talked to Rusty about how wonderful her life was and how she perceived herself to be a great mother. He felt that her mental illness and her psychosis were made worse by childhood experiences and she probably would never be able to see things the way they were until she came to terms with her feelings. Rusty didn't think this was ever going to happen because she wouldn't cooperate, and he didn't have the time or resources to help her. He was sure she had residual schizophrenia and had experienced one or more episodes of the disease, even though she was not currently totally detached from reality. She also fit the onset profile for schizophrenia which manifests itself in the early twenties in men and late twenties in females. Nan was twenty-eight years old when she killed her boys. He had one other patient he suspected might be suffering from both manic depression and schizophrenia. This person was permanently institutionalized. He was sure Nan had inherited both disorders; two distinct abnormalities in brain structure and chemistry. *What a tragedy*, he mused. It wasn't lost on him that her mother was in her forties and her father just about to turn forty when they had Nan. He had read about studies conducted which indicated that children born to older fathers and mothers exhibited more psychosis than children born to younger parents. These studies had been disregarded as outlandish, but Rusty wasn't too sure they didn't have some merit.

Nan would continue taking the relatively new drug, Lithium; and Rusty had warned Nan and Jack in his final session with them that this drug could not be taken during pregnancy or if planning a pregnancy since it could cause harm to a developing fetus. He wanted to advise them not to have any more children, but ethically he was not permitted to say that. It didn't matter at all because somehow he felt they hadn't really heard anything he said regarding this issue, and he knew in his heart that even though they absolutely should not have any more children, indeed they would.

Jack Ramie, he guessed, simply found it easier these days to deny reality in the hope that everything would work out fine. He was a true pacifist whose behavior pattern was most surely the result of a family conflict of some kind, possibly between his parents. The Ramie case proved to Rusty that the system which employed him was too restrictive in nature for his theories, causing him to become stagnant. It was a condition he could no longer accept or tolerate.

It was a quirk of fate that on the same day Rusty submitted his resignation to begin his own private practice in pediatric psychology, Nan Ramie was released from the hospital by the medical board. It would have taken much more than this contemptuous news to dampen Rusty's spirits, but he couldn't stop himself from picking up his nameplate—the one they gave to him on his very first day of employment with the state bureaucracy—and throwing it against the door, watching it shatter into a hundred pieces. It was a pitiful epitaph to his career that a woman who had murdered two human beings was free to return home in less than one year, despite the fact that she had yet to admit to the act. He shook his head in genuine sorrow, convinced she would be back in the hospital as soon as she stopped taking her medication, a common and oftentimes deadly symptom of both manic depression and schizophrenia. The other fact he knew for certain was that Nan was very much an other-oriented manic depressive and schizophrenic; in other words, she was a serious danger to other people during her episodes. She was not at all like other mentally deranged people who harm themselves or take their own lives during their crises.

Katie felt like a wet dish rag by the time the appointed hour for the reunion with her parents was to take place; she had been plagued with diarrhea all morning long. She was in a state of dreaded anticipation mixed with anxiety and fear. She found it hard to cope with her mixed-up feelings of love and hate toward both of her parents. She thought about spitting on them and running away, but she was afraid of what her future would be like without her parents almost as much as she was fearful of what it would be like with them.

What is it that makes a child cling to his or her parents even when he or she is treated abominably? It seems to be something so highly innate as not to be affected by outside influences. The fragile insecurity of the human being and its need to be connected, attached to the originator of its existence regardless of the possible life-threatening consequences, has been proven over and over again. The statistics on child abuse cases that go unreported are staggering, all verifying the highly protective nature of the immediate family unit and the faithful allegiance of even an abused offspring toward his or her parent.

Walking down the dark, narrow hallway, Katie's stomach tightened again, an all too familiar pain that ripped at her constantly during the desolate days. She suddenly felt like the real Katie was outside of her body somewhere, watching everything with intense interest. The new Katie, who was about to turn seven in just a couple of days, moved quickly and with more courage out to the street to await the arrival of her parents. She was an empty shell having been picked clean of her innards, waiting alone on the street for the first reunion with her parents in six months. She looked like a waif standing solitary in her misery.

Katie was not prepared for the ardor displayed by her mother as she enthusiastically ran from the car, extending her arms around Katie in a zealous greeting. Katie's body remained rigid as her mother engulfed her, and her familiar smell, a combination of stale cigarette smoke and cheap perfume, overpowered her. She immediately felt a combination of nostalgia and disgust. As she reluctantly climbed into the back seat of the car, Jack acknowledged Katie's presence with half-lowered eyes and a forced grin.

She was relieved to see Jonathan and the smile she gave him was real, even though she felt animosity toward him because he had stayed with their grandparents and father.

Nan was single-handedly keeping the conversation going, incessantly asking and answering her own questions. The more Katie listened to her bubbly, happy voice, the angrier she became at Nan's lightheartedness. She was distracted temporarily by an urgent desire to watch her father who seemed uneasily tranquil. He had always been quiet, but now he was remote and it hurt Katie to think that he didn't care about her. She tried to take comfort in June's words of reassurance that everything would be fine, but she didn't believe that after only a few minutes with her parents.

A hearty laugh came from Jonathan who had crawled into the front seat of the car, as Nan tickled him under his arms. Katie couldn't believe what was going on as she wondered how this person who killed two people could be so happy. Katie herself was upset and she didn't even kill anyone. Her dad did seem miserable, though. It just wasn't fair. She thought Jonathan was a little traitor for laughing; no one should be laughing as far as she was concerned.

Katie's mood brightened when she was told they were going to visit Barbara, her younger sister, in the Catholic orphanage where she had been placed. The reception room smelled of incense and Katie felt uncomfortable waiting in the confined area. When she saw Barbara, Katie's eyed widened in disbelief at how much she had grown and she quickly moved toward her. Immediately Barbara began screaming, burying her face in the long, black robe of the nun who was holding her. At Barbara's obvious rejection of her, Katie's hands clenched in tight fists. She didn't realize that young children forget people very easily and Barbara was simply frightened by the new face. Instead Katie took it personally. One of the other nuns quickly suggested the family join the rest of the children and try to get to know Barbara better in her own environment. Katie unenthusiastically followed the group into a brightly-lit hall where about thirty children were being fed lunch from very small tables and chairs. A stern-looking nun ordered Nan to supervise the feeding of Barbara, who seemed to relax more now that she was in familiar surroundings. Katie watched with dismay as Barbara let Nan spoon soup into her mouth. Feeling defeated Katie watched with unbelieving eyes as Barbara responded positively to the attention her mother was showing her, causing Nan to grin from ear to ear and squeal with delight. "Oh, Jack, I think she remembers me."

At that moment Katie felt everyone in her family was happy except for her. If she was miserable before the reunion, she was now wretchedly disheveled. She had expected remorse and penitence for the long absence and lack of visits; she had not expected a gay celebration. She was hurting badly and she wanted them to know it and apologize for all of the suffering they had put her through. Instead they acted as if nothing had happened.

Katie tossed sleeplessly that night in her small bed in Mrs. Winkle's kitchen, wondering what kind of impression she had made on her parents with her quietness and lack of affection and enthusiasm. She wondered if she would ever see them again.

The next meeting with Nan and Jack occurred on Katie's seventh birthday. It was November of 1953. Even as she clutched at her new doll and thought about the great movie they had taken her to, Katie couldn't help acting hostile. She refused to answer their questions with anything other than a nod and had declined their offer to sit in the front seat of the car with them. Katie became panic-stricken when she found out one of her birthday surprises was that she would be spending the night with Nan and Jack in a motel room. Never in her wildest dreams had Katie imagined herself in the position of being alone with them overnight. Without Rusty to slow down the progress of Nan's release, Nan had been issued overnight passes within a week after becoming an outpatient. In their eagerness to resume a normal sexual relationship, however, Nan and Jack had deviously kept Nan's new freedom a secret so they could spend the nights alone.

Katie was lying stiff as a board in the small cot which the hotel manager had provided for her. Why didn't they keep her out of their plans? She felt sick to her stomach and didn't want to spend the whole night with them. She was afraid they might kill her and vowed not to close her eyes all night long. Katie flinched when her mother bent down to kiss her good night.

"What's wrong with you, Katie?" It was Nan's voice.

"I hate you both. You killed my brothers and you are probably going to kill me, too. I want to go home!" Katie stared in disbelief at her mother as she realized this was not a dream. It was all real. She had actually said what she thought out loud for both of her parents to hear. Jack remained at the bathroom sink, ignoring what he had just heard from his oldest daughter. Nan looked briefly at Katie and then quickly turned on her heels and continued to get ready for bed as if nothing had been said. Katie buried her face in the pillow and wondered if she had just imagined that she had said something, as it didn't appear that her sharp words had been heard by either of her parents.

On what proved to be one of the longest nights of her life, Katie's glazed eyes focused on the bed which her parents occupied as her mind constantly went over the same thoughts, things which she remembered June Reynolds saying to her what seemed like so long ago. She was not responsible for anything that happened to her brothers. The adults should have known there was something wrong with her mother, and she couldn't have stopped her from doing anything she wanted to do. They were the ones who were guilty, not her. They were the ones who should be sad, not happy. She wondered if June had been right, though, because it wasn't that way at all. Was she sad because she should have helped her brothers and prevented them from dying? Were her parents happy because they could blame her for letting Nan hurt the boys?

This scene, if it had taken place in a psychiatrist's office, would have served to dramatize the serious lack of communication that existed in this family unit, not to mention proved that the patient was not in any way ready for release. Most importantly, though, it was a testament to the lack of concern by society for the emotional stability of a seven-year-old who was trying to deal with the ramifications of a terrifying event without any help. She was crying out for help but was being ignored. Unfortunately, Rusty Gladden had been absolutely right in both his assessment of Nan and his concern for the welfare of Katie.

Chapter Three: The Years That Followed

"Come on, slowpoke, isn't this exciting?" Nan was already at the end of the long, narrow hallway before Katie walked through the front door of the apartment. From the corner of her eye, Katie saw a small bedroom with a giant window and by the time she reached her mother, she had also passed a bathroom and a kitchen located off the hallway. She followed her parents through the living room area where she noticed a set of French doors with panes of glass that had been painted a bright blue. While Katie was wondering what was behind them, Nan enthusiastically threw open the doors to reveal the master bedroom.

"Katie, you and Barbara will be in the bedroom right next to ours. Isn't it cute?" Looking past her mother as she spoke, Katie scrutinized the small room they had just entered until her eyes focused on the window; she was instantly relieved. There was a fire escape connected to the window, so there was no way her mother could throw anyone out of it.

The Ramie family reunion took place in mid-November, shortly after the incident at the motel in which Katie blurted out the fact that she hated her parents. The apartment Nan and Jack rented was on the third floor of a fifteen-floor apartment building.

"How do you like it, kids?" Nan was exuberant but Katie could only manage to smile weakly. She was too busy thinking. She was pretty sure an older person would have a good chance of surviving a fall from the new apartment. As she moved from one window to the next, Katie surveyed the concrete below, thinking that if she or Jonathan fell they would probably break an arm or a leg, but at least they wouldn't die...or would they? She knew a baby wouldn't do well at all.

As she closed her eyes, Katie pictured Barbara smashing to the ground...poor Barbara. Why didn't those hospital people make them get an apartment on the ground floor? Katie was convinced that people who worked in hospitals must be very stupid. She took great consolation in the fact that she was in the room with the fire escape; there was no way anyone could throw her out that window.

Even the fact that Jonathan was to have his own room didn't upset Katie, because the window in his room had no protective railing or fire escape; just a straight drop to the concrete below. All of a sudden as Katie looked out Jonathan's window, a very fleeting image crossed her mind of Kevin with his arms and legs flailing and his wide, frightened eyes looking at her. Someone was carrying him. She shook the thought from her mind quickly; it unnerved her because it seemed so real.

In the months following her release from the hospital, Nan remained typically as Dr. Gladden described her in his psychograph—possessing an unnatural surface calmness and an inability to accept reality. At the time he entered his evaluation in her record, he was not sure whether denying the facts was a deliberate attempt on Nan's part or whether the past had escaped her during electroshock treatments, but he believed the former diagnosis to be true because there were selective past events in her life that Nan recalled vividly. When he was asked to comment on Nan Ramie to the hospital administrators, he replied with confidence, "Unless this woman can be made to face the reality of the event that brought her here before she is released, specifically her part in the death of her two sons, then we will see this patient readmitted to mental institutions again and again."

Nan faithfully took her tranquilizers for the first couple of months, but gradually as she felt better she stopped. Although Dr. Gladden had made it clear to her that stopping the medication once she started to feel good was a serious issue with people who were manic depressive, she ignored his warning. There were also no support programs in place to follow-up on patients released from psychiatric hospitals to ensure they were taking their medications.

During this time, those people who frequently associated with Nan found her remote and extremely sensitive to conversations about the past. The incident in April was considered a taboo subject even when Nan was not present. Everyone in the family wanted to forget about it, especially her mother whose health had failed rapidly after the death of her grandsons. The only time Nan's pretense had been threatened in any way was when Katie, during her seventh birthday reunion with her parents, accused her of killing the boys. For a split second, Nan could see the face of a little blonde boy, a face filled with terror, but it was only momentary and passed quickly, just as Katie's words were forgotten. Nan heard only what she wanted to hear and blocked out anything unpleasant from her mind like a giant eraser.

The fact that Nan was not as physically active as she had been before she was institutionalized was not as crucial because Katie and Jonathan attended school for most of the day. Barbara, who was able to amuse herself without making too many demands on Nan, took a lengthy nap in the afternoon which allowed Nan to sleep during the day. Jack took over the care of the children in the evening and cooked dinner for the first few months; slowly, however, these duties were relegated back to Nan.

If anyone could be accused of deliberately blocking out reality it was Jack. In a desperate attempt to get everything back to normal, he went along wholeheartedly with Nan's obliteration of the past. It hurt him so much to think about what happened that he was totally content to ignore it; however, he knew things were not the same. He worried when she was home alone with the children she might try to hurt them again, but as each day passed he became more reassured that Nan was no threat to herself or to the children.

There was only one person in the Ramie household who couldn't forget about the past. Katie was incessantly filled with troubled anticipation of what her mother might do. Climbing the three flights of stairs to the apartment after school every day, Katie held her breath until she opened the door and saw that everything was okay. Remembering vividly the way her mother looked prior to her breakdown, Katie was constantly on guard for indications that it was happening again. Her mother was definitely not the same, although except for the strange way she acted during those days before she killed Kevin and Marty, Katie had a hard time recalling exactly what she was like.

The air in the home was filled with an undercurrent of tension. Jack was pathetically quiet and every time Katie looked at him, she yearned for the sound of Sam Reynolds' affectionate voice. She wondered why her own father couldn't ruffle her hair and give her big bear hugs like Sam did. She wished he would sit by her bed and tell her stories at night like Uncle Bo did, but instead he barely spoke to her.

The relationship between Katie and Jonathan was awkward. The year of separation and Katie's jealousy toward him for the special treatment he received by staying with his paternal grandparents during Nan's hospital stay caused a slight rift. She probably would have been much less envious if she had known Jonathan, who would turn six in January, had seen and heard a lot of ugliness from his fraternal grandfather during his stay. In any case, each day found them drawing closer together. Because Katie shared a room with Barbara, who would be two in December, she spent a lot of her time attending to the toddler's needs. She avoided her maternal grandmother as much as possible; she was sure that because of the slap she somehow held Katie responsible for what happened that day. Unfortunately, Katie was still not totally sure herself that she did everything she could to save her two brothers.

Katie's stomachaches and severe attacks of diarrhea continued even after the family was reunited. She dared not tell anyone about them because she was sure they were caused by eating dirt, which she did every day, either from the side of the apartment building or from underneath the hoods of parked cars. She figured she would eventually die from it; and, at times, especially lying in bed at night listening for disturbing sounds, she wished she was dead just like her two brothers.

Katie's seventh Christmas, which was also the first one since the family reunited, found her spending the night tossing and turning in euphoric anticipation of what she hoped would be under the tree in the morning. It was the happiest moment of her childhood thus far when she glimpsed through tired eyes the beautiful black and white coach doll carriage, which was her Christmas present. Jack carried Katie's new possession up and down the stairs a number of times on that blustery day in December so she could walk her baby doll up and down the street. She talked to the doll as if it were alive; convincing her that she was a good mommy and she loved her and wouldn't do anything to hurt her. During the holiday vacation, Katie played with her doll as if it were real. Her maternal instincts were strong and she derived great pleasure from taking care of her baby.

After her release Nan was required to visit with one of the hospital psychiatrists monthly. With Dr. Gladden gone, she saw whichever doctor was available. It wasn't long before the monthly visits gradually ended. Dr. Gladden's report on her went unread. Some of her new doctors thought that it was a good thing that she seemed to have amnesia about the deaths of her sons, and that it might even be an effective way of dealing with her life and what she did. It seemed to them that Nan was coping as well as could be expected.

In mid-January of 1954, Nan announced she was expecting again. The realization that they were having another baby came to Nan and Jack as it had on five previous occasions—without surprise or concern. They had not discussed the possibility of having more children, just as they had not talked about it at the beginning of their marriage or as each of the children began to arrive.

Katie felt weak like she was going to fall over when she found out they were having another baby. How could they? She could barely keep her shock hidden as Nan announced she was pregnant. She wanted to slap Nan in the face as she sat on the kitchen chair like a queen gathering them all around her for the announcement.

Later as she rocked back and forth in her bed, her arms across her chest, Katie thought about the new development. She didn't think they could have any more children. She thought for sure the doctors wouldn't let them after what Nan did. Then she panicked thinking her parents had done something they weren't supposed to do and they would come and take Nan away again and break up the family. But Katie didn't think that was really true either because they seemed so happy when they told them about the baby. She broke out into a cold sweat as she continued to think; another baby didn't really mean there would be any more trouble….or did it? She would have been happy with no more brothers or sister at all. She hated her whole family. In the midst of crying tears of anguish Katie fell asleep.

The beautiful baby lay contentedly in the bassinette. Suddenly two ugly hands reached out and circled the baby's neck, lifting it out of the crib. As the baby's eyes fell out of its head Katie screamed. She ran after the lady holding the child until they were on the fire escape outside of her room. The baby was screaming and blood was pouring out of the two vacant holes where the eyes had been. Watching in terror as the woman pulled apart the thick iron bars with one of her hands, Katie snatched the baby from the creature's other hand and fled down the stairs of the fire escape and out onto the street. She stopped at the corner grocery store and bought the baby a pair of eyes and placed them in the bloody holes in the baby's head. The baby grinned at her.

If Katie had been a typical seven-year-old, the impending birth of a baby brother or sister would most likely have been a very exciting event; however, she was programmed only to think of everything in relation to what happened to her family on that fateful day in April. Her thoughts were always negative, causing her to spend much of her young life in a worrisome state. She had the ability, not becoming her years, to determine how a current happening might possibly affect her and the family in the future. Having figured out that bearing so many children so quickly was most likely a big factor in her mother's breakdown, the knowledge that her mother was now free to have more children made her tremble with fear. It was never far from Katie's mind that her mother was capable of committing the same act twice, a fact most adults around her had already dismissed as unlikely. Since moving into the apartment she kept a hawkish eye on Nan, and at night she did not dare close her eyes to sleep until she was sure everything was okay.

In his lengthy report Dr. Gladden had also predicted trouble if Nan were to have any more children, and suggested counseling for the couple that focused on limiting their family to the three children they already had. Obviously nothing came of that suggestion either.

Not prepared either mentally or physically for the demands that a new life was making on her already tired body, Nan experienced more difficulty with this pregnancy than she had in the past. The weariness she experienced while on tranquilizers was nothing compared to the fatigue she felt as the baby grew inside her. To add insult to injury, the varicose veins in her legs began to flare up in the seventh month causing her obstetrician to recommend she stay off of her feet as much as possible. Aside from the usual debasement which occurs when one is not feeling well, Nan was already at a low point due to the fact that she was not taking her anti-depressants.

Because of Nan's deteriorating physical and mental condition, Katie assumed more responsibilities such as shopping, cooking, helping with the washing and ironing, and caring for Barbara. Katie didn't mind washing the clothes in the wringer washing machine, but she hated hanging the wash outside. The clothes had to be hung from lines strung across the alley on each floor of the building. It was always a race to see which tenant could get to the lines first. Because the sun was blocked out by the tall apartment buildings, the alley where the clothes hung was always dark; thus the clothes did not dry unless they were hung early in the day.

Katie always ended up hanging the clothes on the upper floor landings, many floors away from the Ramie's apartment. She was constantly looking behind her making sure no one was coming up or down the stairs who might push her out. She feared suffering the same fate as her two baby brothers, so every time she heard someone coming she would shut the window quickly until they passed and she knew they were no threat to her. Katie was always relieved when this chore was done, except she had to go through it all again when the clothes needed to be pulled in from the line later in the day.

Her shopping duties were limited to occasional trips to the small grocery stores in the neighborhood, mostly for milk, bread, and Nan's cigarettes. The Ramie children ate a lot of grilled cheese, bologna sandwiches, and canned macaroni and cheese, so cooking was very simple. There was no fresh fruit or vegetables on the menu; most everything came out of a can. She ironed almost everything she washed and was an expert at it even though she was only seven. She loved it when things were clean, which was kind of ironic in view of the fact that she was still eating dirt on a regular basis.

Katie was also a fanatic about keeping up her grades and felt pressured as her duties at home increased. Both Katie and Jonathan were enrolled in St. Anne's, a Catholic grammar school. Nan and Jack received a generous waiver of tuition for both children as a result of a program instituted by the church for the needy families in the parish. Katie was not comfortable attending St. Anne's; the walk to school was long and waiting ahead of her was a day of very solemn instruction. Things in the Ramie household were grave enough and the daily seriousness which dominated instruction in this Catholic institution was not conducive to Katie's emotional well being.

Very early in her schooling Katie exhibited a desire to excel. She needed and wanted to be the best at everything, and was frequently disappointed when she failed to maintain the often unattainable goals she set for herself. It didn't really get her any more attention at home as it was expected that she would get good grades because Katie always got good grades. But she had to study to get her high marks; she wasn't like other people who could grasp things immediately. It didn't occur to her to ease up even when she was overwhelmed with things to do; she just kept trudging along.

During the time prior to the birth of the new member of the Ramie family Katie was extremely unhappy. She stood on the long line outside of school every morning close to tears, hating the darkness in the school hallways, the smell of the marmalade sandwiches in the school cafeteria, and the strictness of the nuns and priests, but mostly hating what she might find when she opened the door to her home. She still felt scared, lonely, and unloved; feelings she was sure were not ever going to go away.

"Katie, your mother had the baby. It's a girl." Jack's voice was emotionless. It was October 15, 1954.

"When are they coming home?" Katie wondered how much time she had.

"In a week or so, I guess. I'll be home a little later. Keep an eye on your brother and sister."

Katie wondered if her mother and father were disappointed that they had another girl as she prepared grilled cheese sandwiches for Jonathan and Barbara. She was relieved that she wouldn't have to worry about a boy's name anymore. When Nan found out she was pregnant she asked Katie to think about names for the new baby, but every time she tried to think about a boy's name she cringed at the thought of anyone replacing Kevin.

It was a bright and sunny late October morning when Nan and Jack brought Amy home from the hospital. They had called her Amy just as Katie had suggested, so she already felt very possessive of the beautiful infant. She marveled at her little toes and fingers, and was more content at that moment than she had been since hearing the news of the impending birth.

Everything was going as well as could be expected for Nan until her varicose veins caused her to become bedridden again. Jack took a few days of vacation to help out.

When Katie was home from school she noticed her dad seemed extremely protective of the baby, much more than she could remember him being with the other children. He was reluctant to leave her alone for any length of time. She couldn't quite put her finger on it, but there was definitely something going on because her father was always hovering around. When he had to leave to go somewhere, it was obvious he was very reluctant to do so. Anxiety mounted in Katie as she witnessed her mother's depression resulting in frequent crying spells, and prayed it was because she was upset about her bad legs and the fact that she had to stay in bed all the time.

One night Katie was awakened by the screeching sound of Nan's voice as she and Jack argued. "It's quite obvious you don't trust me to take care of the baby. Every time I turn around you're watching me. My legs are much better now and there is no reason why you have to stay home from work. I can handle it!"

"I was only trying to help until your legs were better. I trust you, honey." Jack's toneless voice didn't sound convincing to Katie, but his reply did quiet her mother down. She thought about how sad it was that her family didn't talk to each other very much. She wondered if her dad was as afraid as she was that her mother would kill again. As she tried to go to sleep, her head pounding with pain, she knew she had to put these thoughts out of her mind. They were just too scary.

When Jack went back to work Katie was burdened with even more responsibility, and the strain of it made her very despondent. Additionally her stomachaches were getting worse and the violent attacks of diarrhea were even more frequent. Lying in bed at night waiting for her parents to fall asleep, she examined her small breasts for lumps, always finding one or two and then drifting off into a restless sleep, dreaming of how she was going to die from cancer.

Sandwiched between the birth of Amy, her mother's leg vein problems which rendered her bedridden, and her father's birthday and parents' anniversary, Katie's eighth birthday was a haphazardly celebrated event; a kind of afterthought. To make matters worse Katie was born on November 2, which in the Catholic religion is a day called All Soul's Day, a twenty-four-hour period of great sorrow and mourning for all of the deceased people in the world. The priests wear black as they celebrate mass and everyone walks around with their heads hung low, praying for the dead all day long. Katie dreaded the day, abhorring the fact that everyone was so sad on her birthday and the day itself never fulfilled her childish expectations.

By Christmas Nan's legs were much improved and she seemed to be in good spirits at being up and around again. She had also resumed taking Lithium after Amy was born and it seemed to be helping her mood.

"I insist you take them to the party, Jack. The kids will enjoy it and I'll be just fine with the baby." Reluctantly Jack complied with Nan's request that he attend the Christmas party his company held for the families of its employees. This would be the first time Nan would be completely alone with the baby since she was born. Usually when Jack left for his night shift job, Katie was always home from school.

From the minute Katie found out they were going to the party, she was thrilled. As they entered the huge theater she was in awe at the amount of people attending the event and sat mesmerized through a magic act and puppet show after which they waited in a long line for hot dogs, potato chips, all kinds of cakes and cookies, and a huge cup of soda. At first, Katie was concerned, sensing that her dad was upset about leaving her mom home alone, but her fears diminished as she enjoyed the wonderful party—the first Christmas party she had ever been to. To top it off Santa Claus made a surprise visit with a gift and a box of candy for each child. Katie thought she would burst from excitement when it was her turn to sit on Santa's lap and collect her prizes. It was a wonderful day she would remember for her entire life, and a welcome respite from her many worries.

However, Jack's heart was pounding in his chest and he felt as if his head was about to burst from his torso, so severe was the headache he had over leaving Nan by herself with Amy. He cursed himself for not having insisted that Nan's sister stay with her instead of listening to Nan's angry argument against the idea. He knew he couldn't continue to prevent Nan from being alone with the children for long periods of time; it was inevitable. Still it didn't make this first outing any easier to swallow as he tried his best to relax. He had long since lost the ability to enjoy himself, so he was both glad and remorseful when the party ended. All the way home, he was preoccupied with sickening thoughts of what he might find when he arrived.

As he turned the car onto the street where they lived, Jack couldn't believe he was seeing flashing red lights and quickly brushed his hand across his eyes to make sure they weren't a figment of his imagination. By his side Katie let out a terrified moan, and she could hear Jonathan's cries of excitement from the back seat of the car.

"You three, stay right here in the car and don't move." Jack was barely able to stand on his two feet to get out of the car. He watched as an ambulance and another police car pulled up. For some reason he couldn't run like he wanted to; instead, he forced himself to put one foot in front of the other and slowly walked up the stairs to his apartment. There was a lot of commotion going on both inside and outside of the apartment building.

As he reached the third floor, he lost his breath when he saw the door to his apartment was wide open. He gagged a few times from the wave of nausea that suddenly hit him, vaguely hearing the commotion in the distance. He used the walls to hold himself up until he was finally in his apartment. Very slowly he walked down the long hallway, glancing to his left to quickly survey the bedroom, the bathroom, and the kitchen; his eyes focused directly on the closed windows. Not knowing whether the quietness was real or whether his senses had failed him, Jack felt whatever had happened was just beyond the French doors. The apartment felt like a furnace as he peered from behind the partially closed doors, his head heavy with pain and soaked with perspiration. The bedroom was empty. He peered into the girls' bedroom, looking disdainfully at the closed window, and feeling that he couldn't stand the suspense another minute longer. Again he found nothing; no sign of Nan or Amy.

"Christ Almighty, where is she?" As he ran back through the apartment Jack could hear lots of commotion coming from above.

"Oh, my God, could she have gone upstairs…the roof maybe? Oh, God, help me please. Not again." Bolting out of the apartment Jack bumped into a stranger and stammered, "What happened? What the hell is going on?"

"I don't know, buddy. I hear someone's been killed." Jack didn't think he could take another step forward upon hearing the man's comment, but he put both hands on the railing and pulled his body up each unmerciful step. He hated the dark hallway with the dumbwaiter staring menacingly at him from each level. The dumbwaiter…a straight drop to the garbage room; he couldn't think about it. The roof…he wouldn't think about it either…had to block it out, block it all out…just get to the top where all the noise was coming from.

On the eighth floor a barricade was set up and Jack could go no further.

In the car Katie sat motionless, staring straight ahead and chewing savagely on her lip. In the backseat Jonathan and Barbara were chattering incessantly about the police cars and fire trucks, seemingly enjoying the commotion. Katie's emotions were always at heightened alert, but now faced with the prospect of having her worst fear come true that her mother had killed again, she had but two thoughts. She really loved little Amy and didn't want anything to happen to her even if it meant they would put her mother away for good this time. Secondly it would be nice not having to worry about being murdered anymore. *Poor Amy*, she wondered what Nan did to her.

Petrified Katie turned her head to see if any of the windows in the Ramie apartment were open. It was small comfort as the tightly closed windows stared back at her because there were three windows on the other side of the building that she couldn't see.

Katie was bleeding now from her lip and from her hand. She had unconsciously been digging her nails into her hand from the time the car pulled into their street. She reached for the latch on the car door; she couldn't wait any longer for an answer to what was going on.

Just as Jack was about to tell the stern policeman manning the barricade why he was so intent with getting through, he saw a few people in the corner murmuring to each other. Through eyes dimmed with fright he thought he saw a familiar figure. In a hoarse voice he half-whispered her name…"Nan!"

She turned then and he could see a baby in her arms. His entire body went slack.

"Jack, you're home." Nan didn't notice Jack's disheveled appearance. She wasted no time filling him in on the details. As Jack leaned his exhausted body against the wall and closed his eyes, a flood of relief washed over him; he did not hear a word Nan spoke.

Katie was standing by the car door contemplating leaving Jonathan and Barbara alone when she saw her father waving happily at her from the stoop. A confused sense of relief spread through her.

It came as a great shock to Katie that the happy-go-lucky owner of the corner grocery store had actually stabbed his wife to death. She liked him more than any of the other Puerto Rican people who had infiltrated the neighborhood over the months. It now seemed to her that what people had been saying about some of them having very bad tempers and carrying knives in their pockets was true. The incident itself did not have the same impact on Jack and Katie as it did on everyone else; it took a backseat to the trauma they had experienced over Nan and Amy during the ordeal.

After recovering from the event, Jack pushed all of his negative thoughts to the far reaches of his mind, convinced that Nan was indeed capable of being alone with the children without harming them. Katie, however, was still not sure.

After the murder of his wife the owner of the grocery store went to jail and the store closed. Katie then had to get Nan's cigarettes from a store a couple of blocks away; she hated these trips. She had to walk past groups of hoodlums standing idly, leering and gawking at her. It didn't matter to Nan what time of day or night it was, if she ran out of cigarettes somebody had to go get them. When Jack was not home Katie was relegated to the task. She moved quickly through the streets, not looking up, clutching at the money for the pack of cigarettes on the way, and hiding the actual pack on the way home. Once she turned the corner to where she lived the ordeal was still not over by any means as getting up to the apartment was also a dangerous task.

When Katie rang the bell it was the signal for Nan to look out the window and assure her she would open the door and wait for her to come up the stairs. The first level of the building had an area under the stairwell that was hidden from view. In many buildings this provided the perfect hiding place for predators and, indeed, many people had been robbed, beaten, and even killed in these very areas. Katie was terrified to go into the building unless someone was waiting for her, but more times than not, Nan didn't answer the bell, and Katie was forced to make a mad dash past the hidden stairwell and up the three flights of stairs, heart pounding in her chest until Nan or someone in the apartment answered the door.

Katie's eighth Christmas was not as spectacular as it was the year before but Jack did his best to make sure each child had something. Katie understood somewhat, knowing from the arguments she always heard between her parents that money was a problem; she was just thankful that thus far her mother had not gotten sick again.

Some responsibility was alleviated from Katie as Nan became more capable of assuming her duties, and she speculated on the thought that maybe things were improving. Amy was three months old and was a very good baby requiring little effort. Still Katie had long since lost the ability to be completely reassured everything would be okay…doubt was always and constantly present in her little mind.

Katie was still having problems getting to sleep at night and often would sneak into her parents' room and watch them in the living room through the cracks in the blue paint on the French doors. One night she saw then making love on the couch; her father on top of her mother, groaning and saying each other's names over and over again. As she began to experience some kind of tingly feeling Amy began to cry. Her crib was still in Nan's and Jack's room, so Katie quickly scurried back to her own bedroom. She was very disturbed at what she had just witnessed. Something deep in her subconscious was sending out warning signals…a premonition of impending doom.

Later that night Katie woke up in a sweat. She remembered very vividly what had awakened her. Little Kevin was in Nan's arms; he was calling her name. "Katie, come get me. Katie, come get me." Nan's back was to Katie as she held the screaming boy in her arms. Kevin was looking directly at Katie, his arms outstretched toward her, his legs flailing wildly against Nan's sides. Was it a dream or was it real? Had Kevin actually cried out to her for help or was she just imagining it? Tears coursed down her face as she tried to settle down, but like so many other nights her rigid body eluded sleep for hours.

Katie was unnerved by the repeated disturbing flashbacks regarding Kevin. She was positive she had been in the living room, hiding with Jonathan the entire time her mom was killing her brothers. Now she was not so certain.

Tensions grew steadily between Nan and Jack. Their financial situation was tight to say the least, but Jack's concerns about money fell on Nan's deaf ears. Nan became more and more upset with Jack and began to complain openly to Katie about his faults.

"Katie, your father is so quiet he drives me up the wall. Talking to him is like talking to a brick wall. He doesn't take an interest in this family at all and he certainly doesn't understand what makes me tick." Katie would always nod in silent agreement; she didn't want to upset her mother by challenging her. Even at her young age, she was smart enough to realize it wouldn't be in her best interest to upset her mother.

A few days later Katie witnessed a conversation between her parents which startled her.

"Did you take your medicine today?" Jack was standing by the sink in the kitchen, rubbing affectionately at Nan's arm.

As she jerked herself away from Jack' touch, Nan shouted sarcastically. "Why, are you worried about what I might do?"

"No, of course not, I was just checking to be sure you hadn't forgotten to take your tranquilizer today. I know how busy you are." Jack sounded apologetic.

What the heck are they talking about? What are tranquilizers? They must be important or dad wouldn't worry so much about her not taking them; something bad must happen if she doesn't. So many unanswered questions just increased Katie's anxieties, and she tormented herself with thoughts that her mother was getting sick again.

The Catholic Church was constantly organizing fund raising events, and getting the students to compete by selling tickets on the street for prizes was a popular activity in parochial schools. The students would get rewards for selling the most books of chances during the time period of the fundraising event. The more threatened Katie felt about her family situation, the more competitive she became in school, so each day of the contest Katie hurried to finish her chores so she could get out on the street and sell as many tickets as she could before it got dark. Even though she enthusiastically took her place on the corner every afternoon, Katie hated walking up to people and asking them to buy a chance; however, the thrill of possibly selling the most books of anyone in the school was overpowering. There was always a lot of recognition for the top salesperson, not to mention a great prize.

The day before the end of the contest, Katie was eager to dispose of her last book of tickets, knowing that if she did she would be the leader for sure. She skipped excitedly up to each prospective purchaser, careful to avoid the people she could remember bothering on previous occasions. When she had only two more tickets remaining in her last book, she spotted a big man in a tan overcoat heading her way and prayed he would take both tickets so she could go home. She extended the ticket book in his direction and started her sales pitch, when the stranger opened his coat. It took Katie's eyes a second or two to travel down his body and focus on the ugly, hairy thing hanging out of his pants. When he was sure that she had seen him, the man closed his coat and hurriedly departed, leaving Katie standing with her mouth open in the middle of the street.

If this man had known that Katie was not easily shocked, he might have saved himself for a more receptive audience. The immediate impact of the incident on Katie was embarrassment. After the pervert departed, Katie quickly looked around to see if anyone had noticed what happened. When she was sure no one else had seen what the dirty old man had done, she resumed selling the last two chances in her book. It wasn't until she was walking home that she pondered over what happened, and she decided that a man's penis was about the ugliest thing she had ever seen in her whole life. She told no one about the incident.

Katie beamed as Father Andrew congratulated her for her outstanding job in the fundraising drive. She was thrilled when he announced that her reward would be to select a prize from one of the booths at the annual church fair. Katie's name was announced by Sister Edward over the loudspeaker that day. It was by far her best day in school.

As soon as Katie fixed her eyes on the monstrous cardboard box filled with small pots, play dishes, utensils, and real cans of soup, she knew that was what she would choose for her prize. When it was passed into her eager arms and she struggled to carry it home, she decided it had been worth all of the hassle of standing on the street corner, getting up the courage to ask people to buy a chance—even what that dirty old man did didn't matter anymore.

The summer of 1955 came hot and humid, and Nan slept as often as eight-month old Amy did during the day, leaving seven-year-old Jonathan, eight-year-old Katie, and three-year-old Barbara, to their own devices. Little did Katie know her mother was already three months pregnant with another Ramie.

"Let's play house." It was raining outside and Katie was bored. "I'll make you both some soup." It was just the incentive she needed to get Jonathan and Barbara to agree to play with her.

"Jonathan, you're going to be the father and Barbara can be the baby," Katie ordered. She took out the utensils in her precious play kit and made each of them a bowl of soup as the three of them chattered to each other in their pretend roles.

"Okay, now it's time for bed. Come on, Barbara, I'll get your pajamas on. Jonathan, you get ready for bed, too!" Jonathan simply flung himself on her bed.

"No, stupid, you're supposed to get undressed," Katie barked.

"You're crazy, I'm not taking off my clothes…forget about this stupid game." As Jonathan snapped up from the bed, Katie put her hands on his shoulders.

"Okay, don't worry about it, I was only kidding. Let's get into bed." Just lying beside Jonathan was enough to send shivers up Katie's spine, especially as she began to recall playing with Roger.

"Hey, Jonathan, do you know what married people do when they go to bed?"

"No, what?" Turning on his side, Jonathan lifted himself up on his elbow.

"They kiss each other a lot."

"Yuuk…disgusting!" Jonathan exclaimed, wiping his mouth in a gesture of repugnance.

"It's not really that bad once you try it, and I have a way to do it without our lips touching." Before Jonathan could react, Katie flew to the top drawer in her dresser and retrieved a small cotton handkerchief.

"See, we use this between us and that way we won't catch each other's germs. Do you want to try it?"

"I guess so." Their lips met awkwardly at first, but once he got the hang of it Jonathan was a very cooperative partner. It wasn't long before he was suggesting it was time for bed, and he even started taking off his shirt.

Sometimes they would build a tent on the bed with a blanket for complete privacy from Barbara, and it was there that they began to explore each other's bodies. Both of them remained fully clothed as Katie was not in the least bit interested in examining Jonathan's naked penis; she knew it had to be ugly and not worth looking at. When they began lying on top of each other, Katie put a small towel over Jonathan's crotch so their private parts would not make direct contact. Katie was surprised to find that her feelings had become much stronger than they were with Roger, and she thought the prickling sensation all over her body was awesome.

Playing house was a frequent pastime during those long, hot summer days, while Nan spent most of her time resting in order to cope with Amy and the new baby growing inside her. Katie knew Nan wasn't right; she slept too much and she was very despondent all the time, always worrying about things that were going on in the world rather than focusing on her family and household chores.

Just before school began, Jack surprised the family with a trip to Rockaway Beach. He rented a small cottage for them—only two small rooms, a kitchen with a table, and a small bedroom with two full beds. Katie was ecstatic; she loved the beach. It didn't matter that they were like sardines in bed at night, or that she had to wash herself outside of the cottage in a fenced off area with only a shower head. As soon as she felt the ocean air and dipped her feet in the water, she had no worries.

Late in the day after cleaning up from the beach, she would walk to the local five and dime and use what little money she had to buy a coloring book of Doris Day or Rosemary Clooney. She spent hours coloring and dreaming about what it would be like to be a big star.

One night her mother's sister, Kate, who had a place at the beach, took Katie to stay with her and her son Paul. She enjoyed being pampered by Aunt Kate, who didn't have any children other than Paul. They ate out and then walked the boardwalk, playing games and winning stuffed animals. When they retired for the night, she fell asleep contentedly in a comfortable bed that she didn't have to share with anyone. Even though it lasted only a few days, she would remember the vacation with great fondness her entire life.

Summer ended, school started, and playing house stopped. Occasionally Katie felt guilty about having taught Jonathan something she knew was wrong, but she didn't make any attempt to talk about it with him to see what he thought. It wasn't that important in the scheme of things and it was just easier to ignore it. Also, Nan's mother passed away—Katie shed no tears over the loss of the grandmother who had shown her not one ounce of compassion in all of her eight years.

Amy was only a few months old when Nan got pregnant again. The new baby was due in December, a month after Katie's ninth birthday. Katie was absolutely numbed by the news but registered no outward reaction when Nan told her; she simply turned and walked away from her mother. How could they be having another baby? She knew they didn't have enough money and her mother was always complaining about the apartment being too small for all of them. What were they going to do with another baby? Why were they so stupid?

Later as Katie picked some dirt off the side of the building and shoved it into her mouth, she agonized about another brother or sister. She knew her mother was just hanging on to her sanity by a thread.

Sometimes Katie was trapped into listening to Nan complain about Jack. As Katie tapped her fingers lightly against the kitchen table, Nan droned on about Jack's inadequacies. "Your father is just too quiet for me. I knew that before I married him, but I thought things would change. I try talk to him, but I don't think he even hears me. Did you see the newspaper today? The world is going crazy. You have no idea what it's like to have a problem or two and not be able to talk to your husband about it. You know we really have to move to a bigger place. I don't know what we are going to do for money. You know, I think he keeps a lot of it for himself...the money, I mean. I hate having to ask him for money all the time. I'm going to get a job so I don't have to depend on him."

On and on Nan ranted as Katie resisted the urge to scream at her the things she really felt. Nan didn't need to gripe to Katie about Jack's lack of communication; Katie was well aware of it. He didn't talk to her, either. But it was confusing for her to hear her mom complain so much about her dad, especially when they were going to have another baby...and she knew very well how that happened. If her mother was so unhappy with him, why were they having another baby? How could she go to work? She could barely take care of Amy. She was positive her mother couldn't handle a job.

These conversations had a very negative impact on Katie and her confusion and feelings of insecurity about her family were heightened after each episode; she was always on high alert for the vacant, faraway oddness in Nan's eyes. She would never forget that stare as long as she lived and, on several occasions since Nan was released from the hospital, Katie had almost seen that dreaded look.

Katie never heard her dad's side of the story, as he didn't talk to her. Even though she had to agree that her father was painfully quiet and unaffectionate, especially toward the older children, it still bothered her tremendously to hear her mother complain about him all the time. After all, he was working very hard at two jobs to pay the bills, and Katie never saw him drunk or acting nasty. He had never hit her or anyone else in the family. Just how much did her mom expect from him?

Katie didn't like the animosity she felt for both of her parents, but she couldn't get rid of it. If anything it was getting worse with each passing day, and she was furious with them for having another baby.

Nan's hostilities also extended to Jack's family, and Katie was painfully aware of her feelings. Oftentimes when they visited the home of one of Jack's brothers or sisters, Nan would walk out of the house in anger over some purported offense, forcing Katie to walk with her. As Nan pushed the baby carriage down many a dark, abandoned street late at night, complaining bitterly to Katie, she despised her mother. She didn't like it at all when Nan took her away from her dad's family—they were so much fun to be around, and she hated to leave the parties. She wished she had the courage to tell her mother to leave her alone when she got mad and go walk the streets by herself, but she was afraid of what would happen to Nan if she challenged her; she was also afraid of what would happen to her family if Nan got sick again.

Katie's ninth birthday in November of 1955 passed uneventfully, with a small cake which also served as a celebration for Jack's birthday and the Ramies' wedding anniversary.

During Mass that same week as Katie watched Jonathan kneeling beside the priest, she experienced a pang of jealousy. He looked like such an angel in his black and white robe. After the service Jonathan introduced his family to Father August, who was in charge of the altar boys. He was a slightly-built Latino with a handsomely boyish face, large dark eyes with long thick eyelashes, a slim pointed nose the perfect length for his small face, thin lips, and a milky white complexion. He won Katie's heart when he smiled at her and his cheeks revealed deep dimples.

"It's so nice to meet you all. Jonathan is doing very well as an altar boy." He patted Jonathan's blonde head affectionately.

"Thank you, Father, and thank you for taking him to and from church. I don't drive and Jack is always working, so we really appreciate it." Katie wondered if she was the only one who noticed the harshness in Nan's voice as she made that statement.

"Oh, it's no problem at all, Mrs. Ramie." The priest drew Jonathan closer to him.

"Please call me Nan, and Mr. Ramie is Jack."

"Very well, Nan and Jack it is." He was still playing with Jonathan's hair, and Katie became even more envious, wishing he was touching her.

"Why don't you stop in for a cup of tea the next time you drop Jonathan off, if you have the time? It's the least we can do to repay you." Katie's heart pounded at Nan's suggestion.

"Fine, I'd like that." As Father August flashed them another smile, Katie quivered. She was truly infatuated by him.

"It's nice to see you all at church," he said.

"It doesn't happen very often, but we try. Usually the kids walk to church by themselves; it's difficult to get everyone ready at the same time." Amy began to cry, interrupting Nan's conversation with the priest.

"Well, I guess we better say goodbye; it's past this little one's feeding time. It was nice to meet you Father August." Jack nodded silently in agreement with Nan's parting words as he took Amy and began to walk to the car.

"I'll take you up on that tea sometime, Nan," Father August said as he disappeared into the rectory. Katie tripped over herself watching him leave.

Katie was totally smitten with Father August. She daydreamed constantly of being with him. In reality it was not that way at all. Father August virtually ignored Katie, giving all of his attention and affection to Jonathan. The priest became fast friends with the Ramie family and Katie sensed he knew what Nan had done. He was overly sensitive to her mother's needs and was constantly stopping by the house to see how things were.

"Would it be okay if I took Jonathan and Katie shopping?" Father August's cheeks were flaming red from the bitterness of the cold November day. Katie thought he was so handsome.

"Well, I guess it would be okay," Nan replied. Katie could have kissed her mother—she was so thrilled at being included in the invitation. Later Katie had to pinch herself as they strolled past all of the beautifully decorated widows in the stores on Fifth Avenue.

"What do you want for Christmas?" Father August asked as he tipped his hat to two old ladies.

"Well, I was kind of hoping for a watch," Katie said, keeping her head down as she spoke. Katie knew her parents wouldn't be able to afford such a gift, but it didn't keep her from wishing.

"Yeah, that's what I want for Christmas, too," Jonathan replied. He was at the copycat stage, always reiterating anything Katie said.

"Well, then, it's a watch you'll have." He pulled them toward a jewelry store and they spent a half hour looking at watches.

Katie waited with eager anticipation for Christmas, knowing she would finally have a nice watch to wear like all the other girls in her class. She was like a lovesick puppy when Father August was around. She was completely oblivious of the fact that he was unaware of her very existence.

On Barbara's birthday—December 18, 1956—Nan gave birth to her seventh child, Sam. It was just about two years since her release from the hospital.

On December 23, the last day of school before Christmas break, Jonathan arrived home with a new watch on his arm—a Christmas present from Father August. The watch for Katie never materialized, and she was grief stricken and bitter. To add to her devastation, Katie spent the entire Christmas vacation taking care of the family while her mother recuperated from giving birth to Sam. The problem with her varicose veins flared up again and forced her to remain in bed for an extensive period of time.

Jack again tried to make Christmas a special day for the little ones. He even bundled up all the kids on Christmas Eve and took them over to Robert Hall's clothing store, where he bought Katie a winter coat which she desperately needed. It was black and white herringbone, mid-calf length, with a hood lined with white fur. It was the cheapest coat in the store, but to Katie it was as if she had been given a coat lined with gold.

She was only nine, but by necessity she was already an able homemaker. She spent the holidays watching Barbara, Amy, and Sam, feeding them lunch and dinner, washing and folding clothes, and ironing. Once a week Jack would do the grocery shopping, armed with a list supplied by Katie. In some ways things seemed to go smoother with Nan out of action than they did when she was up and around.

On a hundred different occasions during that holiday Katie asked herself the same question over and over again—had she heard Father August wrong? Maybe he had only promised Jonathan a watch and didn't mean he would get one for her. She felt so stupid for believing he would buy her a watch. She hated Christmas. She hated Father August.

Nan was feeling better by the time school began, but as soon as Katie arrived home, she began to do what was necessary to assist her mother. On most days this meant helping to start dinner, setting the table, folding clothes, and keeping an eye on the younger children. Many times Katie propped one of her school books on the ironing board to study while she worked. The occasional pain in the pit of her stomach was now a dull and constant ache that spread to her back.

When the little ones were finally in bed, Katie put a large pot of water on the stove. When it started boiling, she carried it carefully into the bathroom. She knew the water coming from the faucets was already cold, and there was no point in even trying them. She stepped into the claw-footed tub and reached for the washcloth which she had earlier removed from her one and only bureau drawer. She dipped it into the pot, took the bar of soap and rubbed it into the washcloth, and scrubbed herself from head to toe with the soapy rag. She then put the rag back in the water and began to rinse herself off. When she was finished rinsing, she dumped the rest of the water over her body. All this had to be done quickly because it was freezing; it was always either too hot or too cold in the apartment—never just right. It was the same with the water temperature. After getting ready for bed, Katie did her homework. It was usually late at night before she crawled into bed; then it took her forever to settle down and go to sleep unless, of course, Nan was still wandering around or Nan and Jack were arguing—then she didn't sleep at all.

Katie shared a single bed with Barbara, who was still in the habit of wetting the bed during the middle of the night, and many times Katie woke up with a start as a warm surge quickly gave way to a cold, damp feeling against her pajamas. All she could do was reach for the towel she kept along with the washcloth in her bureau drawer, and carefully put it over the wet spot infringing on her space in the bed.

Amy's crib was now in Katie's and Barbara's small bedroom, leaving little room for any other furniture. Katie had absolutely no privacy at all. The new baby, Sam, was still in Nan's and Jack's room, but eventually his crib would end up in Jonathan's tiny room. The one bathroom in the apartment was always occupied, and everyone in the Ramie household learned the meaning of patience, especially when it came to going to the bathroom.

On one particular day shortly after Christmas, Katie was in the kitchen doing the dishes and listening to a song on an old pink radio Nan had given to her. She spent days digging dirt out of the crevices of the radio until it sparkled and, even though the music that came from it contained a lot of static, Katie was thrilled with it anyway. Suddenly Nan strode into the kitchen in a very unhappy mood. Katie knew why, too—she heard her parents arguing again late into the night. As usual it was mostly just Nan's angry voice she heard, until they finally stopped and Katie was able to relax enough to fall into a restless sleep.

"Your father is just about the cheapest person I have ever known in my entire life!" *Here we go again*, Katie thought. It was hard for her to give her full attention to her mother at times like these. She felt awkward hearing about problems between her mother and father.

"He has some nerve telling me I can't make telephone calls." Katie often wondered what it cost when her mother called her sister in Rhode Island and spent an hour or more on the phone seeking sympathy from her. Aunt Wilma's husband had been transferred to a military base in Providence and they decided to move the entire family there instead of staying in New York City. Katie missed her cousins, and Aunt Wilma promised her that she could come and stay with them for a couple of weeks during the summer. She was looking forward to it.

"Well, I'm sick of it. I ask him for a couple of dollars more than what he budgeted for food and he thinks I'm asking for the world." The radio was making it very easy for Katie to tune Nan out and Nan sensed it immediately. She stopped complaining, walked quickly over to the radio, reached for the knob, and turned it off.

"You better not get attached to this thing. It isn't yours."

Katie was stunned at the words Nan had just spit out of her mouth, and before she thought about it she said, "I'm going to tell daddy everything you said about him."

Before Katie knew it Nan was flying at her from across the room, slapping her hard across the face. Katie turned on her heels and went running into her bedroom. She beat her fists against the bedspread, silently whispering words of hate for her parents and her life. It was a long time before she got up from the bed. By then she had decided that all adults said and did things they didn't really mean. Every adult she had ever known had let her down and she despised them all. She felt there wasn't a person in the whole world who really gave a damn about her.

A few weeks after Christmas, Father August presented Jack and Nan with two tickets to the Ten Commandments, which was premiering at a movie downtown. Although somewhat improved Nan was still having trouble walking, so she suggested that Katie accompany her father to the movie. Katie held her breath while Nan and Jack discussed the logistics.

"I really don't want to leave you alone with the kids. Jonathan really isn't much help and I don't want you to spend too much time on your feet; the doctor said you should be good as new in a couple of weeks if you are careful." Jack shook his head as he looked at Father August, who was still holding the tickets.

"Well, Jack, I can stay here with Nan and the kids while you and Katie go. Really, you shouldn't miss it." Father August forced the tickets on Jack, who reluctantly accepted them.

"Well then, it's all settled." Father August winked at Jack as he continued speaking. "I'll see you tomorrow evening at about six." Then he was gone.

Katie felt both elated and nervous as she dressed for the movie. She put on her new winter coat, reveling at the fact that she had been the envy of everyone in her class when she told them of her good fortune. She wished she was going with Father August—at least he talked. She worried about what she was going to say to her dad. The prospect of spending time alone with Jack and making conversation was unnerving Katie, and the only thing she managed to say to him during the entire trip to the theater was a comment about how nice it was of Father August to give them his tickets.

Jack only nodded silently at Katie's statement, as he inserted the subway tokens in the turnstile. He never said a word to her as they sat in the dark theater, but Katie didn't care. She was totally enthralled by the huge screen and the fantastic movie, and for three blissful hours she had not a problem in the world. She felt serene and lightheaded as they left the theater.

As the train brought them closer to home, Katie was immersed in her own thoughts. There was so much she wanted to talk about with her dad—about the movie, about Nan, about their life, about her two dead brothers—but she knew he wasn't interested, so why should she bother? She thought he might be worried about Nan, but Father August was with her so nothing was going to happen. Anyway he had no problem leaving her alone to go to work every day. She figured this was the way life was for people—more unhappiness than anything else. She thought she would be so happy that night and she was for a couple of hours, but then it was right back to the same old feelings. She thought they should be talking to each other, thought there was a lot of things they could be talking about. It made her very sad.

Jack sat rigidly in the seat beside Katie. He had not liked the idea of leaving Nan alone even with Father August there, and he was anxious to get home and make sure everything was okay. He barely remembered his oldest child was sitting next to him; his thoughts were only of the children at home. He had long ago lost the desire to relate to anyone. He dwelled constantly on money problems and Nan's mental state. He was not deliberately ignoring Katie, he was just preoccupied. But how could she know that? How could a nine-year old understand that his life consisted of worries on top of worries? How could she understand that he had nothing to say to her; no words of encouragement, or thoughts for her future…nothing.

Looking out the window of the fast moving train, Katie saw only blackness. Her whole world looked just that way. Her throat felt parched and dry, her stomach hurt, and she blinked back tears at the disappointment of it all.

It was a shame Jack couldn't enjoy the outing with Katie, as everything was just fine at home.

Although the Ramies' neighborhood was predominantly Irish when they moved in, the Irish were gradually moving out and being replaced by Puerto Ricans. Katie was a fringe member of a group of very Irish and very Catholic girls. She never really felt like she belonged, however, partly because of her own insecurities and partly because of the difference in their family situations. She was very much aware that she had to take the initiative if she wanted to hang around with these girls—if she didn't force herself on them, they wouldn't go out of their way to include her in their activities.

One of the girls, Maura, was in Katie's class at school. Her family was very stable, and her mother was extremely domestic and protective of her three girls. They got everything they wanted from good home-cooked meals to nice clothing. Maura was an excellent student and Katie found herself measuring her abilities against that of her classmate, even to the point of copying Maura's handwriting because she felt it was better than her own. Katie had to study hard in order to keep up her grades, and the competition with Maura only increased the pressure which she felt from day to day.

Occasionally Katie escaped to Maura's house for the afternoon. When she did, she found herself depressed after the visit because her friend's home was so nice. It seemed to Katie that her own life was an endless succession of problems and disappointments from the lack of money for movies, candy, visits to the local hangout to buy a coke and a bag of potato chips, family vacations, nice things for the house, and a room of her own, to the hand-me-down clothes from older cousins.

The situation at home was definitely deteriorating. Nan and Jack were at loggerheads about money matters. On most days, the tension between them was palpable. Nan's legs were improving, but they were still slightly swollen and the skin ulcers near her ankles were not totally healed. Katie thought her mother had the ugliest legs she had ever seen; her veins were bright blue bulging streaks encompassing most of her legs. Nan's pregnancies had caused the valves in the veins to stretch so that they no longer prevented the blood from flowing backward and collecting or pooling in response to long periods of standing or sitting.

Nan wore heavy beige support stockings while she was up, but spent most of the time sitting or laying down with her feet elevated. Doctor James, the family physician, made a house visit to check on Nan, and Katie remembered him stressing that her mother's legs had to be elevated higher than her heart—it took four bed pillows to make this happen. Katie and Barbara had been sleeping without their pillows since Nan's legs began to swell.

Of more concern to Katie was her mother's obviously deteriorating mental state. There were times—sometimes a full day, sometimes just hours or minutes—when Nan was very energetic and elated. These were good moments, but it didn't take Katie long to realize they were short-lived. During these times Nan would send Katie for cigarettes, but she would include money for a hoagie and a small bottle of soda which she and Katie would share secretly, savoring every morsel of this treat. They would also listen to music on the pink radio that Nan returned to Katie during one of her better moods. Nan's mind raced with mostly unrealistic ideas and thoughts, but Katie listened anyway wishing that many of the things Nan said they would do would actually happen—like a trip to Rhode Island to visit her Aunt Wilma. Also on her good days, Nan taught Katie how to cha-cha and swing dance.

Alas, these moments were fleeting, as Nan's elation quickly turned to depression. She was exhausted from lack of sleep and the physical energy she expended during the mania. It wasn't long before her mental processes slowed completely and the sadness and melancholy followed. She began to sleep more during the day because she was up most of the night. Katie missed a few days of school, and Jack quit his second job at night to help at home.

Katie didn't know Nan had stopped taking her medication until she heard her parents arguing about it one night. She had been trying hard to relax and sleep because it was already after midnight. It wasn't until she heard Nan agree to take a pill that Jack was forcing on her, that she was able to finally fall into unconsciousness. It was a long, rough week before the Lithium began to kick in again and Nan became somewhat stabilized.

"Katie, take this ten dollars and get everything on the list. Bring the cart with you; you won't be able to carry all the bags in your hands. And be careful; don't take the side streets, stay on the main roads." Katie dreaded the task ahead of her as she accepted the long grocery list from Nan. It was the first time she would be doing the weekly family grocery shopping. Nan was not ready to face the world yet, and Jack was busy trying to make up for lost time on the job.

"Hey, baby, where are you going?" Katie tried to ignore the catcalls from the young men lounging on the stoops. She kept her head down and concentrated on the shopping list. Once inside the store, she engrossed herself in picking out the items her mother wanted while calculating the prices in her head to make sure she did not exceed the ten dollars she had been given.

When she was finished shopping and the bill was just under ten dollars, only then did Katie allow herself to relax a little. However, there was still the long walk home through deteriorating neighborhoods, this time with the precious groceries.

Aside from listening to more verbal harassments from idle men, Katie's trip home was uneventful. When it was all over and the groceries were put away, Katie proudly gave her mother unexpected change from the ten dollars. She felt very proud of her and her new accomplishment. However, she did such a great job that grocery shopping was added to her growing list of duties, and she felt even more resentment from the tremendous pressure to do things at home.

Katie's mouth ached so bad that she wanted to die. She couldn't stand it a minute longer and put her head down on the desk. Sister Bernadette sent her to the principal's office after determining Katie had a fever and that her mouth was swollen. The principal called home and about an hour later Jack showed up at the school. When he arrived, he seemed to Katie to be annoyed. The principal, Mother Seton, approached him with concern.

"Mr. Ramie, I believe Katie might have an abscess. She told me she has had a toothache for a week now, and she is running a rather high fever. I think she needs to see a dentist immediately as these infections can be very dangerous."

Jack scratched his head in concentration as he stared at Katie. She felt as if he wished her gone because she was causing so much trouble. "We don't have a dentist," he said flatly.

After a long silence Mother Seton said, "There is a clinic by the ell. Hold on, let me call them and see if they can take Katie on an emergency basis."

The last thing Katie remembered after they placed her in the huge black chair with all of the weird equipment hanging over it in a room that reeked of antiseptic was someone putting a big mask over her face.

She was standing at the bottom of the alley. She looked up and saw her mother at the window holding Kevin. "Here, Katie, catch him," shouted Nan. She threw him toward the other side of the alley, and it was impossible for Katie to reach him before he fell. She watched in horror as Kevin broke up into little pieces. As she frantically tried to pick up the pieces, a baby blanket fell on her head. She yanked it away and looked up to see a doll-like figure descending toward her. She put out her hands to catch it, but it fell right through them and into a hole in the pavement beneath her feet. When Katie looked down into the hole, she saw a troll under a bridge eating the baby.

When they woke her up, the toothache was gone along with three of her second teeth. She was in an anesthesia-induced stupor for the rest of the day, but she did remember the alley and the troll very vividly.

Laurie came into Katie's life at a time when she felt totally friendless and lonely. She was the same age as Katie, just about to turn ten, but that was the only thing they had in common. Laurie was the only child in a very well-to-do family. They bumped into each other a few days after Laurie moved into the top floor apartment in the building around the corner from Katie's apartment building. They became instant friends.

Katie thought Laurie's mother was the most beautiful lady she had ever seen, and her father the most handsome man in the world. Aside from that, Laurie's mother was the only mother Katie ever met who worked full-time. Every chance she got, she escaped to Laurie's house where the two of them played with their paper dolls. Laurie went to public school, and all of the stories she told Katie about what she did in school made her envious, especially the fact that she never had as much homework as Katie did.

Everywhere Laurie went, Katie was invited, and, although the demands at home were such that she couldn't accompany them very often, when she did it was always a marvelous experience for her. Because both of Laurie's parents worked, she had all of the possessions Katie dreamed of. Their apartment was well-decorated and they were constantly going on trips, out to eat, and to the movies—all of the things Katie wished her family could do. They were a loving, warm family, and actually talked to each other about everything.

Laurie was alone from the time school let out until her parents got home. She learned to take care of herself and was a very independent-minded young lady. Like Katie she was mature beyond her years, but unlike Katie her privileged upbringing had made her an extremely happy-go-lucky person. She was good for Katie. By the nature of her lifestyle, Laurie was able to provide Katie with an escape from the constant hardships of her own home.

Katie idolized Laurie. Aside from being a welcome relief from the Ramie residence, Laurie's home was a haven, bright and cheery with all of the things needed to entertain two pre-pubescent girls to their heart's content—fantastic snacks, the latest in television and radio equipment, all kinds of magazines, and closets full of games and clothes.

Laurie's parents were delighted that she had made a friend so quickly and were more than approving of Katie's frequent visits. They encouraged Laurie to invite Katie on their family outings so she would have someone her own age to enjoy.

Katie fantasized about living like Laurie did all the time; she wished Laurie's parents would adopt her. She couldn't help but dwell on the idea that she would eventually lose Laurie as a friend. She had been disappointed so many times before in her life with relationships that terminated just as she was beginning to enjoy them. Still, their friendship was the bright spot in her life at that point, so she worked hard to keep their kinship intact.

"Here, try some of this rouge on your cheeks," Laurie said, as she handed Katie the tube with the bright red cream in it. Laurie had clumsily spread it on her own face.

"You look like a clown, Laurie," Katie said, as she doubled over with laughter. She was thoroughly enjoying experimenting with Laurie's mother's makeup.

"What color eye shadow should I use?" Laurie was busy wiping her cheeks with a tissue trying to get rid of some of the red.

"I don't know. Blue, I guess. Your mom won't get mad, will she?" Katie didn't want to upset Laurie's parents in any way.

"Are you kidding? With all the stuff she has, half of it she doesn't even use. You worry too much, Katie. Let's play house. I'm tired of doing this anyway."

"Okay. I'll be the mother," Katie said, as she quickly put on eye shadow to go with the rouge.

"No, I want to be the mother. It's my house," pouted Laurie. Both girls were extremely stubborn which resulted in many spats. The battles were short-lived, as Katie always gave in right away just to keep the peace. She was an expert at that.

"Okay, this time you can be the mother and I'll be the father, but next time I get to be the mother."

"That's fine by me. We can take turns. I'll write it on this piece of paper so we don't forget." Laurie was pleased with her idea. She didn't want to upset Katie, as she was very thankful for her friendship. Her parents could buy her anything, but they couldn't buy her friends, and until meeting Katie, Laurie had not been very successful in making and keeping friends. Her parents expressed their concern on a number of occasions, causing Laurie to feel pressured, but now she had a good friend and her parents were very happy about it.

The girls began their game of playing house very innocently, dressing up in old clothing and performing household duties to pass the time. Each time they set up housekeeping, however, they talked more and more about sexual things. Katie was much more aware of the birds and bees than Laurie, who did not have the benefit of brothers and sisters, or parents who produced brothers and sisters quite frequently. Katie confided in Laurie about seeing her parents making love, and playing house with Roger and Jonathan, and Laurie listened intently as Katie told her what she saw and what she did.

It never crossed Katie's mind that she could play house with Laurie the same way she did with Roger or with Jonathan, and she was initially disgusted when Laurie suggested that they include bedtime in playing house. Besides, it was Katie's turn to be the husband, and she didn't like the idea of being the man one bit; however, a slight thrilling sensation erupted within her. She hesitantly agreed to the whole thing.

"Oh, I'm so glad you're home from work, honey." Laurie met Katie at the front door the next day, dressed in one of her mother's evening gowns. She looked very pretty—she was a beauty like her mother. Unlike Katie who was flat as a board and painfully skinny, Laurie already had slight bumps and curves in all the right places.

"Gee, you look nice. What's going on?" Katie really meant it.

"Well, I thought we would go out to dinner and then dancing," Laurie said, her New England accent becoming very pronounced. She looked and sounded much older to Katie with her mother's dress and makeup on.

"Here, put this on," Laurie said as she handed Katie one of her father's white dinner jackets. Katie immediately opened her mouth to object, but changed her mind and quietly put the beautiful, but too big, jacket on as Laurie fluttered her eyes at her.

"Now wait until you see where we are going," Laurie said, as she escorted Katie to the dining room which was now the restaurant. Katie's mouth started to water as she fixed her eyes on the feast Laurie had prepared. There were chocolate cupcakes with gobs of vanilla icing, soda, potato chips, and real napkins on the table.

"This is great, Laurie!"

"Come on, Katie, you have to pull the chair out for me. You're supposed to act like a gentleman, you know." Laurie shook her head in dismay as she pulled on Katie's jacket sleeve to get her to move from the seat she had already plopped onto in front of the food.

"Wow! I can't believe it, Laurie. This is fantastic! You must have wiped out all of the snacks in the house."

"Why, dear, I'm so glad you're enjoying it. Hurry up and finish so we can dance." Laurie picked up a short white straw and held it in her hand, pretending it was a cigarette she was smoking, imitating her own mother. Katie didn't like Laurie doing that; it reminded her too much of the way Nan smoked. She hated it.

"I'm going to turn on the radio now," Laurie said, when she was done with her soda.

"Come in the living room." Laurie held out her hand for Katie.

"This is crazy, Laurie. I can't dance," Katie lied. "What are we going to do?"

"Dance slow, silly. We're married, remember." As the music blared, Katie began to perspire as Laurie pressed herself against her. *This is wrong*, she thought, even worse than what she had done with Roger and Jonathan—they were boys. She knew that a girl dancing close to a girl just wasn't right. Katie was trying to ignore the fact that dancing close to Laurie felt pretty good, and the tighter she squeezed her, the better it felt.

Finally Katie decided to exert her masculinity and abruptly stopped dancing. "Let's go home now."

"Why? I'm having fun," Laurie pouted.

"Because it's late and we should go to bed. I have to go to work early in the morning." Meekly, Laurie followed Katie into her bedroom, watching as she removed her dinner jacket.

"Well, silly, get undressed," Katie said, tugging at the buttons of Laurie's mother's gown. Instead, her friend hesitated playing nervously with her hair.

"Do you want to go to bed, Laurie?"

"Sure, sure," she replied, but stood motionless waiting for Katie's next move.

"Where are the tissues? I need tissues and a towel," Katie said, as Laurie pointed to the box next to her bed.

"What do you want them for?" Laurie looked puzzled.

"I'm going to use the tissue on our lips if we kiss so we don't catch any germs." As Katie got closer to Laurie she remembered this was Laurie's first time playing this game so she would have to take the initiative like Roger did. She felt a peculiar type of power in knowing that it was up to her to decide what to do with Laurie. She wondered if she should kiss her first or make her get into bed.

Katie decided on the kiss first, pressed the tissue between her lips, and quickly came down on Laurie's half-turned mouth as she grabbed her around the waist and pulled her closer to her body. Laurie was quick to respond, and Katie found her a much more willing partner than she had been with Roger.

As she continued to kiss her Katie forgot Laurie was a girl, and Laurie began making little sounds that delighted Katie. She knew she was enjoying it, too. When the tissue finally became soggy and started sticking to their lips, it was time to do something else. Laurie reached up and removed the bits of tissue that remained on both of their lips.

"What do we do now?" Laurie's voice was almost a groan. Silently Katie pushed her down on the bed and began to remove the evening gown which Laurie had not succeeded in taking off completely. Even though her street clothes still remained on under the cocktail gown, Katie felt excited as she tugged at the silk cloth, her hands touching various parts of Laurie's body. When the dress was totally off, Katie slipped into the bed beside her friend and began to touch Laurie's small little bumps through her shirt. At first she did this softly, but in response to Laurie's squeals of delight, a little more firmly, remembering how good it felt when she was touched there. She brazenly moved her hand down between Laurie's legs and very carefully rubbed her groin area just a little.

Laurie followed Katie's lead by doing the same thing to Katie. They both felt a delightful tingling in the lower part of their body. They continued like this until Katie couldn't stand it another minute and stopped abruptly, springing up out of Laurie's bed. Katie kept her back to Laurie as she took off her father's dinner jacket, deciding that she couldn't face her friend again after what she did,

"My goodness, Katie, it's only pretend. We didn't do anything wrong! We're just playing house. What's the matter with you?" Laurie was upset that Katie had stopped playing the game. She was used to getting her way, and Laurie didn't hesitate to express her annoyance with Katie.

"You spoiled it, Katie. You spoiled our game." Laurie was crying when Katie left the apartment. She was confused. She felt much different than she did after playing the game with Roger and Jonathan—with them she worried they might get caught. Now, she felt dirty. It just wasn't right for two girls to act that way toward each other, and she was sure there was something wrong with her. By the time Katie reached home, she was deep in disturbed thoughts.

The girls didn't talk to each other for a few days and avoided each other on the street, but both of them were miserable without each other. On the first weekend after the incident, they made up, and the next time they were playing in Laurie's house they resumed the game which had initially caused the fight. Katie convinced herself it was just pretend, like Laurie said, and thoroughly enjoyed the whole thing.

After a few such sessions, Laurie talked Katie into kissing without anything between them, and she had to admit it definitely felt better kissing each other on their bare lips. As the novelty wore off, they played house less and less frequently; however, even though Katie thought of it as just make believe, she couldn't get rid of the feeling that there was something wrong with her and Laurie, but she had no idea why.

One Saturday Laurie invited Katie to go for a ride with her family, and Katie managed to get away. It was a beautiful day, and they drove out to Long Island where Laurie's parents looked at a dozen homes that were for sale while the girls occupied themselves squealing at all of the beautiful decorations, eating junk food, and playing around the outside of each of the different houses.

The girls were busy chatting with each other in the backseat of the car on the way home, when Laurie's dad interrupted their conversation to tell them they had decided to buy one of the houses and would be moving in a month. Instant silence permeated the car as both girls appeared frozen in their seats, and tears instantly welled up in their eyes as they thought of losing each other.

"I'm not moving anywhere!" Laurie screamed, as she crossed her arms over her chest. "I like it just fine where we live now. Why do we have to move all the time?" She continued to spit out the words to her parents.

"I'm going to run away," Laurie finally proclaimed. It was a very quiet and uncomfortable trip home for all of them.

Saying goodbye to Laurie was the hardest thing Katie ever had to do. It was more than just a friend she was losing, as there would be no more special treats for her. It was back to the dreary life.

"You won't tell anyone about the games we played, will you, Laurie?"

"Of course not, Katie, that's our secret," Laurie said through tears. "Mom said you can come and visit me as much as you want." It was a nice thought, but Katie realized there was no way she would be able to visit Laurie. Long Island was a long way from New York City, and there was no one to drive her there and back. She could not ask her father to do that for her; she barely even spoke to him, and she couldn't expect Laurie's parents to pick her up. No, she knew that would never happen. And she was right.

Many letters came from Laurie at first; filled with happy details of her new life, but always ending with how much she still missed Katie. However, it wasn't long before the letters became less frequent, and Laurie started writing more about her new friends than how much she missed Katie. The requests by Laurie for Katie to visit eventually stopped, as did the letters.

It was a long time before Katie could think of her friendship with Laurie without feeling broken hearted. She became even more disenchanted with her life, if that was possible. She was extremely jealous of Laurie's beautiful house, nice clothes, great parents, new friends, money, good food…everything.

While Katie was sharing Laurie's lifestyle it was okay, but now that she no longer benefited from it, she envied all of the things Laurie had that she no longer had access to, at least on occasion. Also, she now knew for certain there was a much better life out there than the one she was living.

Chapter Four: Moments of Anguish

Sam was two months old when Nan's mental health took a serious nosedive. She was lethargic most of the day, and jumpy and jittery by nightfall. Katie often found her staring at nothing while taking long drags on her cigarette. She was up most of the night making calls to her sisters, talking to them in disjointed sentences about nonsense. She read the newspaper and interpreted everything in it in an inappropriate way. She was fanatically preoccupied with events going on in the world, things that wouldn't have normally concerned her. She felt that only she alone could do something to solve all the world's problems, which was a complete joke because she couldn't even keep her own little world intact.

Katie took a deep breath as she opened the apartment door and entered the long, narrow hallway. When she saw Nan in the kitchen sitting at the table smoking, she froze at the sight of her and was instantly on high alert when she saw those eyes. Suddenly she was back in the other kitchen staring at the stranger who was her mother. Her vivid blue eyes were again glazed over, the irises having left their central position so that only the white corneas were prominent. Katie didn't need a second look to confirm that her mother was in trouble again; they were all in trouble again.

Jack was driving a taxicab a couple of hours during the day and working the night shift at the factory, so as soon as Katie got home from school he was ready to leave for his full-time job. As he walked out the door, he said absolutely nothing to her.

At the beginning of the ordeal Katie found only one effective way of keeping Nan relatively calm, and that was to agree with everything she said. The one constant objective in Katie's mind was to get Nan to lie down and sleep, for only then could she get the house in order and do her homework. Sometimes it worked; sometimes, like on this night, it didn't.

"Get out of the room, both of you, and take Amy and Sammy with you." With eyes wide with fear, Barbara and Jonathan were more than willing to follow Katie's instructions and leave their mother in Katie's care. As Katie approached the bed, Nan moved her body from side to side as she let out moans and sobs intermingled with senseless words. Katie's stomach was so tied up in knots she could feel all them in her throat, as she nervously reached out her hand to comfort Nan.

"Please stop crying. Try to stay calm so you don't get sick; you have to stop worrying so much about everything and try to sleep."

As Nan's hands fell from her face, Katie was struck by the agony in her expression. She wished there was some way she could lock her mother up in a room for a long time and let her work her problems out by herself. She hoped that maybe if she didn't have access to anyone else she would hurt herself instead. She couldn't forget for a minute that her mother was a murderer; she could very easily throw them all out of a window at any time. She had to protect them from that eventuality. It was fear of her mother that outweighed any tendency toward sympathy for her plight.

Nan calmed down somewhat after Katie's comforting words, but she continued to mumble incoherently. "Oh, I can't stand it anymore; everything is closing in on me. I'm tired, I'm so tired. No one understands me."

"Yes I know. Why don't you try to go to sleep; you'll feel so much better." Katie's words fell on deaf ears as Nan got up from the bed and headed for the kitchen. And so it went...on and on...as Katie, exhausted herself, consoled Nan with empty words, fixed her tea, listened to her mad thoughts, and never left her side for a minute. When Jack opened the apartment door, Katie quickly left the kitchen without a word, quietly turning her sick mother over to him.

Jack called off from the cab company a couple of days in a row. He knew he couldn't leave his wife alone. On the third day he called off, he was told not to bother showing up anymore.

Nan's condition deteriorated with each passing hour. Usually Jack was able to catch a few hours sleep after coming home from his regular job, but for the last few days the only sleep he got was during his lunch hour at work. It was difficult to tell how much his exhaustive state contributed to his bad decisions with regard to Nan.

Communication between Jack and the children was non-existent. Katie wanted to shout to him on many occasions that he should put Nan in the hospital, but she couldn't get up the courage to do it. It didn't seem like her dad gave any thought at all to taking her to a doctor, and she couldn't understand why he left them alone with her. He knew how dangerous she could become.

When the door closed and Jack went to work, the children were in the hands of Katie, who was their protector. Her instincts told her she was fighting for survival.

Jack and Katie were like ships passing in the night, one going to battle and the other returning from it. They were absolutely exhausted. Katie hurried to feed the little ones while keeping a constant eye on Nan, who during early evening was content to sit in the living room chain-smoking. Sometimes Katie got lucky and Nan actually slept until nightfall, allowing her to get everyone fed and bathed and homework done before bedtime.

All of the children remained in the same room while Nan was sleeping or roaming around. This was Katie's hard fast rule, and she would not allow anyone to break it; their lives depended on it. However, eventually night fell, and along with the darkness, Nan's psychotic behavior manifested itself.

"Why does the government give them more money? My parents were immigrants and they worked hard; they didn't expect everything handed to them. They certainly didn't act like animals either, stabbing each other and all of that nonsense." Nan threw the newspaper across the table. "I think I'll call Wilma and see what she thinks." Nan's hand reached for the phone with a quickness that surprised Katie.

"Mom, she lives in Rhode Island. It's a long distance call. Maybe you should wait until dad comes home to call her." It was her mother's third call to Rhode Island in the last two days, and she was on the phone for at least an hour each time. Katie was well aware they couldn't afford such an extravagance; she remembered all the arguments between Jack and Nan about telephone bills.

"No, he hates me to use the phone. He can't wait to get out of here every day. He doesn't like being around this house, that's why he doesn't talk. I can't raise you kids by myself; he is totally useless." Then the tears came followed by the sobbing, scaring Katie out of her mind as she led her struggling mother to the bedroom just to get her away from the phone and the younger children, who by now were petrified.

"Look, why don't I give you a nice backrub? Stay here while I get the rubbing alcohol." Katie ran to the bathroom as quickly as she could, stopped in the kitchen to warn the kids to stay together and keep the babies quiet, and returned to Nan before she escaped the bed.

Katie's mind was racing with all of the things she needed to say to her mother to keep her calm, as she spread the cool liquid over her perspiring back. She hated even touching her.

"You are a good mother," Katie lied. "I know how hard it is for you to take care of all of us, but you are not doing yourself any good by worrying all the time because it's making you sick. Please try to calm down for your own sake!" Of course Katie didn't believe a word of what she was saying; on the contrary, she thought her mother was a very weak woman incapable of handling her own life, let alone the lives of the children she had borne.

Every word out of Katie's mouth was a desperate attempt to get Nan to settle down enough to sleep. If she could have knocked her over the head with a hammer without hurting her, she would have done it. She had some success in sedating Nan with her soothing words, but it was always short-lived. It seemed as soon as the kids were in bed, Nan started acting up again.

Katie was feeding Sam a bottle while she watched Nan talking to Aunt Wilma on the phone. It was now eleven at night, a full hour and a half before Jack was due home, and Nan was as physically energized as Katie had ever seen her. On the other hand, Katie could barely keep her head up. She listened as Nan talked the ear off of her aunt; never sticking with one subject for more than a few minutes. It was obvious Aunt Wilma was trying to get Nan to hang up, but Nan kept saying, "Don't worry, it's perfectly okay. I can talk as long as I want." Katie wondered what her father would think when he got the telephone bill.

When Jack's keys sounded in the door, Katie felt a small measure of relief. When he walked into the kitchen, she immediately left and put Sam, who was sleeping, in the bassinette in her parents' room. She walked quickly into her bedroom where Amy and Barbara were sleeping. She closed the door behind her and fell into bed next to Barbara without even removing her clothes. Despite the fact that she was completely exhausted, it was going to be quite some time before she was able to fall into a troubled sleep.

As soon as Nan saw Jack, she became hysterical again. As she listened to the commotion from her bed, Katie hoped she wouldn't have to use the knife she had taken from the kitchen drawer earlier and placed carefully under her mattress within easy reach. She was not confident at all that her father could control her mother, and she decided she wasn't going to take any chances by being unprepared.

"Leave me alone, you bastard," Nan's shrill voice quivered. She could tell by the closeness of their voices that her mother and father were in their bedroom now.

"It's your fault that I did it…it never would have happened if you hadn't gone to work…it's not my fault." Katie grabbed the knife and bolted out of bed, putting her ear to the door so she could hear them better. She wondered if her mother was actually referring to how she killed Martin and Kevin. No, she decided, they never talk about that; it just couldn't be.

"Calm down, honey, calm down. Everything is all right." Jack's voice was barely audible to Katie, but it was clear whatever he was saying wasn't working on her mother.

"Yes, that's right, calm down, Nan…Nan, the nut, right; Nan, who has no reason to get upset because she has a saint for a husband. Well, it's not true. You are very hard to live with, but I have news for you. I will not let you drive me to murder this time." Nan was shrieking at this point.

So she did remember what she did to the boys—she was actually talking about it Katie closed her eyes tightly against the unwelcome words that were being shouted in the other room. She was completely petrified as she scrambled back to bed and finally passed out clutching at the knife under her pillow.

Early the next morning, Katie got up and hurriedly dressed for school. She grabbed her books and tiptoed past her parents' bed. They were both asleep. She knew she needed to get out of the house before any of the little ones woke up; otherwise, she would surely have to stay home. She didn't even stop in the bathroom to pee or brush her teeth.

She rushed into Jonathan's room, woke him up, and helped him get dressed. They scampered around like two little mice getting ready to make a quick exit before anything menacing appeared in their path. Only when she closed the door behind them did she feel relieved, glad to be away from the sickness and the fear.

Even though it was a bitter cold and windy day, Katie was actually glad to be going to school—a safe haven for at least a few hours. She worried about her brothers and sisters at home, but her dad would have to protect them. She couldn't understand why he didn't take Nan to the hospital.

"Mom's sick again, isn't she, Katie?"

"What do you think, dope!"

"I'm afraid of her now. Is she going to go away again?"

"How do I know what is going to happen? Anyway, if she does you'll probably go to live with grandma and grandpa again. So what are you worrying about?" As she bit down on her lip in anger, Katie continued. "Hurry up or we'll be late for school."

When Katie opened the door, it was just as cold in the apartment as it was outside, so she didn't bother to take off her coat. Her mother's piercing voice echoed through the apartment with obvious contempt. "That damn super isn't worth anything. There is no excuse for this place to be so cold. I've been telling you since this morning to find him and make him give us some heat. What the hell is wrong with you? Do you want us to freeze to death?"

As Katie held Jonathan's hand, she reluctantly moved down the hallway toward the living room. As they passed the kitchen they saw Jack holding Nan by her arm, trying to prevent her from going somewhere. Both of them had their coats on, and Nan's eyes were wild with fury as Jack struggled to hold onto her. Katie and Jonathan were able to slip past them, and ran quickly into the back bedroom where they found Barbara sitting on the bed with a blanket around her. Amy was standing up in her crib, soaking wet and shaking from the cold, and the baby was nowhere to be found in the room. Katie bolted into her parents' room and over to the bassinette where she found Sam under a bundle of blankets, sleeping blissfully, unaware of the chaos around him. Katie frantically wheeled the bassinette into her room, grabbing up some diapers from the dresser drawer as she passed by it.

For the next hour the children huddled together under the blankets listening to the muffled sounds of their parents' voices. When Sam and Amy started crying miserably from hunger, Katie knew she had to venture out of the bedroom to try to get some food for the kids. The French doors were partly closed and Katie tiptoed up to them, peeking through the crack. Her mother and father were now in the living room.

As she was figuring out her strategy, Katie froze in horror as she saw what her mother had in her hand; it was the big butcher's knife her Uncle Ralph, a meat cutter, had given to her dad. It was so big and so sharp that her dad kept it in a cabinet above the refrigerator, wrapped in two thick towels. Katie wondered how she got it.

"I'm going down there to see why he hasn't put on the heat. If you don't want to go with me, that's just fine. You stay here." Nan was screaming at the top of her lungs as she darted from Jack. Katie watched her father run after her mother, feeling like she was watching some horror movie and not her own parents. Without thinking, she left the room herself in close pursuit.

Just before Jack left the apartment to pursue Nan, he turned and saw Katie at the end of the hallway. "Call Uncle Ralph and tell him to get over here," he barked. Katie's fingers could barely dial the number. She should be calling the police, not Uncle Ralph; she was so scared.

"Aunt Paula, this is Katie. Is Uncle Ralph there?" She could barely get the words out; her throat was parched.

"What's the matter, honey? Is everything okay?"

"Oh, Aunt Paula, mom's sick again. She has a knife."

"Oh, Christ, wait a minute honey. Ralph…Ralph…quick, get the hell over here. Nan's gone berserk again…Katie's on the phone."

"What's the matter, sweetie? Quick, tell me what's going on." It was reassuring to hear her uncle's voice.

"Mom's got the big knife you gave dad. She ran out of the apartment to kill the super. We have no heat and she's mad. Dad ran after her."

"Oh, God, no…okay, honey, I'll be right there."

After her uncle hung up, Katie walked slowly to the front door and locked it. She then sank to the floor with her back against the door. She couldn't think about anything but the superintendent of the building—a big, muscular Puerto Rican with a very bad temper. She had seen him arguing with other people in the building, a look of contempt on his faced that scared the hell out of her. She had heard from one of her friends that he had cut someone very badly in a fight.

Katie put her head in her hands as she realized both her mother and father were heading for a showdown with this monster. The image of her mother carrying that big knife made her want to throw up. Even if her mom got close to the superintendent, she wouldn't have a chance against him. He was huge, and what if he turned on Jack, too, not knowing that he was trying to stop her?

Jack was frantic about Nan's deteriorating mental condition, but he was optimistic that it would pass. He had convinced himself that two years had passed and she was cured. He was satisfied that what had happened before was a one-time occurrence. He figured she would always be fragile, especially after having a baby. He didn't worry too much about the fact that she had stopped taking her tranquilizers. He didn't remember Dr. Gladden's parting words about Nan needing tranquilizers on a permanent basis. He figured at some point when she was feeling better, she could stop taking them.

In the past couple of weeks, however, it became obvious to Jack that he was in over his head, and things got worse for him both mentally and physically when he was forced to give up his part-time job to stay home during the day to make sure Nan didn't hurt anyone. The sharp pains in his abdomen that caused him to double over began soon after that. He had been trying to cope with them without seeing a doctor, as it would be just another expense he couldn't afford.

When he left the house each afternoon to go to work, he was confident that Katie could cope with watching the kids. He didn't think of her as a ten-year-old at all; in some ways, she was more efficient than her mother at taking care of the children and the house. She seemed to have a natural instinct for it. He didn't worry about discussing things with Katie; she never asked any questions or wanted any explanations. She did everything very quietly, and he appreciated that about his eldest child.

On this day, he couldn't go to work because Nan was totally irrational, and he thought it best that he remain with her until she calmed down. The apartment grew colder as the day progressed and Nan became unreasonably upset, venting out all of her anger on the superintendent of the building. By the time Katie and Jonathan returned from school, things were totally out of control, but Jack didn't know what to do about it. He only turned his attention away from Nan for what seemed like a minute when he saw the knife in her hand, and then she was out the door and he was following her down the dark staircase which led to the basement.

Jack knew they were no match for the bad-tempered super, and knew he had to do whatever he could to stop Nan from getting to him. She was already banging on the boiler room door when Jack caught up to her, and just as he reached for her the heavy metal door opened and Nan raised her knife-wielding hand in the air toward the super. As the knife descended upon him, the super blocked it with the poker he was using to manipulate the wood in the incinerator. The poker creased Nan's arm in the process, causing blood to flow instantly from the deep gash. The knife slid across the dirty basement floor with Nan in pursuit of it.

Jack shouted at the top of his lungs. "She's sick, she's sick, she doesn't know what she's doing! Please, please, don't hurt her!" However, the super was enraged that Nan had tried to kill him. He muttered something in Spanish that Jack couldn't understand and rushed at Nan with his poker raised high in the air. While the super's back was to Jack, he quickly picked up a piece of wood that was lying on the floor waiting its turn to go into the incinerator, and without thinking he slammed the wood against the super's back. The blow stunned the big man enough so that he dropped the poker, giving Jack the time he needed to grab Nan's arm and push her out of the boiler room and up the stairs. With strength he didn't know he had, he half carried, half pushed Nan up the three flights of stairs, with the super in pursuit yelling furiously as he closed the distance between them.

"Katie, Katie." She lifted her head when she heard her name. She had no idea her dad's voice was capable of being that loud. "Katie, open the goddamn door!" She shivered as she heard her father's voice…so loud, louder than she had ever heard it before. Her legs were asleep, and she could barely stand on them as she got up from where she was sitting against the door. For just a second she wondered whether she should open the door. Suppose the super got into the apartment; he could kill them all. Without thinking further she reached for the lock. As she turned it, Jack pushed the door open with such force that it knocked Katie against the wall. He shoved Nan into the apartment, then slammed the door shut and locked it.

With just a second to spare, the loud foreign sounds of the super reached their ears as he brought the poker down on the front door again and again. As the irate man continued to attack the door, Jack ran to the kitchen and picked up the phone. Katie crawled down the hallway, slithering past Nan who was sitting motionless against the wall, and then ran into the bedroom to join the other children. Once inside she slammed the door shut, and immediately had Jonathan help her put the bureau in front of the door. She then began to plan their escape out the window and down the fire escape.

As he dialed the emergency number, Jack heard the sound of sirens and prayed they were coming his way. Knowing it was a small miracle that he and Nan escaped the wrath of the super for as long as they had, Jack realized his frantic plea that Nan didn't know what she was doing did not mean anything to the enraged man outside their apartment door; and if someone didn't help them quickly, he would eventually succeed in breaking down the door. As soon as the dispatcher answered the phone the banging suddenly ceased, so Jack hung up and tiptoed to the door. Nan appeared to be in shock and was now in a fetal position on the floor. Jack put his ear to the door, listening intently to the voices outside.

"What's going on here, mister?" Jack didn't recognize the strange voice. The super yelled something in broken English in reply to the question, but again Jack couldn't understand what he was saying. At that moment he did hear a familiar voice.

"Jack…Jack, are you in there? It's Ralph."

"Is it safe to open the door?"

"Yes, the police are out here with a man who says Nan tried to kill him. Let us in now!" Jack felt a surge of relief pass through him as he opened the door and fell into his brother's arms.

"It's true alright; she did try to hurt him. I told him she didn't mean it. She's sick again." All eyes stared at the pathetic woman now sitting cross-legged against the wall, sucking on an unlit cigarette she had retrieved from her coat pocket and panting like an animal. Blood was dripping from the tear in the arm of her paper-thin coat where the poker had cut her.

"Mr. Ramie, we need to ask you a couple of questions; Mrs. Ramie also, if she's up to it."

"Sure, sure…come in."

After Jack carried Nan to the couch, the policeman began his interrogation.

"Mrs. Ramie, I'm Sergeant Wilkes. Do you know what happened here today?"

Staring past the stranger, Nan opened her mouth. "I have to call my sister. The voices are telling me I have to leave right away; can't take it here anymore. My husband is too quiet, you see." Wringing her hands together, she continued.

"Where's Katie? I have to talk to her, tell her how to take care of the house and the kids." As she searched the room for Katie, Nan put her hand in the pocket of her coat and pulled out a twenty dollar bill. Looking directly at the policeman and avoiding Jack who was standing right next to him, Nan continued to talk. "I took this from my husband's wallet; he never gives me any money. Tell him I will send it back as soon as I get to my sister's house." The policeman looked at Jack and shook his head.

"Sir, I think we had better call an ambulance for your wife." As his eyes focused on the slightly opened French doors, he was surprised to see a child cowering behind them. When Katie opened the fire escape window in her bedroom, she saw the police cars heading toward the front of the apartment building. She and Jonathan had quickly moved the chest of drawers away from the door so that she could leave the safety of the bedroom to investigate what was going on.

"Is that your child, Mr. Ramie?" Glancing over his shoulder toward the place where the officer was pointing, Jack shook his head affirmatively.

"She sure looks scared. Your wife is lucky she wasn't killed today. You know that man would have been perfectly justified in defending himself against her. He showed us that knife before you opened the door. Geez, she could have really done him in with that thing."

Suddenly Nan bolted from her position on the couch toward the place where Katie was hiding behind the door. Seeing those evil eyes coming at her, Katie slammed the door with such force that two of the glass panes cracked, sending glass shattering to the floor. One of the officers dove for Nan, grabbing her around the legs and wrestling her to the floor as she kicked and clawed at him.

"Christ, isn't that ambulance here yet? Shit, I think she broke my jaw, Phil. Try to get your handcuffs on her, quick." A few minutes later as the paramedics bandaged Nan's arm and restrained her in a straightjacket, the injured policeman gave Jack a sympathetic look.

"What a crazy broad she is," he remarked to his partner when they were out of earshot of Jack, who had just departed in the ambulance with Nan.

"Yeah, they should lock her up for good. Did you see all those little kids? There must have been five or six of them hiding like rabbits in that bedroom. What a shame. I can't believe my jaw is not broken; it hurts like hell." They shook their heads in dismay as they returned to the squad car.

Even on the way to the hospital, Jack kept hoping Nan would snap out of it so he could make them turn the ambulance around and bring her home. At the admitting desk the nurse insisted Nan sign herself in. Jack didn't understand the legalities—something to do with guardianship and the fact that the state could only admit a person for psychiatric treatment without their consent by court order; otherwise, a patient had to admit or commit themselves.

Much to Jack's dismay, when he told Nan to sign her name she wrote Brenda Starr on the form. Brenda Starr was a cartoon character in the newspaper. After some discussion, the hospital personnel agreed to admit her with that signature.

On the way to her room, Nan told the attendants that she had to go to the bathroom. Nan urinated as they watched, and before they could stop her, she wrenched her wedding ring from her finger and flushed it down the toilet.

When she heard Uncle Ralph's voice, Katie couldn't stand it any longer and ventured from behind the closed doors of the back bedroom.

"My God, how long has she been like this, Jack? Why didn't you take her to the hospital sooner? Katie called, and I knew something serious was happening; that's why I got on the horn to the police right away. She almost got the two of you killed tonight. That guy was nuts with rage; even the cops couldn't get near him at first. Jack, you're crazier than Nan is for going after her."

As she listened to her uncle yell at her dad, Katie wanted only one thing...Nan out of the house as quickly as possible. She didn't care if she had to take care of the kids by herself; it was easier than dealing with her mother. Eventually she got her wish—everyone left at once and the Ramie children were alone.

As Katie cleaned up the broken glass, she wondered why they didn't keep Nan in the hospital the first time. She certainly wasn't strong enough to take care of her family. Couldn't they see that? Why was she allowed to have more children? She wondered what would happen next. Would she have to quit school? Her thoughts were interrupted when the baby started to cry. The kids were starving. It was time to get them fed and ready for bed.

Jack leaned against the scarred door to the apartment, too exhausted to insert the key. His thoughts were on work. How could he do that and take care of the kids, too? First thing in the morning he would call the number they gave him at the hospital. They told him he could probably get some help from the welfare department.

Katie knew it was pointless to wait up for her father, as he wouldn't tell her anything anyway. When all the kids were finally asleep, she crawled into bed exhausted and was unconscious almost immediately. On this night she didn't have to worry about Nan and what she might do. Later as the morning sun filtered into the room, Katie awakened and tiptoed into her parents' room. She watched as her father slept soundly. Deep in her heart she knew she would have to stay home with the babies; she had known it since the night before, even while she did her homework. She seriously contemplated getting her clothes on and slipping out of the house before anyone else woke up, but she couldn't actually bring herself to leave knowing that her dad would have to go to work. Her stomach was hurting real bad and she was sure the end was near for her; all that dirt she was eating was probably killing her. She hoped she would die soon.

Later as she fed the baby, Katie thought about what it would be like to be free of the responsibility of babysitting and household chores. She wouldn't mind setting the table or drying the dishes like her friend Maura did, but she felt overwhelmed by everything that needed to be done in the house. She wished she could spend more time on her schoolwork. She was sure she could be the best in her class if only she had more time to study. In the last few weeks she had barely been able to keep up with her assignments, and it devastated her to think she was slipping further behind her classmates.

Two-month-old Sammy looked up at Katie and smiled, but she couldn't bring herself to smile back at him; after all, he was one of the reasons for her problems. "Why did they have more kids?" Katie said aloud to the contented baby. "How could they be so stupid?"

Jack had left the house earlier without saying a word to Katie. She wished he would talk to her, maybe even thank her for everything she was doing, but she knew that was never going to happen. It was every man for himself in the Ramie household; only the strongest would survive...and she wasn't sure she had that much strength.

True to his character Jack couldn't bring himself to tell Katie what was going on. He was relieved to see she had everything under control when he awoke from his first good night's sleep in weeks. He was relieved. He immediately called the number on the card he got the night before and explained to the welfare department his need for help. Shortly after that he left for work early, hoping to put in some much needed overtime. He didn't think it was important to tell Katie that someone would be coming the next morning to take care of the children so she could go to school.

As she prepared the little ones for bed that night, Katie contemplated running away. She didn't have any money, but if she did she would try to go back to June's house. Just then she experienced a pain in her abdomen so severe that it doubled her over; she was now positive it would be just a matter of days before she was dead.

Early the next morning someone knocked on the door as Katie was feeding Amy; she was afraid to answer it, so the banging got louder and louder until Jack heard the commotion and got out of bed. He opened the door to find a slightly-built, dour-looking black woman in the doorway. She identified herself as Mrs. Warren. Katie was confused, but when Jack told her to get ready for school she was surprised and relieved that she had a replacement. The lady took the baby from Katie and Amy immediately began to scream. Katie tried to ignore the crying as she hurriedly prepared for school; she was already an hour late.

"Did you get a late pass from the office, Miss Ramie?" Sister Charles interrupted the English lesson to acknowledge Katie's arrival.

"Yes, Sister Charles."

"Good, bring it here." Word about Nan's hospitalization spread quickly among the staff at the school, as Jonathan had told Father August immediately upon seeing him the morning after his mother tried to stab the superintendent of the building. Regrettably Sister Charles was a strict disciplinarian and was incapable of providing much needed sympathy to Katie. When she took Katie aside later that day to talk to her, she didn't provide much comfort to the disturbed child.

"It is very important for you to help out at home as much as possible during this time of need. You have to pray to God to give you strength to help you through this ordeal. If you work hard, everything will turn out okay. I don't want you to ignore your studies either over this; there is no excuse for missed work. You can do it; you are a very strong young lady."

There it was then. Sister Charles had made Katie feel guilty that she had bad thoughts about not wanting to help out at home. Katie was more depressed than ever as she walked home from school that day. She was convinced she was a very bad person.

The next day a different social worker showed up at the Ramie household, and it continued that way for a month. Some of the homemakers stayed for a few days or a week, but mostly they came and went in one day. By the time Katie got home from school the social worker was ready to depart, and then it was up to her to care for the children and the house until the next social worker showed up. Katie wasted not a precious minute on anything that wasn't necessary, for that would mean less time she could spend on schoolwork. With each passing day, she performed her chores more quickly and more bitterly than the day before.

On his way to visit Nan one weekend, Jack was summoned by one of her doctors. "Mr. Ramie, your wife is improving rapidly. Fortunately, her breakdown was not that severe. I understand she had one two years ago?" Jack didn't answer the question. He was uncomfortable at the mention of the first breakdown.

Shifting in his chair, the doctor continued. "We administered one shock treatment to your wife and she responded well to that. I know you are anxious to get her home. What is it...five children you have? I'm sure she will be as good as new very shortly." Jack was very pleased with the psychiatrist's statement and quickly left his office to visit Nan.

A little over a month after Nan was institutionalized, she was granted outpatient status, and Jack surprised the children by bringing her home with him one Sunday.

"This kitchen is filthy!" Nan shouted. She was frantically going from one thing to another, pointing out a small smudge on the refrigerator, a speck of dirt on the floor, and a dirty dish in the sink. Katie was close to tears.

Later as Nan changed the baby, she yelled at Katie. "Look at this, Sammy has a rash. Aren't you cleaning him properly when you change him?" Surprised by the attack, Katie responded without thinking.

"But he's always had a rash, even when you were taking care of him. Remember?"

As she glared at Katie in disgust, Nan shouted back. "No, his little bottom was clear when I was taking care of him."

Katie resisted the urge to call her a liar; she just wanted her gone and hoped she would never come back. It wasn't until a couple of agonizing hours later that Jack packed her into the car for the trip back to the hospital. Even Jonathan confided to Katie that he had not enjoyed seeing his mother again.

"She's a witch," cried Barbara.

"Mommy's still sick," Katie explained to her. It had been a terrible day for the Ramie children.

Within a few weeks of that first visit home, Nan was released completely with a supply of tranquilizers and a stern warning to keep up her visits with the psychiatrist who was assigned to her case. As soon as Nan walked through the door Katie relinquished the job of taking care of the children and the house to her mother. She didn't want to be bothered with it for one more minute.

The superintendent of the building did file an assault charge against Nan, but Katie heard her father telling Uncle Ralph the charge was dismissed because Nan was nuts. Katie couldn't help but wonder what would have happened if the butcher knife Nan attacked him with had killed the poor guy, whose only crime had been working hard to try to get them some heat. Katie was sure Nan would have gotten away with murder again.

The end of the school year arrived and summer followed quickly. Katie left the house as soon as she could escape, joining the other children on the block to participate in activities sponsored by the Police Athletic League (PAL). The police closed off an entire city block to traffic and set up craft and game tables. Katie loved making key chains, potholders and other crafty things.

She also won the championship at shuffleboard for her age group. Her absolute favorite game was New York checkers, which was played with bottle caps and a chalk outline similar to the one made for hopscotch, using fingers to shoot the bottle caps into the numbered squares. She played it for hours on end, deliberately staying away from the house as much as possible, knowing it was the only way to prevent additional responsibilities from falling on her shoulders.

In July of 1957, Katie found out her mother was pregnant once again. Katie was four months away from turning eleven. She was hardened to it all by now and realized Nan would probably have another nervous breakdown. She decided to enjoy her freedom while her mother was home, and tried not to think too much about what was going to happen when she got sick again.

In September Jonathan and the other altar boys accompanied Father August to upstate New York for a camping trip. Katie was extremely upset at Jonathan's excitement over the outing. It didn't seem fair to her that he was always being treated specially. She had not recovered from the animosity she felt because he got to stay with his grandparents and father during Nan's first breakdown; she felt he was once again getting favorable treatment.

The night he dropped Jonathan off after the camping trip, Father August stayed for dinner. After the incident with the watch, Katie quickly lost her infatuation with the priest; in fact, she had a real dislike for him. There was something about him that wasn't right, but she couldn't put her finger on it. He didn't act like other men she knew.

"Are you okay, Jonathan?" Nan reached to feel his forehead. His head was practically lying in his plate of food which was untouched. He looked deathly pale.

"Get the thermometer, Katie." As she rummaged through the medicine cabinet, Katie thought it served her brother right if he got a little sick from his wonderful trip.

Throughout the night Jonathan's condition deteriorated. His fever kept going up and he became more uncomfortable with each passing hour. He started vomiting and his neck became stiff. Nan woke Katie up in the middle of the night and asked her to feed Sammy while she put cold rags on Jonathan's body. Katie peeked in Jonathan's room after getting Sammy settled down, and when she turned on the light Jonathan screamed out in pain that it was hurting his eyes. She didn't even recognize him; he had red stuff all over his body. Nan waited until the sun was coming up to make her call.

"Father August, this is Nan Ramie. Listen, Jonathan is very sick. He has a terrible rash all over his body, and his fever is 104 degrees. It couldn't be that high, could it? My thermometer must be broken. Jack is working a double shift. I'm scared. Jonathan has been complaining of a terrible headache, and now when he tries to talk he doesn't make any sense."

"I'll be right over." Within five minutes of the call Father August stood over the ailing child and nervously determined that he was deathly ill.

"We have to get him to the hospital immediately; help me get him out of bed." As they struggled to carry Jonathan out of the apartment and to Father August's car, Nan gave Katie instructions.

"Watch the kids. We're taking your brother to the hospital." Katie glimpsed Jonathan hanging limply in the priest's arms, and for just a second she felt a wave of fear for him. She didn't have much time to dwell on it, though, because the kids were already clamoring for breakfast. She was also upset that because of him she would miss a day of school.

When the trio arrived at the emergency room, the resident on duty took one look at Jonathan and called the attending physician.

While they paced in the waiting room, Nan and Father August comforted each other. "It's probably just a bad case of the flu, Nan, don't worry."

"Father, will you call Jack for me and tell him to come to the hospital?"

"Sure, I'll be right back. Do you want a cup of coffee?"

"Thanks, I'd like that. I feel kind of funny."

Nan popped an aspirin in her mouth as the priest handed her a cup of hot, soothing liquid. It was her third pill since early morning, but she still had a terrible headache. An hour later when the solemn-faced doctor approached the trio, which now included Jack, it was apparent the news he was about to relay was not good.

"Mr. and Mrs. Ramie, I'm Doctor Carter, chief of staff and head neurosurgeon at this hospital. I've just examined your son, and I believe he has spinal meningitis. I think it is bacterial rather than viral." The threesome did not understand the gravity of his remark until he continued.

"We are arranging a lumbar puncture on your son to check the cerebrospinal fluid. We will need your permission in writing for this. This will determine if he does have meningitis. If the test results do prove positive, we will try our best to save his life."

"Save his life? What do you mean, save his life? Are you telling me that my son might die? Oh, my God!" Nan cried out in anguish, and Father August moved to comfort her but she brushed him away. Jack stood motionless in the background.

"We will need to administer large amount of antibiotics. This is all speculation you understand, but if Jonathan survives there is the possibility of permanent damage to his spine which can result in paralysis, sometimes total, sometimes partial. I must tell you also that if the meningitis has spread to the brain...well, your son may be left with some form of brain damage." Stunned beyond belief, the three of them stood quietly in a small circle until the doctor broke the silence.

"I must ask you some questions about Jonathan's whereabouts for the last few days."

In a choked voice, tears streaming down his face, Father August replied. "Jonathan was with me and a group of other boys at a camp in upstate New York."

"That's not good!" I'm sorry, Father, but this means that the origin of the meningitis could possibly be from the upstate area."

"Oh, no, do you mean I caused this terrible thing?" In order to calm down the hysterical priest, the doctor reached out and shook his small shoulders.

"Father, it is vital that you get all of the children who attended the camp to the hospital as soon as possible." Dr. Carter turned around quickly and continued.

"Do you have any other children at home?"

"Yes, we do," Nan replied.

"Well, as soon as you sign some consent forms for me, I want you to go home and get them and bring them back here for a shot." When the doctor realized Jonathan's parents didn't seem to be hearing him, he shouted more firmly.

"Don't you understand me? This is a very serious situation. Bacterial meningitis is highly contagious, and I want everyone who came into direct contact with your son during and after the trip to get in here as soon as possible for an inoculation. Before you all leave the hospital, I will arrange for you to get your shots. Excuse me. I have some urgent phone calls to make. If we don't get all of these people inoculated with the H. influenza type B vaccine, we could have an epidemic on our hands."

As Dr. Carter hurried to the nearest phone he thought about the case. Jonathan was only seven years old, and it was unusual to see bacterial meningitis in someone that young. Generally it was found in teenagers or college age students who engaged in intimate kissing with multiple partners; his patient had been on a trip with a priest and a group of other altar boys. Also, he mused, it was usually difficult to find the origin of the meningitis because the offending organism was usually harbored by carriers who did not have symptoms themselves, but who could transmit the bacteria.

By the time Jonathan was finished with the lumbar test that proved the existence of the illness, his condition had further deteriorated. He was in shock and his brain was swelling. Antibiotics were administered intravenously, and a corticosteroid was used to reduce the swelling in the brain. He was listed in critical condition and was placed in intensive care in complete isolation. The goal was to get him through the next few hours so that he might have a chance of surviving.

After getting his shot and performing the painful task of giving Jonathan the Last Rights, Father August rushed back to the rectory to begin the process of contacting the boys who had been on the trip and arranging for them to meet at the hospital for their shots. Each call involved a long explanation to the concerned parents about the necessity and urgency of getting their child to the hospital.

After talking to twenty sets of very unhappy parents, the exhausted priest prepared himself to go back to the hospital to check on Jonathan. His anguish was apparent as he bumped into the pastor on his way out the door. He explained the entire situation to his superior and promised to call him as soon as he had further news on Jonathan's condition.

Katie was holding Sammy and trying to shake Amy loose from her leg, when the phone rang. "It's me. Get the kids ready; I'll pick you all up in a little while."

As she held the dead phone in her hand, Katie wondered what was going on. She was used to her father's limited conversation, but it was unusual for him to take them anywhere. She bundled up all the kids and waited for Jack to arrive. There was no hint about what was they were facing during the mysterious journey until they arrived at the hospital, and Nan told them Jonathan had some kind of contagious disease and that he might die from it. On top of that they were informed that they all had to get a shot.

Katie was glad the other kids were crying so that no one was paying attention to her misty eyes. It was the biggest needle she ever saw in her life, and it hurt a lot when they stuck it in her arm.

As she watched the kids in the lobby while she waited for Jack to take them home, Katie thought about Jonathan. She couldn't help feeling jealous of him even in his precarious predicament. She wished it was her who was dying. All the way home she felt guilty that she couldn't share in the genuine sadness which everyone else seemed to be experiencing.

Father August still couldn't believe he had performed the Last Rights on Jonathan when just a couple of days ago they were enjoying a wonderful camping trip. He loved being around his boys; he was good to them and they needed his attention and affection. Still he couldn't bear the agony of feeling responsible for his illness, and he was sure God was punishing him.

Katie felt like a celebrity the next morning when Jonathan's illness was announced to the entire school at a special mass said on his behalf. Katie sat with her classmates, filled with excitement and happiness from all the attention she was receiving as the sister of the sick boy. She tried very hard to act as solemn as she could so they would all think she was very sad.

Each time the phone rang Nan's heart stopped beating. She was experiencing severe morning sickness from this latest pregnancy, and it was adding to the turmoil of the last few days. As each day passed there was increased hope that Jonathan would survive, and after three weeks he was removed from the critical care list.

"We are quite certain that Jonathan will not suffer any permanent disability as the result of his illness. His reflexes check out fine and his brain wave activity looks great. We'll just have to wait and see, but the prognosis is very good. He's a lucky little boy." The doctor departed quickly from the room leaving Father August and Nan to celebrate his announcement.

"Surely it's a miracle; thank you, Lord, for sparing the boy." Father August clasped his hands together in joy. He reached out to hug Nan but she stiffened noticeably, so he abandoned the gesture.

Father August had been kind enough to drive Nan to the hospital each day so she could spend some time with her son. She watched as he sat next to Jonathan's bed, stroking him and whispering words of comfort. Since Jonathan's illness something about Father August was making Nan uncomfortable. She had known many priests in her life, but none as preoccupied with young boys as he was. He looked like a boy himself and was very feminine-like in his mannerisms.

Two weeks after Jonathan was taken off the critical list, Katie was granted special permission to see her brother. She was excited more about the actual visit to the hospital than she was about seeing Jonathan; however, she was appalled when she saw her brother. He was thin and chalky white. There was a bunch of sores around his mouth, some of them bleeding and some with white stuff oozing from them, and tubes of all kinds were hanging from his arms. Jonathan smelled awful and Katie held her nose as she approached his bed.

"Hi, Jonathan, how are you feeling?" As Jonathan stared lifelessly back at her, Katie continued.

"I hope you're feeling better?" Katie's eyes were like saucers when she looked around the room and saw all the stuffed animals and boxes of candy her brother had received, mostly from Father August. She put her hands on the railing of Jonathan's bed and whispered in his ear. "Can I have a piece of candy?" Slowly Jonathan raised his head in response to his sister's request.

"No, leave my stuff alone. It's mine." He turned his face from Katie.

At that very minute she hated him and wished he had died. She dreaded the thought of him coming home. She knew he would be more spoiled than ever, and it was just as she feared.

A week later Jonathan arrived home in a wheelchair, and everyone gathered around him telling him how great he looked and how wonderful it was to have him home. Everyone, that is, except Katie, who remained in her room too disgusted to watch them make a big stink over him. It didn't matter to her that he was in a wheelchair and might not be able to walk again; he was getting all of the attention she craved.

There was no doubt in her mind that her parents loved Jonathan the best, especially her mom. She never asked Jonathan to take care of the kids, to do the wash, to go to the store, to hang up the clothes, to clean the house, to make lunch for the kids, to feed the baby, or to change the baby. There wasn't much loose dirt left on the walls outside of her bedroom window, but Katie busily scratched off as much of it as she could to satisfy her for the time being.

Within a few weeks Jonathan was walking with a cane. It seemed at first that he might have a permanent limp, but as it turned out even that disappeared in time. Remarkable and a miracle were the words everyone used to describe his recovery, but Katie did her best to ignore the entire situation, concentrating on her school work and maintaining her straight "A" average. It went totally unnoticed. So did her eleventh birthday. There wasn't even a cake; everyone was busy with Jonathan's recovery. Nan mentioned something about getting one as soon as things settled down, but that never happened.

Shortly after Katie's eleventh birthday the severe chest pains started every night after she went to bed. When she found a small lump in her newly budding breasts, Katie told Nan. Nan made an appointment with the family doctor, and as Katie walked alone to his office she braced herself for the bad news that was coming. She knew for sure she had cancer and that she was going to die. She was disappointed that the dirt hadn't already killed her. She was upset that her parents hadn't offered to accompany her. She thought they were going to be really sorry when she died—really sorry.

Dr. James' office was located on the same street as Katie's school, and she passed it every day on her way home. The doctor was an alcoholic but was very well known and respected in the community.

As Katie sat in his two-by-four dingy waiting room, she became light-headed and sick to her stomach. She could smell the alcohol on his breath as he quickly examined her breast, shaking his head and reassuring her there was nothing abnormal on her chest. Katie was sure the doctor had lied. She knew she was going to die soon; it would be her turn to go to the hospital, her turn to make them suffer and care…soon.

After Jonathan's illness Nan became preoccupied with the impending birth of her eighth child. She told everyone it was her sixth pregnancy, including her obstetrician Dr. Costgrove, who had delivered all of the Ramie children. He never challenged her on this issue; he didn't really think it was that important.

This time Nan obsessed about having a brown-eyed boy. "We don't have one of those yet," she would say to Katie, completely oblivious of the fact that Martin, the infant she killed, had dark brown eyes. Nan spent days writing a poem about the new baby. Katie memorized it so she could recite it to everyone.

> Please, Dear Lord, send me a boy
> With eyes the color of the rich, brown earth.
> Give him a heart full of laughter,
> And a bright, sunny day for his birth.
> Mold him perfectly, dear Jesus

With the finest clay you can find.
And when you're finished, sweet God,
Please give him a wonderful mind.

George, a brown eyed boy, was born on March 18, 1958. It just happened to be a bright, beautiful, sunny day. Katie wondered what it was that made this woman, who shouldn't have been allowed to have any children, get just what she wanted.

A whirlwind of responsibility followed the birth of the new baby, and for a month after his birth Katie prayed every day her mother would not get sick again. Her prayers went unanswered.

Forcing Katie to stare directly into her eyes as she gripped her hair tightly, Nan's spittle landed on Katie's face. "Just get the hell out of the house, you brat. I'm sick and tired of you trying to run my life. I bet you tell your father everything I say, you little traitor." With a squeal that sent shivers through Katie, Nan repeated herself. "Get out, get out." She knew that April morning it was happening again; she could tell by her mother's eyes.

"Mom, I don't tell daddy anything. What you tell me is private, I swear. Please leave me alone, you're hurting me." Suddenly Nan let go of Katie's hair with such force that she sent her whirling across the room.

"Did you hear that? The baby's crying. I'm going to feed him." Panicking as Nan headed for the baby's crib, Katie tried to stop her.

"No, mom, he's sleeping. We just fed him, remember. Please don't wake him up. Let's go in the living room and sit down for awhile." Katie was terrified. She didn't think she could calm her down this time. She prayed for help; it was almost time for her dad to come home and she willed him to hurry up.

Katie had discouraged her mother from disturbing George; it was always her goal to keep Nan away from the babies as much as possible. Once distracted, Nan quickly busied herself setting up the ironing board in the middle of the living room. She filled the steam iron with water and plugged it in. Katie sat on the couch deciding it was safer to watch her mother rather than discourage her from the task. Nan dragged the hamper beside the ironing board and began taking the clothes out one by one and ironing them. The only problem was the clothes were dirty. Nan was mumbling to herself about being overworked and unappreciated. All of a sudden she focused on Katie.

"What are you looking at? Don't you think I'm capable of ironing? Why are you always watching me? You make me nervous."

Katie had to look away from her mother's horribly contorted face. She was now fully alarmed and again asked God for help. Without warning Nan yanked the iron out of its socket and hurled it across the room at Katie, who fell to the floor just as the scalding iron whizzed past her head. The iron came to an abrupt stop as it slammed into the wall behind the couch. Katie crawled quickly behind the sofa, hoping it would protect her from harm; she was trembling.

The slamming of the front door was like music to her ears. She wasn't sure whether Nan had left or Jack was home, but either way it was a relief. Cautiously Katie peered from behind the sofa, watching as Nan dropped to the floor and beat her fists against her chest, screaming angrily. "I want to see my boys. I know they are alive. They won't let me see them. You're my daddy. I know you will make them let me see my children. You always make things right." Liquid was dripping from Nan's mouth and her eyes were like white marbles in their sockets.

Katie put her head between her legs to hide from the ugly scene she was witnessing. The room became deadly quiet. As Nan lay motionless on the floor with Jack kneeling silently beside her, Katie moved swiftly into her room thinking for sure her mother was dead. As she climbed into bed beside her sister, she discovered the sheets were wet from another one of Barbara's accidents, but tonight it was the last thing she wanted to bother with. She put the blanket over the wet sheet and collapsed on top of it. Then she remembered that she forgot something, and quickly got back up. She pulled the knife wrapped in newspaper from the drawer and clutched it tightly in her hands before she slipped it under the bed. She listened hard for any sounds that might mean trouble.

Someone was shaking Katie violently and she fell out of bed onto the floor. Each time she reached for the weapon under her bed it slipped further away from her grasp. Unexpectedly a blunt instrument came down hard on her back, followed by an excruciating pain. She was burning up; she was being ironed by her mother. As she looked around, she saw her father lying on the floor as flat as a pancake. He had already been ironed. Someone began to scream.

As Katie woke up from her nightmare, she realized the penetrating cry she was hearing was coming from her mother. Jumping up quickly, she retrieved the knife from under the bed and raced through the master bedroom. She reached the living room just in time to see Nan hitting Jack wherever she could, as he struggled to get her out of the house. She followed them with the knife still in her hand until they were both out the door. She quickly locked it and breathed a sigh of relief. The sun was starting to come up.

It wasn't lost on Katie that Nan had mentioned Kevin and Martin during her breakdown the night before. It was apparent to her that Nan knew she had two other children, but had convinced herself they were alive. In fact, it seemed Katie now knew more than the many doctors who had treated Nan over the years.

As soon as Katie opened the door to the plump, toothless, and smiling black lady, she knew she was going to like her. Gerta Simms was assigned to the Ramie home by Social Services for an indefinite period of time. A jolly, well-organized, and loving person, Gerta quickly won the hearts of all of the children. Katie adored her; she was not only relief for her during the day, but she was genuinely affectionate toward Katie. It was two long days after Nan's hospitalization before the homemaker from Social Services arrived and Katie was exhausted. Gerta sensed immediately that the child was overwhelmed and informed her that she was in charge and Katie was just to worry about taking care of herself. It was one of the few times in her life that Katie felt totally relaxed. Also Gerta sensed that Katie carried a lot of hurt around with her and made a special effort to be kind to the little girl.

"Can I walk home for lunch today, Gerta? Will you make me a grilled cheese sandwich?"

"Sure, honey-pie; now run along or you're going to be late for school."

Katie couldn't wait for their lunch hours together; she could tell Gerta anything and everything. They laughed and cried together; mostly laughed.

Shortly after Nan's breakdown, Jack got approval to switch to the day shift. When Ms. Simms left at 5 PM, Katie helped Jack with dinner. After the dinner dishes were done Katie was eager to escape the house to play outside.

Katie was very embarrassed by the situation her family was in. She believed everyone thought her family was crazy. She overheard friends talking about how her mother was always in and out of loony bins. In order to compensate for the insecurity she felt, Katie told lies about things that were happening to her. Once she told her friends she was going to be a flower girl in her aunt's wedding. True, there was a wedding and she was invited, but not as the flower girl. Unfortunately that wasn't enough to make her feel special. They were all little white lies, fabrications meant to make them accept her.

The kids met at the luncheonette for sodas and potato chips each evening. She was afraid to ask her dad for any money, so she stole a dime from a jar which Jack kept on top of a kitchen cabinet for Ms. Simms in case she ran out of milk or bread during the day. She didn't really consider it stealing and convinced herself she deserved the money for all the work she did.

Even Jack was more relaxed during this time. He didn't have to worry about the kids during the day, and he was better off financially while Nan was in the hospital. For Katie it was a world of difference, as things were more organized and everything ran more smoothly when her mom was not there. She could even go to sleep in peace at night...no knife under the bed.

Ms. Simms arrived at the Ramie household at seven in the morning. By 7:30 Katie was ready for school. Katie told her friend Maura that they had a maid and she was so impressed by that fact that she told Katie she would knock on her door and they could walk to school together. Maura was anxious to get a look at the maid. Katie worried that Maura would find out the truth, but it was worth it to have her friend envy her.

It was a dreary, rainy morning with just about two weeks to go before school let out for the summer, and Katie and Mrs. Simms were in the kitchen preparing lunches and feeding the little ones breakfast. All of a sudden they heard a loud scream coming from the hallway. Ms. Simms picked up a spatula and as quickly as her pudgy body would allow, ran out into the hall with Katie close at her heels. When they reached the ground floor landing, they saw Maura fending off a man dressed in black who was attacking her. Maura's raincoat was ripped and her umbrella was lying on the floor. Gerta charged at him and started beating him with the spatula until he fled out the back door and into the alley.

Maura was hysterical. Her clothes were disheveled and bruises were beginning to appear on her face. From that point on Katie would never feel comfortable coming into the hallway. She hated the first floor landing with its hidden back entrance leading to the alley. The dark area behind the stairs was a perfect place for someone to hide and not be seen, and that is exactly what Maura's assailant had done. This incident proved to Katie that her fears were well-founded.

From that point on Gerta insisted they all ring the bell and wait for her to come down and escort them up. Katie was relieved when the older kids were hanging out in the hallway, for it meant she didn't have to dart up the stairs like a jackrabbit...especially when Jack was home and ignored or didn't hear the bell.

Katie didn't want to think about her mom coming home; it was so much better with Ms. Simms watching them. It was wonderful not having to worry what her mom would do next, but unfortunately Nan was released from the hospital just before summer began.

Nan knew the drill...a few weeks of intensive therapy followed by lots of talk sessions. This time she had needed only one shock therapy treatment. She spent the days napping, reading, and crocheting. It was nice to paint her nails without being interrupted. It was good to be away from the kids for awhile; they were so demanding. She promised herself when she got out this time that she would learn to drive and get a job. She even liked Jack better when he visited her in the hospital. He was nicer and always brought her cigarettes and candy without being asked. She wondered how long they would let her stay.

Katie noticed immediately that Nan was more nervous than she had been after her prior releases from the hospital; she was always popping a pill of some kind or another. For Katie it wasn't long before the tense feelings returned along with the stomach pains and diarrhea. Nan complained more about Jack than ever before. As Katie sat in the living room at the end of a hot summer day half listening to Nan, she felt sorry for her. Nan looked terrible; she was overweight and doughy-looking. Her once-pretty face was showing the impact of years of medication due to her illness as well as her heavy smoking habit. Her skin was sallow and wrinkled; her crystal blue eyes were dull and streaked with red. She was slow to react to things; she reeked of stale cigarette smoke and medication.

"Katie, run down to the store and buy a pack of cigarettes for me."

"Oh, do I have to? It's dark outside."

"Yes, I'm all out."

"Why don't you go?"

"Don't get smart with me, young lady. Get going." As she nervously made her way to the store, Katie wondered how Nan could allow one of her children to go out at night when the neighborhood was so dangerous. To add insult to injury when Katie completed her errand and rung the bell for Nan to watch her come up the stairs, Nan didn't respond. Katie waited ten minutes before finally mustering up the courage to enter the hallway. She almost broke her neck running up the steps with lightning speed before someone grabbed her. She was scared out of her mind. At times like this Katie reaffirmed her hatred for her mother; she missed Ms. Simms desperately.

Jack resumed his part-time job driving a cab. He was determined to save money for a house and get his family out of the deteriorating neighborhood. One night shortly before school began, he came home badly shaken up. He had been involved in a serious accident with the cab; the first of his driving career. The incident really worried him.

Two weeks later Jack's maternal grandfather, a spry German in his eighties, stopped by the house and offered to cook dinner for the family. He was a superb cook and whipped up a meal of sauerkraut and spareribs that the whole family delightfully devoured. Katie enjoyed her great grandfather's infrequent visits. He was so much fun, always singing and breaking out in a dance.

Three hours later Jack collapsed on the floor of the living room after a short period of intense abdominal and chest pains. He couldn't get himself up. Nan called Dr. James who arrived at the house within fifteen minutes. Nan and Katie helped the doctor get Jack into bed, and Dr. James said something about the possibility of a heart attack.

Katie watched from behind her bedroom door as Dr. James worked frantically on Jack, taking his blood pressure and listening to his heart. She couldn't believe how bad her dad looked and how quickly it all had happened. He kept asking Jack where the pain was and shaking his head in confusion at Jack's response…the excruciating pain was mostly in his back and right side.

"Could be something else…maybe," the doctor mumbled to himself. His heart rate seemed fine and his blood pressure was only slightly elevated. Just as he was about to call an ambulance, Jack squeezed the doctor's hand and said the pain was subsiding. Dr. James began to suspect a digestive issue and asked Nan what Jack had eaten for dinner.

The doctor injected Jack with morphine and sat by his side throughout the night as a worried Nan looked on. After the shot took effect, Jack slept peacefully.

By morning the patient was feeling remarkably better and Dr. James made the pronouncement that he had probably had a gallbladder attack and passed a stone or two. He told Jack that the attack was probably brought on by the stress of the taxi cab accident and the sauerkraut and spareribs he had eaten the night before. He advised Jack to go to the hospital as soon as possible for x-rays of the gallbladder...but Jack never did.

It was now the fall of 1958. Katie was twelve years old, in sixth grade, and in love with Mitchell O'Keefe, an adorable redhead who was in her class. She was devastated when she didn't get Mitch as a partner for the school's dance performance. She didn't even notice Harry Pedro, the Spanish boy who was assigned to be her partner, was head over heels in love with her.

Katie's infatuation with Mitch was one-sided and when she finally realized this, it made her even more insecure and unhappy. She still felt awkward with her friends; like an outsider. She was mortified by her mom's frequent illnesses and the way she looked. She hated having a big family. There was never enough money to buy the things other girls her age had, and she had to rely on boxes of hand-me-down clothes from relatives in order to get something to wear. It was a blessing that she did wear a uniform to school every day, so she didn't have to deal with the issue of what to put on each day. It was quite obvious to her that unless she called on the girls she played with and pushed herself on them, they went about their business without her. She always felt like a third wheel. Also after Maura's attack, they were all afraid to venture into her building.

Shortly after Katie's twelfth birthday, Jonathan began complaining about Father August's peculiar behavior. Because of his illness Jonathan never caught up with his class and had to be held back. He struggled with his grades and it was hoped that repeating the year would be the best thing for him. It also meant he could serve another year as an altar boy; a fact which delighted Father August.

"Mommy, Father August tried to kiss me on the lips again the other night while we were watching a movie." Father August often picked Jonathan up for altar boy practice and for masses and funerals. "Mommy, Father August keeps touching me on my behind all the time."

It took a while but Nan finally reported Father August's behavior to the pastor. Shortly after that Father August was gone with no explanation or announcement. Katie knew something terrible had happened between the priest and Jonathan and she imagined all sorts of things. Rumor circulated around the parish that Father August liked boys better than girls and Katie was sure of it.

The events of the past few months were quite a strain on Nan's limited tolerance level, and she was showing signs of another breakdown.

Nan was inconsistent when it came to going to church on Sunday. If she was feeling good and things were going well, she insisted they all go to mass. Those days were few and far between. Because the church was within walking distance of the apartment it wasn't always necessary for Jack to drive the family, and so the fact that he did not accompany them all the time was not a problem. Only when Nan was in the throes of a mental breakdown did she harp on Jack's broken promise to practice Catholicism; otherwise, it was ignored.

Katie remembered how obsessed her mother was when she was released from the mental institution the first time about her and Jonathan making their Holy Communion. Even though their attendance at church was inconsistent, in Nan's mind it was essential that the kids receive all the sacraments. As it turned out Jonathan and Katie did eventually make their Holy Communion together in 1955. She was eight and Jonathan had turned six in January of that year. The family made a big deal out of the event. Katie wore a beautiful white dress and veil and received a bouquet of white and red carnations that smelled heavenly. Jonathan wore a navy blue suit with a white shirt and white tie, and a huge white bow tied around his left arm. They even had their picture taken professionally, holding their Child of God prayer books and rosaries. Jonathan's were black and Katie's were white. Ironically they didn't go to church again for many, many months after that day.

One Sunday shortly after the disappearance of Father August from the parish, Nan announced that the whole family was going to church. "Come on, help me get the kids ready or we'll be late," Nan barked at Katie. Butterflies fluttered in Katie's stomach as she watched Nan haphazardly preparing the children for church. It was a bitter cold day in January just after Jonathan's eleventh birthday, but Nan was dressing the children as if it were the middle of summer.

"Listen, hon, I don't think it's a good idea to go out today. It looks like snow." Jack weakly protested the venture as he peeled off the inappropriate clothing from each child, replacing them with winter garments. But, before long, they were all jammed in the car heading for the church. A premonition of impending doom hung over Katie as she held George, who was extremely cranky at being bundled up. For the millionth time in her life Katie wished with all of her heart that she belonged to another family as she anguished over what was to come.

The church was packed to the brim with people by the time the Ramie clan arrived. Before Jack could stop Nan, she marched down the middle of the aisle with George in her arms and Sammy and Amy toddling beside her. Barbara, Jonathan, and Katie remained in the back of the church, knowing there were no seats available for them up front and completely reluctant to follow their mother. They watched as three-and-a-half-year-old Amy separated herself from Nan, reversed herself, and began walking back down the aisle calling Katie's name loudly. Red-faced Katie moved forward to collect her. She thought she was going to pass out from embarrassment as she tried to shut Amy up.

When Nan reached the front of the church, she boldly entered the altar area and headed toward one of the red velvet chairs reserved for the altar boys and priests. As soon as Nan sat down with George on her lap and two-year old Sammy squeezed in beside her, she realized the rest of the family had not followed her, and in an annoyed voice shouted down the aisle. "Bring the other kids up here, Jack, and sit with us." Katie's face turned beet red when she saw hundreds of faces turn around to look at her family, all of them as shocked as she was. She couldn't stand the humiliation another minute. She let go of Amy's hand and ran as fast as she could out of the church. She didn't stop running until she was home.

The tips of Katie's fingers ached, they were so cold. As she boldly entered the hallway which under normal circumstances she dreaded, she huddled under the stairs, the same stairs that harbored drunks and perverts. The acrid smell of urine permeated her nostrils as she blew on her burning fingers to warm them. She was filled with rage. Why did her father let her do those things? Why didn't he take her right to the hospital as soon as she acted up? This time as she looked around the dingy stairwell she hoped someone would attack and kill her.

All of the years of anxiety because of Nan's mental problems were taking their toll on Katie. She was much more than her twelve years in a sad way. The carefree attitude that should accompany childhood had passed her by; irretrievable and producing a miserable little girl who had been forced to behave like an adult from the age of six. The hurt she was feeling was unbearable...with an irresponsible mother who was in and out of hospitals and barely functioning most of the time; with too many brothers and sisters which caused financial and emotional strains on everyone; with no real friends because of the abnormality of her family life; with the stress of trying to perform to her maximum potential in school despite the extreme demands made on her at home; and with a father who refused to act responsibly to thwart her mother's dangerous behavior, thus jeopardizing their very lives. She asked herself a thousand times how he could have had any more children with her after what she did.

Katie was totally and completely convinced her parents did not really care about their children. Even when Nan was home from the hospital all the two of them seemed to care about was going out together whenever they could. She couldn't begin to count all of the times she had to babysit while they went off somewhere, and Nan would spend hours before that painting her nails a bright red and fussing with her hair and makeup.

There was never enough money except for necessities, and Nan and Jack were constantly battling over it. But Nan usually got her way when it came to getting things for herself. Now as she huddled in the hallway realizing no one was going to attack her, she wished her family would have a car accident on the way home and die. She knew she would be better off without all of them.

An hour later Jonathan and Katie huddled together on his bed as he filled her in on the details of what happened after she left, his blue eyes twinkling with amazement. The other children sat quietly on the floor, exhausted from their ordeal. The baby was sleeping in Katie's arms.

Since his illness with spinal meningitis, when Jonathan got excited he tended to stutter a bit. He was definitely pumped up as he began his story. "My go-goodness, Katie, you should have seen her. She wo-wouldn't move from the ch-chair on the altar, so Father Ramsey continued saying mass, you know, and just let her si-sit there. Sammy kept running up and down the st-stairs and when Amy saw what fun he was having, she ran back up the aisle and started playing on the stairs, too. Barbara and I stayed in the back of the church.

"What did daddy do?" Katie asked, excited to hear more.

"No-nothing. All he did was glare at mo-mommy the whole time. Then when it came time to serve co-co-communion, mommy insisted the priest give some to George and Amy, and even Sammy. Can you believe it?" Jonathan paused to catch his breath and pounded his fist against his knee.

"Sh-she made such a big stink about it that the priest let Amy have some. Katie, I co-could have died! Amy chewed it and then spit it out all over the carpet. She told mommy in a loud voice that it tasted yuuky. Father Ramsey got down on his knees and used his cloth to pick it up, bl-blessing it or something. He sure looked mad. The altar boys were laughing, though. They were trying to hide their fa-faces." Jonathan stopped talking, but Katie urged him to continue.

"Then two of the ushers, one of them was Mr. Fi-Finnegan, came rushing up to the altar. He grabbed George from mommy and the other one gr-grabbed her arm. Boy, she started swearing at him and kicked him a few ti-times. George was sc-screaming at the top of his lungs and then Amy and Sammy started cr-crying when two strangers in the front of the church picked them up. Then dad finally came up to help and he and Mr. Finnegan go-got her outside. It was so fr-freaky. They wa-wanted to call the police, but dad told them she was having a nervous breakdown and that he would ha-handle it…big joke, ha." Jonathan laughed at his dad's statement as he continued.

"We-Well, anyway, it ended up that Mr. Finnegan had to dr-drive us home because mom was hitting and ki-kicking everyone. Holy smoke, it was really awful." As Jonathan finished his story, Katie put her hands up to her face and covered her eyes. It was too horrible to think about what her mother had done.

"I will never be able to show my face in school or church again. If she was my wife I would have dropped her off at the hospital and told them to keep her. I wouldn't let her get away with all of this," Katie muttered aloud.

Unfortunately, Nan was still just a few feet away in the master bedroom being comforted by Jack.

"I hope they both leave for good. We don't need either of them. If the welfare people let Ms. Simms come back, we wouldn't even need parents." Katie put the sleeping baby in Sammy's crib when the other kids started clamoring for lunch. She quickly fed them in the kitchen, all the while trying to keep them as quiet as possible and away from the back bedrooms. She was relieved that neither of her parents surfaced while she was feeding everyone.

Toward mid-afternoon Jack emerged from their bedroom looking tired and pale. He reached for the phone and made a few calls which Katie tried to listen to without success. He then returned to the bedroom. A couple of minutes later he and Nan emerged from the room with their coats on. Katie avoided looking too long at Nan's vacant eyes. She was curious as to where they were going, but didn't dare ask.

A half-hour later, Jack's sister, Dee, and her husband arrived at the house with cold cuts. Uncle Ralph and his wife showed up a short time later with all kinds of goodies. It wasn't long before Katie was enjoying their infectious good humor. Each time Nan went to the hospital Jack's relatives rallied to the aid of his family with food and drinks, and they would party and have a great time. It was such a relief to have Nan out of the house and to be able to laugh again. She was grateful to her aunts and uncles for doing that much. Katie loved those times, but it wasn't long before they would go home and take that fun away with them.

A welfare lady arrived the next morning...and the next...and the next. Much to Katie's dismay Gerta Simms was not one of them. Katie didn't miss any school; this time the social services department was really on the ball when it came to the Ramie family, placing a caretaker in the home the next day. Unfortunately it was the one time Katie wished she could stay home. Just as she expected there were whispers, rude stares, and outright cruel comments about her mother's behavior in church, especially from the kids in her class. It really upset her, but she held her head up high and acted like she didn't care. She was good at that.

Nan was released from the hospital a few weeks after she was admitted.

Nan was just another number in the mental institution system; her repeated breakdowns were expected with her diagnosis of manic depression and schizophrenia. The object was to send her home as quickly as possible with as normal a psychological disposition as they could restore to her; all therapy was geared toward getting rid of the immediate symptoms. No effort was made to understand why she kept breaking down so frequently; it was considered a waste of time as most of the patients with Nan's psychological disorder stopped taking their medications as soon as they felt better. Each time Nan was admitted to the hospital, it was noted she had not taken her medication for weeks or months prior to the breakdown,

Nan was home by February and preoccupied with getting a job; her first one ever. She disappeared one Saturday for a few hours and filled out an application at the five and dime store a short distance from the apartment. She lied on her application about a lot of things; the new Nan had no children, drove a car, did not have any mental problems, and had been working in retail on and off for the past fifteen years.

She was hired as a part-time cashier for the evening shift from five to nine at night. She left the house to catch the bus as soon as Katie got home from school, and wasn't home until close to ten at night. Katie would watch for Nan from the living room window because she had to walk one block from where the bus let her off each night. Sometimes Nan would bring home a pack of bubble gum or some other treat. It helped, but it didn't quite make up for the stress of watching all the kids in the evening and trying to do homework.

Within a few days Nan began complaining about the new job. She was tired, overworked, and afraid of the commute on the bus and the walk home. After only two weeks Nan announced she had quit. Katie was relieved for it meant she could spend more time on her school work. Many years later Katie overheard a conversation between two of her aunts, and found out her mother had actually been fired because of cash shortages in her register.

The entire experience was very discouraging for Nan, as she honestly believed she could work if she wanted to; now she knew she would always be totally dependent on Jack. Her failure to keep a job which would have given her an income of her own, increased the bitterness she felt at her inability to be independent. She lied to everyone about why she wasn't working any more, using the excuse that Jack thought it was too dangerous for her to walk the streets in their neighborhood at night. Actually the neighborhood had deteriorated tremendously in the last couple of years; from any window in the their apartment they could watch gang fights and other crimes being committed.

That summer was one of the all time scorchers, so the kids started opening up the fire hydrants to cool themselves off. Of course it was illegal to do this, but that didn't deter the sweltering adolescents. One of the hydrants was located directly across from the Ramie's apartment building and Nan spent many an afternoon running from one window to the next, closing them quickly before a spray of water entered the apartment. As soon as one of the boys opened the hydrant with a wrench, the girls scattered in all directions so they wouldn't be dragged into the water. It was always predictable that the kids would be allowed about ten minutes of hydrant fun before the police arrived and shut it off; however, in a matter of minutes another hydrant would be pried open.

As she did during the previous summer Katie was quick to leave the house each day before getting stuck with the kids or chores. The Police Athletic League had again closed one of the blocks to traffic and provided entertainment in the form of games and crafts. In the evening after the PAL block was closed, she visited the luncheonette or just hung out on one of the stoops around the block.

One incredibly hot day in late summer—the kind of day when it is difficult to breathe—Katie saw a police car pull up to her building. She took a deep breath and ran as fast as she could to the entrance. The police were already in the apartment house and Katie climbed the stairs two at a time, breaking into a cold sweat when she saw them knocking on her door. "I live here. Can I help you?" she was breathless.

"Someone called us from this apartment. Can you let us in?" Katie felt like she was going to faint as she began banging on the door, wondering what was going on now.

Nan finally opened the door and Katie knew instantly from her frantic look that something was very wrong.

"You reported a missing child?" The policeman posed it more as a question, hoping the child had been found since the call and their arrival.

"Come in...yes, my daughter is missing. I'm on the phone with one of her friends. She said Barbara stopped by her apartment earlier this morning to ask if she could play, but she couldn't go out and so Barbara left. They haven't seen her since and neither have I." Nan was on the verge of hysterics.

"How old is she?" The younger policeman reached for a small notebook from his back pocket.

"She's only seven, but she looks much older than that. She's got blonde hair...it's short. She has brown eyes. What else?" Nan was wringing her hands together as she rambled on. "She's wearing a dress. I forget what color it is. Katie, do you remember what color dress Barbara was wearing?" Katie shrugged; she was deliberately gone from the house before the little kids got up.

"Well, mom, if Barbara is missing, she probably has at least three other people with her. Don't worry." Katie didn't know anyone who had more friends than Barbara; she was never without at least five other kids by her side, but Nan had contacted every one of them and no one had seen her. Katie went through some other possibilities of where Barbara might be, but these proved to be dead ends. Katie was excited to be involved with the police in locating her missing sister. They asked her all kinds of questions, none of which she could answer very helpfully.

Nan began to cry and Katie could see she was losing it. All of a sudden it occurred to Katie that maybe Nan had done something with Barbara…and maybe the other kids. She quickly ran into the master bedroom and checked the crib to see if George was okay; he was sleeping soundly. It was nap time, and Amy and Sammy were also sound asleep in Katie's room. She knew Jonathan was playing outside; she had just seen him before the police arrived. *So it was only Barbara this time*, Katie thought. *She's finishing the job she started last time.* It was then that she realized something terrible might have happened to Barbara.

Jack arrived home having been summoned by Nan when it was clear Barbara was nowhere to be found. Katie was dismissed from the room while the police and her parents gathered for a discussion. A short time later she heard the older officer radio into the police station for assistance in finding Barbara. Three agonizing hours later a policeman searching the rooftop of the building where Barbara had last been seen found the child.

Katie was peeking through the crack in the French doors; it gave her a good view of the living room couch. She saw a policeman carrying a bundle wrapped in a white blanket.

"Is she okay? Is she all right?" Nan kept screaming over and over again.

The police officer gingerly placed the bundle on the couch and the blanket fell away to reveal a pale and sweaty Barbara. Her eyes were wide open but she wasn't blinking, just staring straight ahead. There were at least five policemen in the room and one of them was holding onto Nan, preventing her from going near Barbara.

"Mr. and Mrs. Ramie, we did call for an ambulance. The child needs to be examined at the hospital even though there doesn't appear to be any obvious injuries. It's policy. Sorry."

"Where was she?" Nan implored.

"We found her on the roof of her friend's building." Nan gasped and clutched her throat as Jack moved closer to Barbara to comfort her.

"It's okay." Jack mumbled as he fixed his eyes on his daughter.

"Barbara, what happened?" His voice was calm, but inquisitive.

"How did you get up on the roof?" Jack got no answers to his questions as the child continued to stare into space. Nan began sobbing.

"Quiet down, you might scare her more." Jack's voice was stern as he talked to Nan.

"Mr. and Mrs. Ramie, I think it would be better if you both left the room. We can take over from here. The ambulance should be here any minute now. You can follow it to the hospital if you like, but I think we had better leave the child alone until someone professional has had a chance to examine her."

Except for the fact that she was dehydrated, Barbara got a clean bill of health at the hospital and was home by early evening. She was her usual self; as talkative and outgoing as ever. She acted as if nothing had happened, and

Katie couldn't believe Barbara was the same person she saw just hours earlier. When she finally got her alone, she asked her little sister how she had gotten up on the roof.

"What roof, Katie...was I on a roof?"

Whatever happened or didn't happen to Barbara on that day remained a complete mystery to Katie, for it was never discussed or mentioned again. Everyone in the neighborhood and at school asked Katie about the incident, but she couldn't begin to explain it to them any more than she understood it herself. She did overhear her mother talking on the phone to her sister Wilma, who had recently moved from Rhode Island to California. She told her how lucky they were nothing happened to Barbara and that the worst of it was that she got dehydrated from being on the hot roof for so long. Katie could totally understand Barbara getting upset because she didn't have any friends to play with and doing something silly like going up to the roof to wait for her friends to find her.

What surprised and intrigued Katie more than anything about her sister's disappearance was how many gentle words her father had spoken to Barbara once she had been found. She would never forget that.

Nan was apparently taking her Lithium on a regular basis, as Katie heard Jack reminding her mother over and over again each and every day that she needed to take her medication. She even saw him counting the pills in the little brown jar they came in just to make sure. Katie knew the pills were the only thing keeping Nan somewhat together. The three toddlers were a handful and even on the best of days; they kept Nan busy from early morning until late night.

The Police Athletic League program only ran through the second week of August, so Katie didn't have any excuse not to help Nan, especially after the incident with Barbara shook her up so badly. By the time the last few weeks of August were over, Katie was looking forward to the start of school. She would be in the seventh grade with only one more year to go before high school.

For Katie's thirteenth birthday in November of 1959, Maura and some of the other girls bought her a dog biscuit corsage to celebrate becoming a teenager. Katie was so used to not having a fuss made over her birthday that she didn't know how to respond to the attention. She felt embarrassed and awkward that they had acknowledged her birthday. She really didn't know how to celebrate and enjoy her birthday; she had convinced herself it was just another day. Getting the corsage was a complete shock, but unfortunately it was too little too late to make her feel better about her birthday. If anything it made her feel guilty that people actually went out of their way to do something for her. In any case she still felt miserable about the day, but now there was guilt added to it that she somehow didn't appreciate what they had tried to do for her.

Each year the seventh graders produced a Christmas play with the students depicting the nativity scene. The parents were invited to attend. The cherished roles of the Blessed Virgin Mary and Joseph were chosen by a lottery system. The nuns put the names of each boy in one hat and each girl in another; one of them then picked a name out of each hat. When Katie's name was announced as the winner to play the Virgin Mary there was never a happier little girl in the whole world. She was the absolute envy of every girl in the school.

Two weeks after the drawing was held for the lead parts in the play, another contest took place to determine which child would carry the statue of the baby Jesus down the aisle and place it in the manger at midnight mass on Christmas Eve. When Katie's name again came out of a hat full of more than 500 names, the nuns were amazed. After hours of serious discussion regarding Katie getting both roles, four more names were drawn from the hat and the five children were asked to report to the principal's office. Katie immediately felt sick when she was told the principal was expecting her. She wondered what she did wrong or if something was going on at home, as her mom was acting funny again.

Katie was in complete shock when they told her that her name had again come out of the hat to carry the baby Jesus down the aisle. She listened intently as they explained to her that because she had already received the honor of being the Blessed Mother in the school play, they were going to try to give someone else a chance. Immediately Katie wished she could trade being the Virgin Mary in the play to carrying the baby Jesus at midnight mass. She had always dreamed of all the people in the church watching her as she brought the infant to the manger. Just to be able to attend midnight mass was a real treat in itself. She didn't have the nerve to speak up for fear she would be considered ungrateful.

The nuns decided to conduct a short straw lottery among all the people whose names had been drawn out of the hat. The person who picked the short straw would be the winner. Katie would be the last person to pick from the handful of straws. When she showed Sister St. Charles her straw, the nun shook her head and looked up at the ceiling as she dismissed the other children. Katie had the short straw, and she wasn't going to fool around with divine province any further.

A week before Christmas and after she had finished being the Virgin Mary in the school play, Jack took Katie shopping for a new coat as a Christmas present. Jack was his usual quiet self, but Katie assumed he wasn't very happy about having to spend money on a coat for her. She grabbed the first one she saw because she was afraid Jack would change his mind if she took too much time. She wore her new coat to midnight mass on

Christmas Eve and felt like a queen. She met Sister St. Charles in the vestibule of the church.

"Katie, did you wear your boots to church? It's raining out." Her voice was very stern as she looked down at Katie's feet. She made Katie so nervous that before she could think about it, she lied and said that she had. As soon as the words came out of her mouth she knew she was wrong.

Looking at Katie suspiciously the nun replied, "Katie Ramie, I want to see you and your boots right here after mass!"

The whole night was spoiled for Katie as she nervously anticipated her meeting with Sister St. Charles minus the galoshes; she didn't even own a pair of rain boots. What a witch Sister St. Charles was! Katie was sure if she knew she hadn't worn boots, she might not have let her carry the baby Jesus down the aisle. Katie felt she was looking for any excuse to take the baby Jesus away from her. What business was it of hers to worry about what Katie was wearing on her feet? Why were the nuns always meddling in other people's business?

Katie decided that after mass she was going to have to make a quick getaway from the church before she encountered the nun. She just couldn't face her with the lie, especially after being chosen to carry the baby Jesus down the aisle and being the Virgin Mary in the play. So as soon as the service ended, Katie darted down the steps and ran to the corner where she waited for Maura and the other girls to join her for the walk home. She knew she hadn't really gotten away with anything; Sister St. Charles would know why she didn't meet her, and anyway the worry over the boots had spoiled her whole night. She wouldn't think about it until after the Christmas vacation; she was sure Sister St. Charles would forget all about it by that time.

The holidays were always the worst time for Nan. It was almost a sure thing that before or after Christmas she would suffer some sort of mental issue. The preparations for Christmas always fell heavily on Jack, as Nan complained of tiredness and general depression. Jack did everything possible to take the pressure away from her, succeeding many times in preventing a total breakdown. At these times Katie and Jack were always on high alert, watching Nan's every move especially around the young children.

Jack took Nan out more frequently during the holidays and, as Katie watched the children she wondered why it was that all or her vacations seemed to be spent looking after the kids and the house. She thought about how much fun her other friends were having going to the movies, bowling, and skating. She envied them their material possessions and freedom from responsibility. She would listen with envy as they talked about everything they did over vacation. She felt life had cheated her thus far and she wondered what was in store for the future; a future she hated to think about.

She was carrying the beautiful baby down the aisle and thousands of people were watching her with adoring eyes. She put the baby in the cradle and looked at its face closely; it was little George. Suddenly Nan was next to her smiling lovingly at the baby. As soon as Katie turned and walked away, Nan snatched the naked baby and ran out the door with it. All she had on her was a pair of red rubber boots. A cold rain was falling as Katie ran after her. The baby was frozen solid when Nan reached the incinerator in their apartment building. "This will warm him up!" she yelled. She turned and looked at Katie with a wicked smile as she threw the baby into the raging inferno.

Katie's head shot up from the table as she awoke from this most recent nightmare; she was always relieved to realize she was just dreaming. She knew as long as she was afraid of her mother, she would have the awful nightmares. She hurried quickly to her bedroom; too tired to wait up any longer for her parents to return. She lay down next to Barbara, grateful for the warmth her body provided and the fact that the bed was dry, but as she looked across the room the closet started moving closer and closer to her. She turned her head quickly before it hit her. She was terrified...she knew she was wide awake and she wasn't dreaming...it was real. When she looked at the closet again, it was back in its usual place, but the longer she stared at it the closer it moved toward her. She quickly pulled the sheet and blanket over her head; she figured she was going crazy just like her mother.

Nan spent a lot of time smoking, crocheting, and sleeping during the holidays, but she did make it through the season without any major incident which might have required hospitalization. Katie, on the other hand, was having more frequent nightmares.

Spring and nicer weather finally arrived, but everyone remained indoors as the neighborhood continued to deteriorate rapidly. The street gangs were increasing and many families had long since packed up and left, with others threatening to move as soon as possible.

The fire alarm box was situated on the corner directly across the street from Katie's apartment, and it was always being set off by pranksters causing constant commotion. Many times the firemen were hindered from attending to real emergencies because of these false alarms. Katie began looking out the window all the time to see if she could catch the culprits in the act. One night she actually saw someone set the alarm.

"Mom, we have to call the police. I saw the person who rang the fire alarm!" Katie actually had the phone in her hand when her mother took it from her.

"No, we don't want to get involved with stuff like that." Katie couldn't understand what her mother meant, but she would eventually find out why she had told her to mind her own business.

The first time Katie saw the Mohegan gang members her eyes almost popped out of her head; they were the scariest people she had ever seen. Their heads were shaved, but one strip of hair remained down the center of their scalps. They stalked the streets where the children once played, wearing black leather outfits and carrying chains. They looked as mean as could be and Katie believed all of the stories she had heard about them hurting people.

Peeking out through the Venetian blinds Katie watched as the gangs assembled on the corner, yelling and screaming at each other before they disappeared in the direction of the park. One night she noticed a different gang hovering around the fire alarm, carrying all sorts of weapons...bats, chains, and knives. They had long hair and wore white hooded jackets with a skeleton head on the back. As they hit their chains up against the side of the building and flashed their knives at each other, Katie remembered the rumor about a gang war and realized it was probably going to happen right there.

Katie snuck into the kitchen and quietly dialed the police and reported what was happening, giving her name and address as requested. Within a couple of minutes screaming police cars arrived from every direction and surrounded the delinquents. Katie watched intently from her place behind the window blinds and was flabbergasted as the officers pressed the unruly group up against the wall and confiscated their weapons.

Later a policeman knocked at the apartment door to thank the informant for reporting the incident and preventing a gang war. After the officer left Nan angrily approached Katie.

"Don't you realize everyone knows that it was us who called the police? Now we are really in trouble. How could you do such a stupid thing? They will get even with us for sure."

The children sensed the danger and had already begun to walk home from school in groups for protection. Maura, Jonathan, Katie, and Billy Goodfellow made up one such band.

"Did you guys hear someone called the police on the gangs the other night as they were getting ready to go at it? Boy, I pity that person if they find out."

"Shut up, Billy, don't even talk about it. It makes me sick just to think about them." Katie was sorry she had made that call. She was afraid to death of what was going to happen to her and her family.

The group was caught completely off guard as they turned the corner to their street. They were confronted by a bunch of greasy-looking teenagers with fiery dragons on the back of their black leather jackets.

"What are they doing out during the day? I think we're in trouble, guys!" Billy moved closer to his three friends.

"Hey, you little punks, what are you doing out all by yourselves? Where's your mommy, skinny boys?" A fat kid with a severe case of acne hurled obscenities at them as they passed. Katie's body stiffened up and she stumbled over herself as she quickened her pace; she prayed they wouldn't hurt them because of what had she done. She was positive they knew it was her who called the police and now they were going to kill them.

"Why don't you bullies leave us alone?" Billy bravely shouted once they were past them.

"Oh, would you listen to the brave little boy. We aren't interested in you little punk, or are you one of the girls?" A tall, skinny guy with a knife in his hand began following Billy. Katie started walking faster toward the apartment, her heart beating so hard in her chest that it hurt. She heard a lot of commotion behind her. When Jonathan and Billy buzzed past her, she wasted no time in following in their footsteps. Maura dropped her books as she broke out in a full-fledged run. Something hit Katie's leg, but the impact made her run even faster. A bottle whizzed past her head and Billy cried out in pain as it hit him in the back of his skull, sending blood gushing from the gaping wound. As the injured Billy fell to the ground, the group stopped dead in their tracks and knelt down beside him. The attackers fled from the scene as soon as they saw all of the blood. By the time an adult came to the aid of the children, Billy had lost a lot of blood from his head wound.

Billy spent two days in the hospital recovering from a severe concussion and a dozen stitches in his head. The news of the incident confirmed the worst fears of the people living in the neighborhood—that no one was safe.

The repercussions for Katie were much worse as she felt she was completely responsible for the incident. Little did she know the gang members had no idea she had turned them in and that the bottle was thrown was not meant specifically for her. She thought it happened because she didn't mind her own business like her mother said. It was horrible to carry around the burden of being responsible for someone almost getting killed. She vowed she would never get involved with stuff like that as long as she lived.

Jack was switched back to the night shift at the factory. The one good thing about his new hours was that the monotony of staying at home every day during the summer was broken up by occasional visits to the beach.

On one particular sweltering day in mid-summer, Jack and his brother Ralph arranged to meet at Rockaway Beach with their families. When it came time for Jack to leave in order to go to work, the rest of the family was having so much fun that Ralph offered to take Nan and the children. It would be very tight in his station wagon, but it was worth it to spend some more time at the beach.

Everyone was totally exhausted later that day as they climbed the stairs to the apartment. The little ones were tired and cranky, and Katie and Jonathan were arguing with each other over who was going to get in the bathroom first. It was Katie who noticed the knob on the front of their apartment door was broken off.

"Look, something's wrong with the door." Panic surged through Nan as people were getting robbed and attacked on a regular basis lately. Then she remembered Jack wasn't with them; he had come home earlier to change for work.

"My God, I hope your dad is okay." As she said it the fear inside her was mounting, and her worst thoughts became a reality as she entered the apartment and saw the mess of overturned drawers and furniture scattered throughout the house. Charging through the living room and into the bedroom with Katie and the other kids close at her heels, Nan looked around for Jack.

All concern for her father vanished as Katie stopped in stunned disbelief at the entrance to her bedroom. The entire room was one big mess of torn clothing and broken furniture strewn all over the floor. Falling to her knees in a mound of clothing, she began to cry.

Nan ran to the phone and dialed Jack's number at work.

"Jack, we've been robbed." Nan sobbed into the phone. "It must have happened after you left. The place is a mess, Jack. You have to come home. We have no lock on the door. They broke it off. I'm going to call the police as soon as I hang up."

As Katie sifted through her belongings, she tried to salvage as much as she could. She didn't own much; but what she did have she cherished. The bastards had taken everything including worthless pieces of costume jewelry they probably would end up discarding. What they didn't take, they broke. Katie was heartbroken.

The most urgent requirement was to get the lock on the front door fixed, and the police suggested a locksmith whom Jack called immediately upon his arrival home. The fellow complained of being busy but promised to make it sometime that night to replace the lock.

The police questioned the neighbors, but of course no one saw anything suspicious. They were not surprised. There was no way the place could have been robbed in broad daylight without someone seeing it, but no one was about to come forward with any information. After the incident with Billy, Katie could hardly blame them.

As Nan and Jack went through each room to determine what was missing so they could provide a list to the police, Nan became more upset. Their television, radio, camera, and record player were all gone, along with some clothing and jewelry and essential items that were needed on a day-to-day basis like pots and pans and silverware. To make matters worse they had no homeowner's insurance; they couldn't afford it, and thus had no hope of receiving any financial help in replacing their stolen property.

As night fell Nan's behavior became more disturbed. She absolutely panicked when Jack indicated the locksmith might not make it to fix the door. "Oh, no, if he doesn't come to put on a new lock, we are not staying in this apartment. I don't want them coming back again." She was getting up and down from the kitchen table like a yo-yo and becoming more and more disoriented as the hours went by. She was exhausted.

"I'm going to call Wilma. I've got to talk to her."

"Nan, why don't you call Madge or Bev? They live right around here and it won't be as expensive as calling California. There is nothing Wilma can do for you all the way across the country." Jack was tired himself and becoming concerned that he would have to spend the entire night guarding their unprotected apartment.

"That's all you care about, isn't it? It's always about what something costs. It doesn't matter that I need to talk to my sister. No, all that matters is how much money you are going to have to pry loose from your wallet." Her lips were quivering as she got up from the table and walked toward Jack. "I have really tried lately to ignore my feelings. Yes, I have. I know it is not good for me to get upset and you will never change, but I am not going to sit here calmly while that door remains unlocked. So I am getting the baby and we are going. Do you understand me? I am taking everyone to my sister's. If you don't want to come, that's fine. Stay here and try to prevent them from killing you." As she moved toward Jonathan's bedroom where George slept, Jack caught up with Nan and pulled on her arm.

"Look, you're overreacting, hon. The locksmith will be here. He knows how important it is for us to have the house secured. If we all leave, anyone can get in and take the rest of our stuff. Why don't you calm down, please? Why don't you go to bed and let me take care of all of this? Let me get you a tranquilizer, too. That will help."

"No, don't bother. I've already made up my mind. I'm taking the kids and leaving. This place isn't safe for us anymore!" Jack wouldn't let go of her arm.

"Nan, I can't let you do that. You're not yourself and I won't let you touch the baby." As he finished his ultimatum Nan whirled around to face him and began shouting.

"What do you mean by that? You don't trust me, do you? You think I'm going to hurt him. Maybe kill him. Is that what you think? Well, I'll show you. I'll show everyone. No one trusts me. You think I don't know you have spies everywhere watching me. Katie and Jonathan are your little spies. I know it now. They watch me like a hawk all the time, wondering when I'm going to kill them. Well maybe I'll just do it right now while you watch. How would you like that?" As Nan struggled to disengage Jack's hand from her arm, Jack threw her against the wall. Stunned, she fell to the floor.

"Jesus, I'm sorry, Nan, but I can't let you near the baby like this. Come on, I'll help you to bed and get you your medicine."

All the while Katie had been listening to the entire dialogue between her parents, prepared to defend herself if she had to. And now her father was bringing Nan to the place where she stood. Katie quickly darted back to bed, placing the knife in her hand under the mattress for the time being.

"Now you lie down and take this and in no time you'll be asleep. Tomorrow everything will look better. Don't worry about the door, I'm going to stay up all night and guard it. I'm sure it will be fixed by morning. Come on, drink this." Jack forced the pill and water on his agitated wife.

"Katie, are you awake?" Jack's unusually loud voice reached Katie's ear. She pretended to be asleep; she didn't want to get involved. She berated herself for not leaving using the fire escape. But where would she go? It was just as dangerous outside as it was inside her home. Her father's voice reached her ears again, only this time much louder.

"Katie, wake up." She got up and walked to her parents' room rubbing her eyes as if she had just woken up.

"Listen, I want you to sit here and watch your mother for a minute while I make a phone call. Don't let her get up. She's about to doze off I think. Call me if she starts to get up and I'll come back." Katie wanted to tell Jack no; to run back to her room and get the knife so she could stab her if she moved, but instead she quietly watched as her father left the room.

She turned her gaze on Nan and watched as her chest heaved up and down with her heavy breathing. She thought briefly of leaving her for a minute to get the knife, but she couldn't take that chance. Suppose she got up? Suppose she started opening the windows? She would be to blame. She decided she couldn't take her eyes off of her for a minute; she would kill her with her own bare hands if she had to. She wasn't going to let her mother hurt her no matter what, and while she stood guard over her Katie heard lots of commotion at the front door followed by male voices.

"Thank goodness, I'm so grateful you came. I was just on the phone to your wife. You don't know how much I appreciate this."

"No problem, buster. I'll tell you, I'm working until midnight every day trying to keep up. It's a damn shame the way people are getting ripped off lately. I don't know what this world is coming to. I'll tell you, I could sure use a cold drink while I fix this here door."

"Sure, right away."

Katie was getting impatient. She wished her dad would get back to them; she didn't want to stand guard over her mother for another minute. She wondered if he forgot about them, forgot how dangerous she could get.

It was at least another hour before Jack appeared in the bedroom. Katie assumed the lock was fixed on the front door although Jack didn't say one way or the other.

"How is your mother?"

"She hasn't moved since you left, but I don't think she is really asleep. Can I go back to bed?" Katie yawned to prove she was tired. She desperately wanted to get out of the room, away from her mother, and back to her weapon.

Katie, Jack, and Nan did not sleep a wink that night...or the next night...or the next...until on the brink of collapse, Jack finally admitted Nan to the hospital—again. As far as Katie was concerned it was two days later than she should have been hospitalized. Between caring for the children, cleaning up the house from the robbery, and dealing with Nan's antics, both Katie and Jack were at the limit of their tolerance.

As she hung the wash out on the line from the alley window on the second level, looking over her shoulder constantly to make sure no one was sneaking up on her, Katie thought about the past two days, wondering again why her dad always let it go on for so long.

The morning after the robbery Nan tried to leave the house again with the baby and almost succeeded, before Jack interceded and wrestled her back into bed where she catnapped briefly. While Katie prayed this was the day her father would take her mother to the hospital, she carefully avoided the bedroom, keeping the other children away from Nan. All day long she worried Jack would leave them and go to work, but he surprised her and remained at home. She decided that this time she needed to tell him he had to get her out of the house right away; that she wasn't going to get any better.

That night all of the kids huddled in Jonathan's room. It was stinking hot and they were wall to wall bodies trying to find a comfortable place to sleep. Only Katie and Jonathan were unsuccessful in dropping into blessed unconsciousness.

"Katie, what do you think is going on?" Jonathan had relegated his bed to Barbara, Amy, and Sammy, and made himself a makeshift bed on the floor with an old blanket.

"I don't know, but I'm sure they aren't sleeping. At least I know mom isn't and I hope dad isn't either, or we are all in big trouble."

"Suppose she comes blasting in here? It could happen you know. Dad doesn't move too fast. He could fall asleep."

"Don't worry, Jonathan, I have something to protect us." As he watched Katie slid her hand under his bed and pulled out the shiny object she had hidden earlier.

"Oh, my goodness! Where did you get that?" Jonathan backed away from Katie.

"I got it from the silverware drawer in the kitchen. I've had it for a long time. I keep it in my room under the mattress just in case. I was so happy the robbers didn't get it. There were a few times I thought I would have to use it on mom. And I will, too. I mean it." Katie shook the object at Jonathan.

It wasn't long before Jonathan dozed off, and only Katie was awake to hear Nan threaten to come in the room and get them all.

"I mean it, Jack. You can't stop me this time. They are my babies and no one can keep me from them. I can do whatever I want with them, and it is not safe in this neighborhood any more. I'm taking them away from all of this right now." As she heard Nan's threat, Katie got up and closed the window even though it was already like an oven in the small, overcrowded room. Then she crawled over to the door and stood behind it with the knife in her hand. She vowed that if Nan came in the room she was going to kill her. She stood like that for the rest of the night while Jack and Nan argued.

Katie was sure Jack would take Nan to the hospital soon. He had to; they couldn't go on like this. But she was wrong. The next day was an ugly repeat of the day before, and nightfall found them back in Jonathan's room, hiding from the monster in the other room. All of the kids were hot and fussy, including Katie, and many fights broke out among them as they tried to survive in the confines of the small room. Finally a cool breeze from a threatening storm made the air more comfortable, and one by one they dropped off to sleep except for Katie, who sat across the door to the bedroom blocking it from entry by anyone. Soon even she succumbed to exhaustion, as her body slid down across the door and onto the floor.

A couple of hours later the clapping sound of thunder and a bolt of lightning illuminating the room woke her up, sending her scurrying across the room to close the window against the downpour. When it was shut, she realized there were other noises she was hearing…and they weren't connected to the storm.

"Leave me alone, you bastard. If you touch me one more time I'm going to kill you. What have you done with my children? I want to see them. You hurt them, didn't you?" Katie trembled as she opened Jonathan's door slightly so she could hear them better.

"No, no. The kids are all sleeping in Jonathan's room; nothing has happened to them. Now come on, let's try to get some sleep. You'll feel so much better with a good night's sleep."

Katie wondered why her dad was still pleading with Nan as she dropped to the floor and felt under the bed for the knife. She was ready to depart from the room; this thing had gone on long enough.

"You think I'm sick, don't you? Well, I've got news for you. You're the one who is nuts…not me." As Nan began to dance around Jack, shouting over and over again how crazy he was, Katie made her way closer to the living room until she was in full view of the ludicrous scene taking place. When Nan finished circling Jack, she slyly moved her body toward the hallway and the children's room, not realizing Katie was in her way until her devil eyes saw the knife in Katie's hand. She was holding it high in the air pointed directly at Nan.

"You're not going anywhere. If you don't back up I'm going to kill you with this knife, and don't think I won't do it." Like a wounded animal Nan moaned and recoiled in Jack's direction.

"My God, Katie, put that knife down!" Jack pleaded with her as Nan fell at his feet.

"Not until you get her out of this house. We are not going to spend another night like animals locked up in that room because of you two. You're driving us all crazy. Now, go right now or I swear I'll use this on both of you."

"Calm down, Katie. I was going to take your mother to the hospital in the morning. Please go back to bed."

"No, I don't believe you. You still think she is going to snap out of it. Take her now." Katie was sweating.

"Okay, okay. You're right. I'll take her. Just put down the knife."

"No, not until you're both out the door. I heard her talking about killing Jonathan and me the other night. Just go." He and Nan slowly shuffled into their bedroom where they spent some time gathering up clothing. Eventually Jack led Nan to the front door, as Katie stood in the kitchen doorway still holding tight to the knife. When the front door closed Katie ran to it and locked it, slipping the safety latch on so they couldn't get back in unless someone in the apartment opened the door. And that was not going to happen tonight. It was just the way she wanted it.

As she turned around she met Jonathan's sleepy gaze.

"Is everything okay now, Katie?"

"Yes, Jonathan, you can have your bed back now."

After the little ones were safely in their own beds, Katie collapsed into her own bed. She fell asleep wondering if she would actually have had the nerve to stab her mother if she had not backed off. As she slipped from awareness, she felt sure she would have.

Katie was able to sleep for a few hours before the babies woke her up. It was mid-morning before Jack arrived home alone. He said nothing to Katie about the incident the previous night ignoring it as if it never happened. He went directly to bed. She was sure he was scared out of his mind that she was going to be just like her mom. It served him right; next time maybe he wouldn't wait so long to get her out of the house.

That night Jack went back to work.

For two weeks Katie took care of the children by herself, as Jack made no attempt to contact the social services office. Katie was angry that another of her vacations was being ruined. It was really a shock when Nan arrived home at the end of the second week looking rested and, like Jack, acting as if nothing had happened. Katie figured her father must have known she was only going to be hospitalized for a short while and that was why he didn't get any help for them, or maybe she was giving him too much credit and he just didn't want to deal with it. Just like before Katie quickly turned the responsibility of the house and the children over to her mother; she was glad to be rid of it.

At first it started out simply as talk. "We have to move out of this neighborhood. You know it's just not safe here anymore." Jack nodded his head, silently agreeing with Nan's assessment.

Although she hated what was going on in the neighborhood, it frightened Katie to think about moving. She would be in her last year at St. Anne's when school started, and then she hoped to attend St. Regina's High School where Maura and her other classmates would most likely go. Secretly she prayed that moving was just a lot of talk, like so many other things. Much to her dismay, however, Nan and Jack began searching for another place. At first they looked at other apartments until they realized that most of the areas they could afford in the city were basically in the same pitiful state as their own neighborhood.

Nan's sister convinced them to look for a house on Long Island. With six kids and no money in the bank, Jack thought it would be next to impossible for them to buy a house. Nan was set on the idea, however, and so to please her Jack drove the family to Long Island every weekend to look at houses. Usually the kids had to stay in the car while Nan and Jack inspected a potential house; each time Katie's heart pounded with fear. She had only one more year at St. Anne's and she certainly didn't want to start a new school.

After two months of looking, it was obvious they were not going to be able to afford the homes they had seen thus far. With six kids, the real estate people were showing them houses with at least three bedrooms; houses Nan and Jack couldn't hope to qualify for. Katie breathed a sigh of relief the first weekend that passed without the family making a trip to Long Island to go house hunting. The weather was getting colder and the holidays were approaching; clearly not a good time to think about moving.

Katie turned fourteen in November of 1960 with no fanfare...which suited her just fine. Shortly after her birthday she took the high school entrance exam and passed with flying colors. She was accepted to St. Regina's the day after the test results were received. Katie was summoned to Sister St. Charles' office where she was informed she had been nominated to receive a scholarship for outstanding academic achievement. She was further informed that after much deliberation, it was decided that based on her family situation she was the most deserving student to receive the financial aid.

"Oh, my goodness, does that mean I can go to St. Regina's?"

"If that's what you want, dear."

"Thank you, thank you so much!" As Katie got up to leave the office she stiffened when she heard Sister St. Charles' parting comment.

"And, Katie, I do know that you don't have any rain boots."

Katie and Nan took the train to St. Regina's a week later where Katie was measured for the burgundy and gold uniform she would wear each day. She would have to take a bus and train to school every morning, but she was thrilled. Maura was attending St. Regina's also, as well as many of her other classmates. Even after being officially enrolled in the high school, Katie couldn't shake the uneasy feeling she had about what was to come.

A Christmas dance was planned for the eighth graders in the parish hall and every girl, including Katie, waited patiently to be invited by one of the boys. Some months before, Mitchell O'Keefe moved from the neighborhood, and Katie had still not recovered from that. Not that he paid any attention to her, but she missed looking at him every day and dreaming about them together.

Katie was caught completely off guard when Harry Pedro asked her to the dance. He had been her partner for the Irish jig in the school musical play. Katie's sense of decency wouldn't allow her to say no to her first invitation even though she really didn't want to go to the dance with him. She figured no one else would ask her anyway.

On the day of the dance, Harry, a slightly-built Puerto Rican, arrived for Katie looking surprisingly handsome in a new suit and presenting her with a beautiful corsage. The dance was a success and Katie had a much better time than she thought she would. Harry was a lot of fun to be with and much nicer than she expected. He was also a perfect gentleman, treating her like a queen.

During the months following the dance, Katie was pursued by Ray Arms, a tall, lanky fellow. He was the school renegade from a broken home and was always in some kind of trouble. Every day he appeared on the corner across from the Ramie apartment, smoking a cigarette and looking up at the window, waiting to catch a glimpse of Katie. Even though Katie knew he was a loser, she was thrilled at the attention. After stalking Katie for awhile and repeatedly asking her to go out with him, he finally gave up. Katie missed the attention, but knew she had done the right thing in refusing to go to the movies with him.

It was a rough winter in the Ramie apartment; they were without heat for the majority of the time. The children all got terrible colds and by the time everyone was well, an entire month had passed.

Nan was very fragile. She smoked more than ever, well over three packs a day. She had to plan carefully to make sure she always had her cigarettes; even she recognized it was not an option anymore to send Katie on errands in their hostile neighborhood. There were occasions when she was down to one cigarette and panicked, making comments about needing someone to go to the store. Katie just ignored her; there was no way on earth she was going to step one foot out the door after dark.

Jack was constantly counting Nan's Lithium pills to make sure she was taking them. On really bad days Katie would come home from school and find Nan had done nothing all day. Jack was still working night shift and even though he slept in most mornings, it was imperative he was in the apartment so Nan was not alone with the children.

Nan was content to sit and crochet most of the time. The veins in her legs were very bad and the pain was constant, so she wasn't very mobile. There were days when she couldn't even get out of bed, when her legs were so swollen she had to keep them elevated. Katie, Jonathan, and Barbara took care of the younger children most days, especially during the evenings and on weekends. Amy was five, Sammy was four and George was two. They were all very good children; almost as if they knew they had to be in order to survive. They didn't get out very often especially during the winter and learned early to amuse themselves with the limited toys and games they had.

The building was infested with mice, and on any given evening while sitting in the living room, a mouse or two appeared somewhere in the room. Jonathan and Barbara would leave crumbs on the floor for them, and everyone would watch them eat and play. The situation with the mice became uncontrollable and Nan decided they needed a cat. Jack was not an animal lover and neither was Katie, but he agreed to the cat in order to pacify Nan.

It was very easy to get a cat; people were always giving them away. The new member of the Ramie family, a black cat, was named Springy. He did manage to keep the mice out of the apartment, but unfortunately he was a very malevolent animal, always biting or scratching one of the kids. Katie was actually afraid of him. He kept appearing but of nowhere scaring her to death. One evening about three months after he arrived, Springy jumped from behind the top of the couch onto Jack's neck, scratching and biting him very badly. That was the end of Springy.

During early spring of 1961, Nan and Jack resumed house hunting. Katie did not accompany them on the trips, preferring to stay at home even if it meant taking care of the other kids or cooking dinner, usually spaghetti and meatballs.

Katie knew her mother was hanging on by a thread. The idea of moving to a house in the country was the only thing that was keeping Nan partially sane. She knew if they didn't get a new home soon, Nan would eventually crack.

As Katie looked out the window at the ground below which was now littered with garbage, she thought about how frightened she was when they first moved in. She was sure her mother would throw someone out the window eventually. She recalled all the breakdowns her mother had since they moved in, and how on guard she was against a possible attempt by her mother to harm any of the children. She wondered if she might have been directly responsible for preventing her mother from killing again; all those late nights sitting half-asleep watching her, watching every move she made. Would Nan, if given the chance, have harmed any of the other children? Katie believed in her heart there was no doubt she would have... and still could.

There were so many near-misses. Like finding Amy when she was two years old in the kitchen playing with a steak knife, with Nan right beside her. Luckily she suffered only a small cut on her finger before Katie wrestled it away from her. And Sammy, when he was three, standing on a chair by the gas stove while a pot of water was boiling with Nan nowhere in sight. And a near miss again with Sammy just after he turned four, leaning precariously out one of the windows which had been left open in the living room, while his mother sat on the couch oblivious to what he was doing. These incidents occurred during times when they were not on high alert. During her breakdowns Nan wasn't left alone for a minute, except when she locked herself in the bathroom.

There was little comfort for Katie in thinking she had prevented any further disasters in the Ramie family, for there were too few good times and too many bad times in her life. Coming back to the present Katie realized the old fears were still very much with her, and she would always be on guard against the possibility of death from a mother so fragile that Katie was forced to spend her life looking over her shoulder. She was very fearful of what the future would bring; even now Katie could see the warning signs. It would take only one seemingly small incident occurring at just the right moment to set her mother off; the mother who would never be normal. Katie realized their neighborhood and the thought of having to live in it permanently just might do it.

She was disgusted at the thought of moving. She was at a very critical point in her life; it had all been arranged...attending St. Regina's, taking business courses, going to school with people she knew, a scholarship, and a new uniform. Yes, everything was perfect; but she knew it would be fouled up somehow.

As she departed from the train with Maura and the other girls, Katie's heart was pounding. This was her first real party; one where both boys and girls would be together. Maura was the only other person her age attending the party, but Katie always thought of her as being much more sophisticated than she was because she had always hung out with the older girls.

Katie was worried about fitting in with a bunch of high school kids, and just as she thought, as soon as she walked into the room a feeling of not belonging surged through her. Everyone looked preoccupied with what they were doing, which was mainly flirting, and she became even more uncomfortable when none of her friends took the time to introduce her to the other kids. Loud music was playing and some people were dancing. Katie prayed someone would ask her to dance, but no one knew she existed. One by one, the other girls abandoned Katie as they found someone else to talk to until only Katie and Maggie were left together. Maggie was a small, bird-like person who usually said exactly what was on her mind. She was the oldest of the girls in Katie's circle of friends and was already in high school, but she looked even younger than Katie. She was also not having any better luck than Katie in attracting attention that night.

After about a half-hour of idly standing together Maggie whispered in Katie's ear. "I'm not having any fun at all; let's split this dump."

"Should we? It's okay with me if you want to?" The idea of getting away from the party suited Katie just fine.

"Let me tell Maura we are leaving. I don't think she will mind at all." She left Katie standing alone in the corner as she made her way over to Maura, who was animatedly conversing with a couple of guys. She watched as Maggie broke in and pulled Maura aside. It was obvious Maura was not agreeable to leaving, and Katie was sure of it when Maggie began walking across the room without her.

"She doesn't want to leave; says she's having too much fun but we can go if we want. She'll go home with Carole and Kathy." Looking dejected the two of them departed, walking down the dark, deserted streets to the ell, scared and miserable. The deal was that they were all supposed to stay together. Katie breathed a sigh of relief when they arrived at the train station.

"That was really a horrible party; everyone was so stuck-up." Katie tried to console Maggie, but she knew it was only because the girl found herself in the same boat as Katie that they shared this comradeship. She knew for sure Maggie would be right back with the tightly knit group tomorrow. Tonight she was glad she had someone to share her misery with. As much as they sympathized with each other, Katie still couldn't help feeling like an ugly duckling. She didn't need to be thrown into a situation which would make her more insecure than she already was; and indeed this was what happened. Because all of her friends with the exception of Maura were older than Katie by a year or two, she was treated indifferently and didn't have the maturity to realize it was just her age and not her personality or looks that caused her to be dealt with that way. She was not self-assured and aggressive enough like Maura, to incorporate herself into an uncomfortable situation and make the best of it.

Shortly after the first boy-girl party disaster, Maggie's parents gave her a party to celebrate her birthday. Again Katie found herself in the position of being ignored. As she sat alone on a chair in the corner of the crowded room, Maggie's brother suggested they play some games. Katie had a secret crush on one of the boys in the group, Pat, who happened to be dating Carole, the prettiest and sexiest girl in the neighborhood. The boys adored her and she flirted with them all the time; Katie wished she could be just like her. Carole was pleasant to Katie, but Katie had seen her bad temper surface during an argument over a boy which resulted in Carole scratching a girl's face very badly.

"Let's play spin-the-bottle first!" They formed a circle, but no one encouraged Katie to move from her place in the corner so she just sat there. The bottle was spun, pairing up a girl and a boy who disappeared into the bedroom to kiss, returning shortly and blushing to the cheers of the other kids in the room. On the fourth spin the bottle stopped in front of Pat, Carole's boyfriend. The bottle was spun for the girls and stopped directly in a gap in the circle, pointing right at Katie sitting on the chair. The room grew so quiet you could hear a pin drop as everyone stared at Katie.

Pat broke the silence. "I guess it's you and me, little girl!" He reached for Katie's trembling hand, and because she needed something to hold onto or she would fall on the floor, she quickly put her hand in his. When he closed the door to the bedroom behind them, he teased Katie.

"So I bet this is your first kiss from a guy, huh?" Katie dared not speak. She felt like there was cotton in her mouth. Her heart was pounding in her chest as Pat came closer and put his burly hands on her shoulders. His lips were moist and big and she felt like she was drowning in fluid only seconds after he started kissing her. Before she knew it, it was over...and much too quickly for her to enjoy any of it. When he let her go she put her hand on the doorknob to leave, but Pat's hand stopped her from opening the door. He winked at her. "Let's stay in here a little while longer, let them wonder what's going on." He had a mischievous grin on his face.

"I don't know, Pat. Carole is going to be awfully mad." Katie bit her lower lip.

"Oh, let her stew. She's too possessive anyway; she's always mad about something.

"Now where were we? Why don't we try another kiss?" Pat moved closer to Katie. This time she opened her mouth just a little wider and relaxed, fully enjoying the second kiss. "Now that was a lot better; you're a quick study alright...you learn fast!" Pat put his arm around Katie's waist and opened the door. No one cheered as they walked out of the room, and Katie caught sight of Carole throwing daggers at her with her eyes. The last thing she wanted was a hassle with Carole over Pat. It wasn't her fault the bottle came her way; what did she expect her to do?

To make matters worse when the music resumed after the game was over, Pat came over and asked Katie to dance. The dance was over before she could relax enough to really enjoy it. Katie kept her distance from the irate Carole for the rest of the night and hurriedly departed before the party was over. She was scared out of her mind about making the short trip home without anyone accompanying her, but she would rather die than ask anyone to walk her home. She was prepared to run like hell to the next building and up the stairs, but as it turned out Pat caught up with her before she left Maggie's building and escorted her right to the front door of her apartment. He gave her a final short kiss before she knocked on the door and was let in by Jonathan.

She was on top of the world. She sat on the windowsill in her room looking out at the darkness through the fire escape railings. She honestly couldn't remember ever feeling this good. It was a moment to cherish; a moment she did not want to end. It was a beautiful evening; school was almost over, she would be graduating in a few weeks, and a boy had kissed her for the first time—an older boy at that.

She looked over at the beds; Barbara was in one, and Amy was in the other. Tonight she didn't even mind that she would have to move one or the other so she could have a bed all to herself. It would probably be Amy; Barbara was getting so big she didn't think she could lift her anymore. She danced across the room to imaginary music. She felt like Cinderella at the ball, but suddenly she stopped dancing. She knew tomorrow she would be back to the old Katie again because nothing good ever lasted.

Sure enough the next time she saw Pat, he was sitting with Carole on the front steps of Maura's house; they were tongue kissing. Katie was back to being the Cinderella who swept the ashes.

Shirley and Karen Flannigen lived with their father on the eighth floor of Katie's apartment building. The story was their mother abandoned them when they were very young, and they had been raised completely by their father, who was an alcoholic. Karen was fifteen and Shirley was seventeen. Both girls were as independent as two birds and used to coming and going as they pleased.

One afternoon at the beginning of summer, Shirley darted up the stairs and frantically knocked on the door to the Ramie apartment, throwing herself into Nan's arms sobbing.

"An ambulance just took Amy to the hospital. She's hurt real bad." Nan couldn't get anything else out of Shirley about what happened or where they took Amy. Jack was still home preparing to leave for work, so he got on the phone and called several hospitals before he determined where she was. He and Nan left immediately for the hospital leaving Katie to watch Sammy and George. Barbara and Jonathan were both playing outside with friends.

Jack dropped Nan off at the front of the hospital and she ran wild-eyed to the first person she saw behind the desk. "Where is my child? Where is my daughter?"

The prim-looking nurse behind the desk took a step backwards and asked Nan in an unpleasant voice, "May I get your name? Then maybe I can find your child."

"I'm sorry." Nan started to cry. "Her name is Amy Ramie; she's only five and a half years old. They told my husband on the phone that she was taken here by ambulance. My husband's parking the car; he should be in any minute." Somehow it seemed important to Nan that this rude woman know there was a man coming soon.

"Hold on, I'll check it out." After a short period of time the nurse returned and told Nan that Amy was indeed in the emergency room. When Jack came in she escorted both of them back to where the doctors were working on Amy.

When Nan entered the small cubicle and saw Amy, she thought she was going to faint. She was as white as the sheet that covered her stiff body and her eyes were shut tightly. She looked like she was dead. Nan couldn't bring herself to say anything and remained frozen at the entrance to the room.

"We are going to have to get her up to surgery quickly if we are going to save the foot at all. It's going to be close; I think the Achilles tendon is totally torn. Is the heel still on ice? Has anyone gotten hold of the parents yet? We can't move on this without them. We need a signature from someone. Who the hell is working on that?" Nan heard it all, but she couldn't get her mouth to work to tell them she was there. Jack was apparently having the same problem.

A tall man in a starched green outfit came bounding toward Nan and Jack when he saw them standing in the doorway.

"Who are you? Are you this child's parents?" The doctor's voice was impatient, and Nan could only shake her head.

"We need your permission to operate on her immediately!"

"What happened?" Nan found herself saying weakly, afraid to find out.

"She lost part of her heel in the spoke of a bicycle. Someone had the good sense to retrieve the remainder of it and we have it on ice. If the nerve tissue doesn't die, there is a good chance we can sew it back in place. I have to examine it more closely before deciding whether it will work. I may have to do some skin grafting." The doctor was talking too fast and Nan found it difficult to comprehend what he was saying.

"I can't say for sure yet, but there may be severe tendon damage. If this is the case we could be in for real trouble. She needs that part of the heel to carry the weight of her body when she walks. If the Achilles tendon is damaged in any way, well…I hate to say it, but she may not be able to walk on that foot again.

"We'll sign whatever you want us to. Please make her well again, please." Nan implored.

"As I said, I haven't been able to assess the full extent of the tendon damage. We need to x-ray, but from what I saw there is the possibility that it exists. Would you stay here please until I get the paperwork?" He didn't really wait for Nan's answer as he bounded down the narrow corridor, his green coat trailing behind him.

Nan gingerly planted herself on the nearest chair she could find in the room. She couldn't look at Amy who was unconscious. Her head was swirling, twisting her brain until it pounded. She leaned against the back of the chair and closed her eyes as they began to twitch. She wondered how it happened; Amy didn't even own a bicycle.

Before she knew it someone was pushing papers at her to sign. She saw lots of words on the papers, but she couldn't really comprehend any of them. She signed her name next to Jack's. She gripped the chair firmly with her fingers as the nurse removed the papers from her.

"Are you okay, Ms. Ramie?"

"Yes, I'm fine." It wasn't really true. She felt like a ton of bricks had come down on her head.

Meanwhile Katie was at home wondering what was going on. They had the day off from school and here she was watching the babies. She heard Shirley tell Nan that Amy was at the hospital. Katie was outside when Karen and Shirley asked Amy if she wanted to go to the park. Katie warned Amy she shouldn't go, but she ignored her and got on the back of Karen's bike and off they went. Amy had no shoes on.

Two hours later the same doctor in the not-so-starched scrubs, now wet with perspiration, walked quickly toward Nan and Jack.

"We were able to reattach the severed heel with only minimal skin grafting. However, there has been some tendon damage and so I cannot say for sure that Amy will recover completely from the injury. I wish I could tell you more but until the wound heals, and that in itself is something we have to be very concerned about, we won't know if she will be able to walk on the foot again." Nan was glad Jack was with her; she was having a hard time standing and she needed him to lean on.

Amy's wound had to be bathed and the dressing changed three times a day, and Jack was the only one who could cope with doing it. The injury was grotesque looking and all manner of liquid oozed from it. Jack was as gentle and thorough at performing the chore as any medical doctor would have been. For three solid weeks he didn't miss a day of changing the dressing. When Amy went for her check-up the doctor marveled at how well the wound was healing, suggesting Jack's attention to it had put the recovery process well ahead of schedule. The reattachment and skin grafting showed no signs of rejection or infection.

When Katie got up the courage to look at the much talked about foot, she thought she was going to throw up. There were ugly brown stitches everywhere and white stuff seeping out. She wondered how her dad could look at, bathe, and touch that awful thing every day.

The details of the accident were finally relayed to Nan and Jack by Amy. She and Shirley and Karen had set off for the park, with Amy riding on the back of Karen's bike barefooted. When they got to the park, Karen's bike picked up speed coming down one of the steep hills, scaring Amy. She apparently moved her feet closer to the wheel and when she did, the heel of her bare right foot caught in the spokes of the bike immediately severing it.

None of the Ramie children had a bicycle, but after seeing Amy's wound Katie vowed she would never ride on the back of anyone's bike. She felt sorry for Karen Flannigen, too. The girl had attempted to apologize to Nan and Jack for what she did, but they only yelled at her. She wondered why Nan was so hard on the Flannigen girls; at least they didn't kill Amy.

For almost a month, Amy remained in a wheelchair until the doctor felt it was time to test her foot. It was a chore convincing her that she had to try to stand on her foot, and when she did she collapsed on the floor immediately.

"It doesn't mean she can't walk on it, but after sitting in the wheelchair for so long the muscles in her legs have grown weak. You have got to force her to use her legs more often. The wound has completely healed; it's time to test the foot." After the doctor's conversation the whole family worked with Amy every day without success. It seemed to Katie that Amy was afraid to put her foot on the floor because she was sure it was going to hurt.

"Amy, if you don't try it at least once you might have to stay in that wheelchair forever. Look at all the stuff you're missing out on." Katie and everyone in the family kept talking until Amy finally agreed to put her weight on the foot, first standing only on her good foot and gradually lowering her injured foot to the floor. Each day she put more of her weight on the injured foot until one day she was finally comfortable putting all of her weight on it. It was just a matter of time before she was walking normally again.

Nan was becoming extremely restless and talked incessantly of moving; she was having a hard time recovering from the ordeal with Amy. Everyone in the Ramie household was on high alert again as Nan did foolish things, like leaving George and Sammy alone in the tub by themselves while she sat in the living room smoking a cigarette. Luckily, Jonathan and Amy found them quickly and safely finished their baths.

Terrible stories were circulating of increased violence in the neighborhood—rapes, robberies, and murders. Nan was sure they couldn't get through another year. Everyone could see she was on the verge of falling to pieces again, so Jack humored her by again taking her to look at houses every chance he got. Sometimes the kids got to go on these expeditions, and sometimes they even got lucky and were allowed to walk with them through the houses. No matter what shape they were in, they all looked good to Katie. She was surprised at how much she wanted to live in a nice place. It was so frustrating; she really didn't want to go to a public school, which was what she would have to do if they left the city, but Long Island was so pretty and it would be nice not to have to worry about getting attacked every time she went outside.

Katie was not with Nan and Jack when they finally put a contract on a house. They were by themselves and Katie was home watching the children. Nan was grinning from ear to ear as she announced the news. "If the contract goes through we'll be out of here by July."

Immediately Katie had to use the bathroom as she was sick to her stomach at the prospect of moving. She wouldn't be attending St. Regina's, and she was afraid to death of the public schools. She knew it was too late to enroll in another Catholic school, and anyway the scholarship she received was only good at St. Regina's. She almost hoped the contract on the house didn't go through. It did.

Chapter Five: Every Minute an Eternity

The entire Ramie family was preoccupied with packing and making all the arrangements for the move to Long Island, so the turmoil going on inside of Katie didn't get any attention even from her. She knew this move had to be for the mental well-being of her mother and the safety of the entire family, but she was not one to make friends easily and to leave even the lukewarm relationships she had was traumatic. What would going to public high school be like? She could just see it now—a bunch of juvenile delinquents hanging out in the hallways, smoking, and using dirty language. They might be escaping the crime in the city, but she heard the kids who went to public school were bad everywhere.

A chill passed through Katie's body and goose bumps appeared on her arm as they got closer to the new house; none of the kids had seen it. She wished they had moved a year ago so she wouldn't have to start high school without any friends. She was positive she wouldn't meet anyone during the summer.

It was almost midnight when Jack drove the car into the driveway of their new home. They had gotten a very late start from the city and the traffic was horrendous. It was so dark it was impossible to see the house. There were lots of trees and bushes everywhere. As soon as the car doors opened, everyone scurried out anxious to see their new home. It took only a few minutes to make the rounds of the incredibly small house. It was like a box; a paltry hall surrounded by a tiny kitchen, a small living room, one miniature bathroom, and two pitifully little bedrooms.

Oh, my God, Katie thought. *There just has to be more rooms somewhere.* Her mouth hung open in astonishment, hunger pains giving way to mounting anger at the size of the house. She didn't think they even made houses as small as the one she was standing in. Katie felt sick; it was late and she was very tired and hungry. They hadn't eaten since lunch and missed dinner because the traffic was so bad. Nan had packed a few hard-boiled eggs, several pieces of cheese, and a small bottle of milk which they all shared. They would have to go shopping first thing in the morning.

"Katie, you girls will share the smaller room, and the boys can take the bigger bedroom." Katie laughed to herself at Nan's use of the term bigger…there was nothing in the house that could be classified as big.

The furniture and boxes were strewn throughout the house by the movers, and it took every remaining bit of energy Katie had to find some sheets to put on her mattress and the one Barbara and Amy shared. Putting the beds together was not an option; everyone was exhausted.

"Your dad and I will sleep in the living room." Finding out that the living room was also going to be a bedroom was the last straw; Katie cried herself to sleep that night.

It was close to noon the next day before Katie opened her eyes. The sun was shining brightly outside sending a warm, yellow glow into her new bedroom, and she could smell bacon and eggs cooking. Things certainly looked a lot better in the daylight, and she enthusiastically got out of bed knowing there were a million things that needed to be done. But first she had to eat. She was famished and so apparently was the rest of the family, who were already in the process of devouring the food as quickly as it appeared on the table.

It was hard work getting the house in order and Katie did her share; cleaning, polishing floors, and watching the kids while her parents went shopping. There was one thing about the new house that she liked; there was no way her mother could kill anyone by dropping them from a window. The windows were all less than two feet from the ground.

Something else was nagging at Katie. She hadn't really noticed this in the hectic months leading up to the move, but her mother was definitely gaining more weight. She was sluggish and tired all of the time, too. If she didn't know any better, Katie thought Nan could be pregnant again; and maybe even pretty far along. But she reminded herself that all of their pregnancies had always been announced with much fanfare, usually in the first couple of months. No, it couldn't be. They would have told everyone by now…or would they?

It wasn't until the middle of the second week of the move that Katie had time to check out the neighbors. Jonathan already had a few friends, and Barbara was the social queen of the neighborhood. While sitting on the front steps Katie saw a frightfully thin redheaded girl bounding toward her; she had never seen anyone so skinny in all her life.

"Hi, I'm Elaine. That's where I live." She pointed to the house directly across the street. "What's your name?"

"I'm Katie, this is where I live. I guess we have the same type of house?"

"Yes, do you have to share a bedroom with anyone?" Before Katie could answer Elaine continued talking. "I have to share a room with my older sister who is a pain in the neck." As Elaine finally paused for air, Katie seized the moment to speak.

"I share a bedroom with my two little sisters."

"Gee whiz, how do you all fit in? My sister has her junk everywhere. I'm lucky I have room in my bed to sleep at night. How many brothers and sisters do you have? My mom says there sure are a lot of people coming in and out of this place."

"I have two sisters and three brothers," Katie replied with a huge sigh. Dumbfounded, Elaine's mouth dropped open. *She may be skinny*, Katie thought, *but she sure has a big mouth*.

"How do you all fit in there? It must be terrible. I thought I had it bad. What a mess. I'll never complain again." Elaine was depressing Katie and she wished she would just go away, but she continued to ask questions and then suggested they play a game of Monopoly.

A few days later after their first meeting, Elaine introduced Katie to the Santigo sisters, who lived around the corner from them. Carmen and Maria were Puerto Rican. Katie liked them right away; they reminded her of Harry Pedro. Carmen was as pretty as Maria was homely, but it was Maria whom Katie adored. She was as nice as Carmen was spoiled and selfish. By the time school began Elaine, Katie, and Maria were a close threesome.

There were other big changes in the Ramie household. Jack found a new job closer to home. He had tried commuting every day into the city, but that only lasted a few weeks; he was spending most of each day on the road. Katie tried to stifle a hysterical laugh when she was told Jack had accepted a job as an attendant at one of the biggest mental institutions in the United States— Pehlam State Hospital—which just happened to be located right around the block from their new house. Katie was encouraged thinking maybe her dad would get Nan to the hospital a little bit sooner the next time she had problems. *Heck, she could even walk there herself*, Katie thought.

The rest of the summer passed quickly. It was early afternoon each day before things settled down enough in the Ramie household to allow Katie to meet with her friends to play Monopoly or sit on the stoop gabbing.

"Elaine, who is that boy sneaking around the house?" Katie was intrigued. She had seen him on previous occasions lurking about.

"Oh, him, that's Billy Lattey. He lives next door to me. What a creep he is!" As she stuck her tongue out at Billy, Elaine picked up the dice and threw them hard against the board.

"Hi, I'm Billy. You must be the new kid." He looked even worse from close up—dark black circles under his eyes, yellowish skin, long oily hair, and painfully skinny. He was not as thin as Elaine though, but she looked much healthier. He reminded her of Ray, the boy who had stalked her in the city; probably just one of the many juvenile delinquents she would run into now that she would be going to public school.

Katie was shocked when Billy pulled out a pack of cigarettes from his pocket and began to light one up.

"Are you allowed to do that?" Katie's voice squeaked when she spoke.

"Who is going to stop me?" His reply was sarcastic as he blew out loads of smoke.

"Just ignore him, Katie. If we're lucky he'll go away." Elaine was irritated that Katie was even talking to Billy.

"Shut up, Olive Oyl. I'm not talking to you anyway." A nasty grin appeared on Billy's face as he shouted at Elaine. Katie had to chuckle to herself at Billy's nickname for Elaine; it fit her perfectly. She did look like Popeye's girlfriend.

"You two certainly aren't very nice to each other." Katie was uncomfortable as Elaine and Billy traded unfriendly stares.

After that encounter, wherever Katie was Billy suddenly appeared, always asking her to do something. "You want to ride on my bike? I'm taking Jonathan fishing. Do you want to come along?" It wasn't that Katie liked Billy all that much that made her accept his invitations, it was merely the fact that he paid a lot of attention to her which she responded to. She liked riding on the handlebar of his bike; she had refused to ride on the back explaining to him what happened to Amy. Although he looked like a strong wind would blow him over, he was very strong and had no trouble maneuvering the bike with her on it. She felt very safe with him. When they played kick the can in the woods, it gave her a good feeling in the pit of her stomach as she waited for Billy to find her. He was very aggressive about his feelings for her and she enjoyed hearing him tell her that he liked her a lot, but she made it clear to him and everyone else that she didn't like him that way at all.

"I know something you don't know." Katie wasn't going to give Barbara the satisfaction of thinking she was one bit interested in her news.

"Big deal...you brat." Katie stuck her tongue out at Barbara.

"Well, I don't care if you don't want to know. I'm going to tell you anyway." Barbara sat on the edge of Katie's bed and gestured extravagantly with her hands.

"Mom's pregnant again." Her big brown eyes searched Katie's face for a reaction. Katie opened her mouth wide and flung herself dramatically against her pillow more for Barbara's benefit than anything else.

"Can you believe it, Katie? I think it stinks. Where are we going to put another human being? I mean we're already squashed to the brim. Why, I'm ashamed to bring my friends home." Katie thought Barbara was so much older than her nine years.

"Is that why you spend so much time in their houses?" Katie lifted her head to see Barbara biting on her lip. "That's okay, Barbara, I don't blame you. You escape to your friend's houses and I hide behind my books.

"You know, Katie, mom used to be really pretty. Do you remember what she looked like when you were young?" Katie seldom had conversations like this with her sisters and brothers, especially about the past.

"No, I forgot." Katie honestly had.

"Well, she sure is different now. She'll be a tub of lard after this baby. Those veins in her legs are gross as it is. I can't imagine what they are going to be like after she has another kid."

"By the way, when is the blessed event?" Katie tried to change the subject; the way her mother looked was a constant source of embarrassment to her.

"Some time in November."

"You mean it might be born on my birthday?" Katie laughed remembering the last time she heard her parents going at it. She never thought about when she was conceived, but it probably was around the end of January or early February. She wondered if they made as much noise conceiving her as they did the other night.

"Hey, Katie, are you asleep or something? I'm talking to you." Katie was deep in thought.

"Go away, Barbara; leave me alone."

"What a snot you are, Katie. You never want to talk to me." Barbara stalked out of the room slamming the door behind her, upset that Katie had dismissed her so suddenly.

When she was alone, Katie thought about this latest development. It was strange that they waited so long to tell everyone. It appeared the bloom was finally off of the rose at least with regard to the big, exciting announcements about Nan's pregnancies. Maybe they were beginning to realize they weren't such wonderful news events; but if that was the case, why didn't they just stop having children? It was too late anyway as far as Katie was concerned; one more child wasn't going to make things that much worse than they already were.

She shook her head. One thing she knew for certain was that two people didn't have to be in love or really even like each other in order to have children. There was nothing but complaints about Jack from Nan, but here she was having another baby. Katie would never understand that as long as she lived.

Katie didn't ask Barbara how she found out about the baby; she also never acknowledged to Nan that she knew about the pregnancy. Nan and Jack never made a formal announcement to them that she was pregnant.

It certainly was easier on Katie waiting for the bus to come on the first day of school, knowing she already had two good friends in Elaine and Maria. Still as Katie took her seat, she felt a familiar pain attack her back and upper abdomen and prayed it would subside. She concentrated hard on all of the new faces on the bus, and breathed a sigh of relief as the cramping finally ended low in the pit of her stomach just as they got to the school.

Katie was visibly shaken as the bus unloaded her at the front door of the school. She watched as people whizzed by her at great speed, all seeming to know where they were going and what they were doing. She barely found her homeroom before the bell rang and entered it with a look of panic on her face. She had just enough time to take a seat and raise her hand when her name was called for attendance, before another bell rang and she found herself back out in the hallway which was packed with bodies going in every direction. What astounded her the most was they were laughing, giggling, shouting, happy bodies; this was completely different from Catholic school.

By the time lunch period arrived, Katie finally knew what the nuns and priests meant all those years when they talked about dying and going to heaven. Katie felt like that was exactly what she had done by going to public school. So far she adored her teachers, and it appeared they were not going to be very strict; not anything she couldn't handle anyway. She was also thrilled to find Elaine and Maria both had the same lunch period as she did. She hadn't really met any new people and it was comforting to see their familiar, friendly faces.

"How's it going?" Maria was genuinely concerned about Katie, knowing it was her first time in public school.

"Just great, Maria, really great. I think I'm going to like it. Everyone is so carefree. I can't believe it."

"It's just the first day," piped in Elaine. "They'll get over it. Just wait and see. As soon as the homework and tests start everything will change." Elaine had a way of putting a damper on even the merriest of occasions.

By the end of the day Katie knew she was in a new and better world. If the kids she met in school today were juvenile delinquents then she wanted to be one of them, and it was with great elation that she arrived home from school on that day thinking she finally had it made.

It wasn't too long before Nan realized living in the suburbs was a lot different than living in the city. The easy accessibility to parks and stores did not exist in this new place, and she no longer could take a five-minute trip on foot to the grocery store for a forgotten item. There were no parks to walk to, and her nearest relative was fifty miles away. The fact that Nan did not drive became a serious problem very quickly, as Jack was working a lot of overtime at the hospital. The only time Nan was able to get away from the house was on Jack's day off, and those outings consisted mainly of grocery shopping or medical appointments.

So Nan's contact with the outside world was limited to occasional conversations with the neighbor next door, Anna. Nan had been a city girl all of her life, and it was difficult to adjust to the isolation she was feeling. She became extremely frustrated at her total dependence on people who drove.

She was already tired of having to rely totally on Jack for everything she wanted.

Another serious problem that resulted from the move involved mass on Sunday. Because the church in the city was within walking distance of the apartment, there was no problem regarding attendance at mass when Nan felt like it. When Jack wasn't available or didn't feel like going, they simply walked. Now that the nearest church was five miles away, there was no possibility of walking, and Nan found getting Jack and all the kids together for one mass was almost an impossible chore. In the city, they didn't attend mass faithfully, but when the mood was right and the weather was good, they did go.

Now Sundays were a disaster for the Ramie family. Of course, Nan turned her frustrations with the entire living situation, plus her advancing pregnancy problems, on Jack, accusing him of never being enthusiastic about the Catholic Church. She reasoned that because the kids were no longer going to Catholic school, it was important for them to at least attend mass on Sunday. She saw it as a breach of their wedding vows that he wasn't more enthusiastic about driving them, and many fights ensued. In reality, Jack was very compliant in hauling the family to church every time Nan demanded it, but it was on those Sundays when things weren't going well and Nan was becoming increasingly upset about her new life that the issue became complicated and ugly.

Nan's problems were compounded when Jack began to work on weekends. Unless the kids could hitch a ride with a willing neighbor, no one went to church. It was apparent to everyone that Nan was extremely unhappy with her new situation in the suburbs, and Katie knew it wouldn't be long before there was big trouble.

School continued to be the highlight of Katie's life, and her competitive spirit flourished in the public school environment as she excelled in all of her classes. It was difficult to find a quiet place at home, but Katie learned early how to study with lots of noise and activity going on around her. Absorbing herself in school-related activities became her escape from the reality of the problems at home.

The house was so frightfully small that there was no hope of privacy for anyone, especially for a teenage girl who desperately needed it at this point in her life. Katie daydreamed often about a room of her own as she lay across the only thing she didn't have to share with anyone: a small twin bed. Ten-year-old Barbara and six-year-old Amy slept together in the second twin bed. The bedroom was just big enough to accommodate the two small beds and a bureau for their clothes. The three boys were in the so-called bigger bedroom, which was still small by most standards. They needed that room because George, who was only three, was still in a crib. Jonathan, who was thirteen, and Sammy, who would be five in December, slept in a double bed together.

All things considered, it was a happy time for Katie. The transition from city to country had not been as bad as she expected. In fact, in many ways, it was much better. Elaine was a loyal friend, and it was the first time since Laurie that Katie felt like a peer was genuinely happy to be around her. She knew her girlfriends in the city had more or less just put up with her. Katie thrived on the boost of self-esteem the new school and friends on Long Island provided.

"Put those books down, Katie. I need you to set the table for dinner."

"I can't right now. I'm stuck on an algebra problem. I'm so frustrated; I don't have a brain for math at all." It was the one subject Katie couldn't master.

"Listen, don't you worry about it right now. Just do the best you can. There are bigger problems in this world, you know." It was a typical reply for Nan; she didn't understand there weren't bigger problems in the world for her oldest child at that moment.

As Katie entered the kitchen, she watched Nan light one of her endless cigarettes and take a long drag on it. As Katie busied herself putting plates on the table, Nan started to complain.

"You know, I hate this house. I have from day one. I'm not a country girl, I guess. I'm used to walking to the store and the park. I despise having to depend on people who drive."

Katie knew Nan had been thinking about what she said for a long time; she was just waiting for the right moment to get it all off of her chest as she continued to complain.

"When I ask your dad to take me somewhere, I have to wait most of the day for him to get ready. Honest to God, he's so slow, it's incredible." She flicked a long ash off the cigarette she was smoking into an ashtray she was holding in her left hand before she took another long drag on it.

Katie took a good look at her mother and noticed she was extremely swollen. She was in the final months of pregnancy but had probably gained sixty pounds already. Her legs were like two huge tree stumps with ugly blue veins sticking out everywhere. Her face was wrinkled from smoking. But what was most concerning to Katie was the fact that her eyes didn't look right; they were not the eyes of April 1953, but they were not healthy eyes, either. The perfectly manicured nails with the bright red polish looked totally out of place on her mother's body.

"Why don't you learn how to drive?" The question was out of Katie's mouth before she even thought about the reaction. She knew driving a car was not as much of a priority in the city; it wasn't really necessary with stores, churches and parks so close and easily accessible by foot or mass transit. Actually, there wasn't a woman Katie knew who lived in the city who drove a car. She couldn't help thinking how different things might have been if her mother had been able to drive. Then she had second thoughts about that; with Nan's mental issues, maybe that would have been a disaster.

Nan answered with scorn that no one was willing to teach her. Katie wondered if her mom could even get a license now, with all those nervous breakdowns on her record somewhere.

"Didn't dad try to teach you when you first got married?" Katie persisted, as somewhere she remembered hearing a story in which someone said Nan was such an erratic driver, no one felt it was safe to be in the car with her when she was at the wheel.

"I really don't remember." Nan squashed out her cigarette in the ashtray and put it on the counter as she changed the subject. "I'm telling you, I can't stand his quietness anymore. He never tells me anything, and I have no idea where we stand financially. I have to ask for every penny I get, and I'm sick to death of it. One day I'm going to take you kids and leave."

Katie thought to herself that Nan truly lived in a dream world. Where would she go with no money and six kids...soon to be seven? Katie had heard that same story for years. It didn't impact her one bit anymore. When she was younger, she used to be afraid that Nan would actually do that; now she realized it was all just talk.

Halloween was a big disappointment that year. In the city, it was easy to fill up a pillowcase with candy just by knocking on the doors of one building with one hundred or more apartments. Some years, Katie and Jonathan had been able to hit two or more buildings, resulting in three candy-filled pillowcases each. During the last year they lived in the city, it had become too dangerous to leave their own building. In their new neighborhood on Long Island, you could walk for three or four blocks and only get candy from twenty-five houses. Also, some stories had been printed about people putting pins and razors in candy, so many people didn't even give out treats for fear that they would be accused of hurting the children. The kids spent a lot of time examining their meager stash of candy when they returned home to make sure it was okay to eat.

Katie turned fifteen a couple of days after Halloween. Nan made a small chocolate cake, which was devoured in short order as soon as the singing ended. Katie almost forgot it was the "Day of the Dead"; not being in Catholic school certainly did have its advantages. Maria and Elaine had also celebrated her birthday with a cupcake during lunch period in school and insisted on singing so loudly that the entire cafeteria eventually joined in. It was the first time Katie's birthday had been acknowledged while she was in school. It felt pretty good, although she was still uncomfortable with all of the attention.

The first Thanksgiving in their new home was fun. They put the kitchen table in the living room, and Jack borrowed some folding tables from the hospital so everyone could sit together. Nan invited her sister, Madge, and her family of three girls and a boy to dinner to pay them back for all of the wonderful Sunday dinners Madge hosted for them. Katie enjoyed helping fix the meal and set the table. The kids, including Katie, all had the giggles by the time dinner was ready and spent most of the meal trying not to choke on their food as they laughed their way through the event.

The next day, Nan gave birth to her fourth girl and ninth child, Carrie. It was a cold, crisp, gorgeous November morning. Katie placidly received the news of the birth, already resenting the responsibilities and trouble that most surely would come because of it.

Every bone in Katie's body ached as she focused her tired eyes on her mother, who was sitting on the edge of the couch, smoking a cigarette and staring out the window at nothing. She had to go to the bathroom so badly, she could hardly stand it, but she knew she couldn't leave her mother alone for even a minute.

Katie thought about the last three days—too many hours filled with emotional outbursts—and shook her head to get rid of the awful words Nan shouted at Jack the night before. "If you would talk to me, let me know what's going on, I wouldn't get like this! You're cheap and I'm sick and tired of it! We live in a matchbox, and the kids are driving me crazy!" Nan had gone on for hours, verbally abusing Jack, and then ended up throwing a vase in his direction. Luckily, he ducked just before it hit him in his head.

Katie didn't dare go to sleep that night for fear that Nan would do something violent and Jack wouldn't be able to control her. Her trusty knife was under the mattress, exactly where she put it as soon as they moved in and her bed was set up.

It had all started shortly after Nan came home from the hospital with Carrie. Nan was practically crippled with her vein problems. Jack was working the night shift at the hospital, so he took care of the babies during the day while the older kids were in school. As soon as Katie came home, Jack left for work.

Nan was a nervous wreck about the holidays approaching. It was the same thing every year, even though she was not expected to do much of anything. Jack did most of the shopping and always got the Christmas tree at the last minute, but no matter what he did, it wasn't good enough as far as Nan was concerned. Katie was beginning to realize Nan talked herself into most of her nervous breakdowns. Here it was, the night before Christmas Eve, and Nan was in the midst of another crisis.

Both Katie and Jack were physically and mentally exhausted by the third day. It wasn't taking care of the kids and the house that was the big problem; Katie knew she could handle that with no problem at all. It was dealing with Nan that was so stressful and tiresome. She had to be watched constantly, day and night. The smaller children had mercifully become very tranquil, as if they sensed something was wrong and they shouldn't rock the boat and stir up Nan's dander. They learned very quickly what to do and what not to do to escape her wrath.

Carrie was a sleeper, just like Katie had been, and Katie loved her for it.

It had been snowing all day long, and as Katie closed the living room curtain against the night, she took a few seconds to watch the clean, white world outside. It looked like Christmas, but Katie certainly wasn't in the Christmas spirit. What was the Christmas spirit, anyway? She heard people talking about it all the time and singing about it in many songs, but she really didn't know what it was like to be in a holiday mood. Most of the Ramie holidays were so stressful and filled with problems that just getting through them was a chore.

Katie looked disdainfully at Nan, sitting placidly in a chair in the corner of the living room, and decided it was time to make a quick run to the bathroom. She had so many questions. *Why does mom always do this, especially around the holidays? Why doesn't dad take her to the hospital right away? Why does he go to work and leave her here with us, especially after she killed two of his kids already? Does he even care what she might do to us? Why did I have to be born into this family? It stinks. I hate them both.*

Even though Katie had stopped eating dirt when they moved to Long Island, she still felt there was something very seriously wrong with her and she would eventually die from it. Many times, she actually hoped whatever it was would take her quickly. As another wave of pain passed through her, Katie felt faint and put her head down on her legs, making a fist with her hands. Slowly, but too slowly, the hurt went away. Feeling as if all of her innards had taken leave of her body, Katie emerged from the bathroom, pale and sweating. Tasting blood in her mouth, she quickly glanced at herself in the small mirror just outside the bathroom door and noticed her lip was bleeding. She had bitten into it during one of the waves of pain she had just experienced.

Suddenly, Katie remembered Nan. How long had she left her alone? She couldn't remember how much time she had spent in the bathroom. Katie's head was throbbing, and all she wanted to do was lie down and go to sleep, but she walked back toward the living room, stepping over the snowsuits and sweaters, which the kids had thrown around the heating grate in the small hallway to dry after playing in the snow. As the weather got colder, they soon realized the only way to stay warm was to gather around the grate, where the heat came up from the oil-fired furnace in the unfinished basement, which could only be reached from outside the house.

Leaning her shoulders against the edge of the wall, Katie stared at the misshapen figure standing by the door. Sighing heavily, Katie wondered how she was going to talk Nan away from the door. She wished her mother would open the door, walk out, and disappear into the night. She wouldn't stop her—that was for sure. She knew her mother would never do that; it was too cold out there, and she never did anything to put herself in danger. But something didn't seem right to Katie. Maybe it was the bits of snow caked around Nan's slippers or the rim of wetness around her robe. But Katie was just too tired at that point to wonder how it happened.

"Come on, mom. You better close the door. There's a terrible draft coming in, and you might catch a cold."

As Katie tugged at her arm, Nan shot her an evil-looking smile as she shuffled back to the couch, dropping bits of melting snow over the thin carpet as she walked. Katie wondered why she had gone outside, but her thoughts were interrupted by a whimpering sound coming from the girls' bedroom. What now, for God's sake? She had hoped the kids would remain asleep so she could keep an eye on Nan exclusively.

Katie tiptoed into the bedroom, afraid to turn on the light for fear of waking up the baby, and waited a second for her eyes to adjust to the darkness. She soon saw Amy curled up in the corner of the bed she shared with Barbara, crying.

"What's the matter, Amy?" Katie whispered annoyingly as she put her finger to her lips. "Be quiet. You'll wake up the baby!"

"I'm afraid, Katie. Mommy woke me up when she was in here, and she scared me."

"Mommy wasn't in here. You must be dreaming. Now go back to sleep." Katie took the blanket and covered Amy, patting her head quickly.

Barbara stirred restlessly beside Amy, and Katie was about to exit from the room when she decided to check on Carrie. She looked into the crib and thought at first that her eyes were playing tricks on her in the dark. It was empty. Groping with her hands, Katie felt every square inch of the crib as if the baby would materialize at any moment.

"Oh my God…the snow…the snow on her feet. Ahhh, no!"

Katie's terrified scream woke up the other children. Flying into the living room, Katie saw her mother standing once again at the door and charged at her, flinging her aside with such strength that Nan fell backwards against the door.

"What have you done with her? Where's Carrie?"

Nan was silent.

Katie pushed open the screen door and followed the quickly disappearing footprints Nan had made earlier. *Oh my God, please let me find her.*

Even though Katie was in her bare feet, she didn't notice the cold wetness on her skin. When the footprints she was following ended, Katie fell down on her knees, swinging her arms wildly across the snow-covered lawn, hoping to make contact with the baby. She had already made a path across the lawn to the driveway in an unsuccessful attempt to locate Carrie. Katie was in a panic. She was conflicted. She knew she should go back inside before Nan did something else to the other children but not until she had the baby. She began to cry as her teeth chattered from the cold. It was all just too much.

"I hate you...you murderer. I'll kill you...I swear I will. Do you hear me? I hate you." As she beat her numb fists against the cold snow, Katie heard a familiar sound. "Carrie, Carrie, oh God. Carrie. Keep crying, baby. I'm coming. I'm coming."

She began jumping frantically from one place to the other, following the faint cries, and finally found her partially covered by a big evergreen bush in front of the house. She was wrapped in a thin receiving blanket, lying on her back in the cold, wet snow. She quickly picked up the wet bundle, pressed Carrie's trembling little body close to hers, and made a mad dash for the front door.

When Katie stepped into the living room, panting and holding Carrie tightly, Nan glared at Katie. She was sitting in the middle of the floor, her expression so sick, so hateful, that Katie screamed at her.

"Get out, get out of here, you murderer! You're not going to hurt anybody else! And don't pretend you can't hear me! If anything happens to Carrie, I'll make sure you pay! I'll make sure they put you away forever! Not like the last time. You're sick, sick, sick, and I hate you!"

As Nan collapsed backwards on the worn-out carpet, her eyes opening and closing rapidly, Katie readied herself for a confrontation. *This time*, she thought, *I'm not going to use words; I'll kill her if she comes close to any of us.*

"Daddy, daddy, why did you leave me? I miss you so much. You knew I didn't want to be alone, and you still left me. Nobody understands me now."

None of what Nan was saying made any sense to Katie, and she really didn't care to listen to any more meaningless jabber from her.

"Didn't you hear me? I said get out of here!" Katie's words fell on deaf ears.

Jonathan came into the room, his eyes red from sleep, confused at all of the commotion.

"Take the baby, Jonathan, and get Barbara to put dry clothes on her right away. Make a warm bottle. Hurry up. She's freezing. And call dad at the hospital. Tell him to come home right now or I'm calling the police. Move, Jonathan, move it!"

Katie's voice was hoarse already, and her feet were stinging from the cold as Jonathan swept the soaked bundle from Katie's limp arms and scurried off. She could hear the kids whispering to each other in the bedroom.

Searching the room frantically, Katie picked up the closest thing she could find for protection. It was a big glass ashtray. She dumped the cigarette butts on the floor and spread her legs apart in a defensive stance.

"If you move one inch from that spot, I'll clobber you with this. I mean it!" Katie shook the ashtray at Nan, who remained still as low gurgling sounds erupted from her mouth.

"I couldn't talk to dad, Katie. Someone said they would give him the message as soon as they saw him. I told them about the police. Are you really going to call the police?

"Yes, and I might need you to make the call, so stay close."

But Jonathan disappeared before Katie could finish her sentence.

Katie turned around and saw why. Nan had gotten up from her prone position on the floor and was crawling toward her.

"Oh, no, you don't! If you want to leave the house, get out right now, but if you stay, you are not leaving this room." Katie shook the ashtray menacingly at Nan, wondering how far this was all going to go.

Nan started sobbing dryly.

"You're not crying. You can't fool me. We don't need you; all you do is have babies and get sick. I don't feel sorry for you anymore."

As Katie screamed at her, Nan, who was still on her knees, charged at her and was halfway in the hallway before Katie grabbed her, halting her progress.

"I told you, it's over. I'll kill you before you hurt anyone else." Katie meant every word of what she said, although somewhere in the struggle, she had lost her weapon, the ashtray.

As Katie tried to push Nan away from the hallway and the heater and back into the living room, Nan remained stiff and immobile. Katie realized how heavy she was and wondered if she could really do anything if Nan decided to attack her. She remembered June Reynolds telling her how strong people were when they went crazy.

As if Nan had heard Katie's thoughts, she began screaming and flailing her legs and arms in the air, and Katie felt a sharp pain on the left side of her face as a long nail dug into her.

"That's it. You've had it now."

She slapped Nan hard across the side of her face, sending Nan's upper body toward the edge of the living room wall, where her head hit it with an awful thud. Her upper body slid down the wall. Her eyes were closed and she lay on the floor, not moving.

As he walked slowly up to the front door of his house, Jack was petrified of what he would find on the other side of the door. He had been getting his patients ready for bed when the message reached him that he needed to get home immediately. He quickly made arrangements for another attendant to cover him while he made the five-minute trip home.

When he opened the door, he could see Nan lying across the entrance to the hallway. Her eyes were closed. Katie, with blood running from her face and lip, stood over Nan. When Katie realized Jack was in the room, she turned to him, her eyes filled with fear.

"You need to get her out of here right away. She tried to kill Carrie. Put her out in the snow to die." On the verge of hysterics, Katie continued. "Take her away. I don't ever want to see her again. You will never leave us alone again with her like this. Never again! Do you hear me? Never again! She could have killed Carrie, and it would have been your fault, too. Just like the last time."

Katie's words stung Jack—hit him deep in his subconscious, where he kept the guilt he felt buried.

"Take her away. Take her to the hospital right now. If you don't, I'm calling the police. She almost killed Carrie, and I'm going to tell them everything." Katie's harsh words came once again to Jack's ears.

Jack leaned over Nan to get a better look at her face and saw her eyes fluttering. He realized she was not really unconscious, just blocking out the world or faking it. "Why don't you get your mother's coat for me?"

As Katie rummaged through the closet in the boy's room, looking for Nan's coat, Jack shook his wife's shoulders.

"Nan, I know you hear me. I'm taking you to the hospital. I don't think I can leave you here with the kids. Now get up so we can get you ready."

Suddenly, Nan grabbed Jack's arms with both of her hands and jumped up quickly, throwing him temporarily off balance just long enough for her to dart into the bathroom, locking the door behind her. After Jack slowly regained his composure, he calmly knocked on the bathroom door.

"Nan, come out of there right now. You know I can get in there if I want, so stop playing games." His tone was soft and patient.

Katie stood in the doorway of the bedroom with Nan's coat in her hands, watching the scene unfolding in front of her. She was not surprised Jack had lost control of the situation and Nan was not responding to his pleas. After fumbling unsuccessfully with the doorknob for a while, Jack walked to the kitchen and retrieved a small screwdriver from the top of the refrigerator. He took his time walking back to the bathroom door, placed the screwdriver in the hole in the lock, and opened the door. Nan was sitting in the bathtub, eyes focused on the ceiling. Jack leaned over the tub and struggled to lift Nan to her feet. He pushed her gently out of the tub and into her coat and guided her out the door and into the car, without either of them saying a word.

As soon as she closed the front door, locking her parents out, the kids converged on Katie, who was now standing at the window, watching the car pull out. They were all talking at once, blabbering about what they had seen or heard or thought they saw and heard.

"Okay, all of you. Please be quiet for a minute!" Katie rubbed her face vigorously with her hands as if to wake herself from a nightmare. She had a long, deep scratch on her cheek, which was still bleeding.

"What are we going to do about Christmas, Katie? It's ruined!" Barbara was in a sad state.

"Christmas will be just fine. We don't need mommy to have Christmas." Katie thought about how many holidays her mother had ruined already.

"Now why don't you all go to bed? We'll talk about it tomorrow. I have to check on Carrie. Barbara, did she drink her bottle?"

"Yes, and I changed her diaper and all of her clothes." Barbara was proud of herself.

"Good job. I'm really worried about her being out in the snow for so long. I hope she doesn't get sick."

"Yeah, she was really shaking all over." Jonathan did an imitation of the baby, waving his arms and legs as if he were shivering. "What the heck did mom do that for?"

"She doesn't know what she's doing, Jonathan. That's why it's important to get her to the hospital as soon as she starts to get sick."

"Then why does daddy let her stick around until she does something really bad? She sure does scare me."

"I don't know, Jonathan. It beats me."

With that, Katie lifted Carrie out of the crib and walked with her to the living room. She sat on the couch and brought the small infant close to her face. Carrie's eyes were two huge deep brown circles, and Katie was pleased to see she looked very alert.

"Oh, little baby, no one would believe how good I feel now that your mommy is out of the house."

Carrie actually smiled at Katie.

A short time later, in a state of complete exhaustion, Katie tucked the sleeping baby into her crib and dropped on her own bed. But as tired as she felt, she couldn't get to sleep. She felt guilty about some of the things she had said to her parents. They both deserved it, she thought. Her mother was lucky she dropped the ashtray and didn't smash her over the head with it. *Don't worry about it. You did the right thing*, she said to herself over and over again until finally her body succumbed to its urgent need for rest, and she fell into a deep sleep.

I've got to ask him today, Katie said to herself.

It was New Year's Eve, and Jack still hadn't said anything to her about what he planned to do with the babies once the older kids went back to school. It had been another ruined vacation, of course, and Katie couldn't wait to get back to school.

"Um...school starts the day after tomorrow. What are we going to do with the kids?"

Jack shrugged his shoulders at Katie's nervous inquiry and didn't say anything. That was the end of the one-sided conversation.

Katie was in the kitchen, preparing a bottle for Carrie, when the next-door neighbor knocked on the side door.

"Yoo hoo, is anyone home?"

Katie opened the door in response to Anna's familiar voice.

"How's everything going, hon?"

Anna's New York accent was very pronounced, and her manner very aggressive and assertive. Katie really liked her.

"Oh, just awful. I don't know what to do. My dad hasn't mentioned a thing about what he plans to do when school starts. I just can't stay home from school."

Anna looked pensive at Katie's predicament. She knew the Ramie household was in crisis; the entire neighborhood was shocked to discover Nan had suffered a nervous breakdown.

Christmas Eve, the day after his mother was institutionalized, little George, who was three, was playing with Anna's son, Stan, and blurted out that his mother was in the hospital. Anna immediately hurried over to the house to get the scoop and found a house full of relatives. When she left, after being told Nan had a breakdown, she figured the kids were in good hands. It wasn't until the next day that she realized they were really on their own. She checked on them each day and was amazed at how Katie, Jonathan, and Barbara were able to keep everything together. She gradually found out the details of Nan's mental history and was saddened at what the children had been through.

"Look, hon, I can watch George for you. He and my Stan get along great, and they will be good company for each other. Also, Sammy can stay with me when he gets off the bus from kindergarten."

Katie reached for Anna's arm and hugged it. "Thanks so much, Anna. That's such a big relief."

"I'll talk to your dad. He needs to make arrangements for the baby soon. He can't keep you home from school—it's against the law—and I will report him if he tries something like that." Anna became very agitated as she pointed her finger at Katie's face.

"Thanks again, Anna. You're a lifesaver."

Katie was in bed when Jack returned from work that night. When she heard him talking on the phone, she immediately got out of bed and tiptoed over to the door. It was almost impossible to hear Jack—he was talking so low—but she strained to make out the conversation. There were long periods of silence, but from words put together, she determined he was talking to Aunt Madge, her mother's sister. She heard Carrie's name mentioned and something about a place for her to stay. He also mentioned Social Services and the fact that they couldn't help him out this time. He ended by saying, "We'll see you soon," or at least that's what it sounded like to Katie.

As Katie hurried back to bed, she wondered if Aunt Madge was going to take Carrie and drifted off to sleep, feeling relieved that everything seemed to be settled. As sunlight filtered into the bedroom the next morning, Katie awoke to Carrie's cries. She was grateful the baby had slept through the night, and she began the routine of helping the younger children get dressed and attending to the baby's needs.

Each time Katie passed the living room, she glanced at Jack, lying motionless on the pullout couch. It was finally Anna's boisterous voice that woke up Jack.

"Hello, Katie. I talked to your dad yesterday. I told him I'd be willing to watch George and get Sammy off the bus until you get home from school." She spoke even louder as she continued. "Did he make any arrangement for Carrie?" She crossed her arms over her immaculate house dress and rested her chin in her hand as she waited for Katie's reply.

"I'm not sure," Katie whispered. "I heard him on the phone late last night talking about Carrie, but I really don't know what's going on."

"Let me know what happens. I'll be ready for George tomorrow morning, and I won't forget to get Sammy off the bus. What a shame this is." She shook her head in sympathy with Katie and then called to George to come play with Stan.

Jack puttered around the house until it was time to go to work. He started to take down the Christmas tree he had purchased on Christmas Eve, along with some last-minute gifts for each of the little kids. They had squealed with delight as they opened their gifts, totally unaware of Nan's absence, but for Katie, it was just another somber holiday ruined by her mother.

Just before Jack left for work, he and Katie awkwardly faced each other in the kitchen. This time it was Jack who broke the silence.

"We will be taking Carrie to your Aunt Madge's tomorrow morning. She has agreed to watch her until your mother gets home. Pack up all of her stuff. She has a crib, so we don't need to bother with that." And with that, he left for work.

The next morning, after hectically getting all the kids off to school and George over to Anna's, Katie and Jack left for Nan's sister's house to drop off Carrie. As Katie held the baby on her lap in the front seat of the car during the hour-long drive, she wondered what she was missing in school that important first day back. Jack did not speak a word to her during the entire trip—she might as well have been sitting next to a wooden dummy. All he did was eat, sleep, work, watch television, and have kids—and all without saying a word.

She could almost sympathize with her mother getting sick all the time—oh, no, what was she thinking? Her mother was just as bad; she had no right to get sick, especially when she had a new baby to take care of. So what if her dad was quiet; at least he worked hard and didn't leave them all the time like she did. What gave her the right to always get sick? She didn't really have it that bad. Katie couldn't wait to grow up and leave her family.

Everything was prepared for the baby when they arrived; Aunt Madge was very organized and efficient, unlike her sister. Katie loved her aunt's house and reminisced about the many wonderful Sundays spent in it, eating delicious roast beef with potatoes, rolls, and fantastic cakes. She envied her cousins for getting Aunt Madge as their mother instead of Nan. They all seemed so happy and content. She wondered what it would be like to live in a normal family, one where the kids had their own rooms, the father talked and laughed, and the mother never got sick and went away all the time.

During the trip back, Katie was lost in her own thoughts. Why did she have to spend her vacations mopping floors and wiping dirty faces? That was her mother's job. The only time she felt a little bit happy was when her mom would leave for the hospital after giving them so much trouble. But that feeling was short-lived, especially when all the work taking care of the kids started. How horrible it was that something like her mother being in a mental institution was the only thing that made her happy. She hated life. As far as she was concerned, it stunk.

"I told you, only one towel for your bath, and I mean it, Barbara!" Katie rushed back to the kitchen to continue her homework but was interrupted again.

"Katie, Amy won't leave me alone!" Sammy cried.

"Stop teasing him, or I'll slug you one, Amy!"

Katie was already mad at Amy for wetting the bed the night before. That morning before she left for school, she had to wash the sheet out by hand and hang it outside in the cold air, struggling to get the clothespin on the frozen piece of material. When she retrieved it from the clothesline later that day, the sheet was still partially wet, so she draped it over the heater and watched it carefully so it wouldn't burn. She wondered when her dad was going to get the washing machine fixed. Even though it was in the dark, dank basement and she had to go outside and open up a heavy wooden door to get to the machine, it was still better than washing everything by hand. Once a week, usually on his day off, Jack brought all of the clothes to the laundromat. The clean clothes had to last the entire week and because there were no extra sheets or towels, one bed-wetting accident or the use of more than one towel a week by anyone was cause for major turmoil.

Every night, Katie raced through the household chores to get the kids settled down so she could do her homework. On one particular night, as she tried to beat the clock to finish a school project, she heard a knock on the door. She hoped it wasn't Elaine; even though she had been a big help over the Christmas holidays, Katie couldn't deal with her right now. Elaine had been shocked to learn Nan had mental problems and was very sympathetic regarding Katie's situation. Elaine loved helping Katie take care of the babies—it was a novelty for her—and Katie was more than happy to have her help.

"Oh, it's you, Buddy," Katie said as she reluctantly opened the door. It was obvious from her tone of voice that she was unhappy with the intrusion. As she stared at her friend, she thought he looked like someone who had just been released from a concentration camp. "I have a lot of homework to do, Buddy. Did you want to talk to Jonathan?"

"No, I came to see you." As he hovered over Katie, sitting at the table trying to finish her homework, Buddy brushed his lips faintly over her ear-lobe.

"Stop that!" Katie slammed her book against the table and jumped up, pushing Buddy away from her. "I think you better leave right now!" Katie opened the kitchen door and waved her arm for him to exit.

When he was out the door, she thought about what had just happened. It was too bad she really didn't like him; it sure felt good when he touched her. She was confused at what that feeling was all about.

"Well, okay, I guess we better go ahead with it if you think it's important. We'll be there on Sunday."

As Jack hung up the phone, Katie sensed her father's annoyance and knew why he was angry. Aunt Madge had told Katie in an earlier conversation that she was anxious to get Carrie christened, and Katie knew her dad didn't think it was that important.

"Jack, they won't let us christen the baby Carrie. It's not an acceptable name." Madge's whisper was aggravated as she rocked the baby in her arms.

Katie heard the commotion at the baptismal font and quickly walked over to find out what was going on.

Scratching his head, Jack replied meekly, "Gee, I don't know. What do you think we should do?"

"Well, we better come up with a suitable name, or the priest won't baptize her."

They stood in awkward silence for a few minutes until the priest motioned to Aunt Madge that he was about to begin.

"Look, Jack, this is it. What do you want to do?" Waiting impatiently for his reply, Madge looked nervously at Jack and then the priest.

"You're looking after her now, so why don't we name her Margaret, after you?"

As he shrugged his shoulders to imply it was okay, Jack took Madge's arm as they walked toward the priest. It was then Katie heard Aunt Madge tell the priest Carrie would be christened Margaret. The priest grinned widely and began the ceremony. It was a religious name only as everyone continued to call the baby Carrie. It was a good thing, too, because Nan was absolutely furious when she finally came home and heard the story.

"I would have walked right out of the church rather than change Carrie's name." Katie chuckled at her mother's comment and remarked to herself, *Yeah, right, mom, and after that, you would have come home and had a big, fat nervous breakdown.*

Nan was biding her time during her first stay at the huge mental institution on Long Island. It was like a city in itself with a bakery and fire department on the site. Jack was able to visit Nan a couple of times a day, as she was being treated in one of the buildings close to the one in which he worked. She liked the hospital; the grounds were beautiful and she could take nice, long walks. It wasn't at all like walking the dark, depressing hallways of the hospital in the city. The doctors were easy; they didn't ask that many questions and didn't pressure her at all for any answers.

The children survived until Nan was released from the hospital a little over a month after she was admitted. There were times during that month when there was barely enough food in the house to make dinner, and Katie had to remind her dad they needed bread or milk. He always came through with the food once he was told, but Katie cursed his lack of concern for such things. Of course, she wasn't as aggressive or demanding as her mother was in dealing with him, and she didn't realize where matters of the house and children were concerned, he relied on Nan to push him into taking her shopping. He and Katie barely said two words to each other unless it was absolutely necessary.

Nan came home considerably more irritable after this confinement than she had been at any time before. She was on strong tranquilizers that didn't agree with her, causing extreme mood swings. One day she appeared almost comatose, and the next was a bundle of nerves. Nan was never one to take her medications according to instructions; she skipped pills and then tried to make up for the missed dosages, which also caused her erratic behavior.

A week after Nan came home, she and Jack picked up the baby from Aunt Madge's, and Katie couldn't get over how much Carrie had grown in the few weeks she was away.

"I don't care what you say, Jack. I bet she is going to be deaf in that one ear. There's no doubt in my mind. You shouldn't have brought her there." Nan was fuming, her voice shrill with anger.

"I really don't think being around a piano for such a short time would cause a baby to lose its hearing, Nan." Jack was trying to be patient with Nan's ridiculous fears, which had started as soon as they left her sister's house with the baby.

"But you saw it—her crib was right next to the piano. Look at her. She constantly turns her head to one side to protect her ear from noise." Nan was really getting worked up, pointing at Carrie in her crib.

"Well, that must mean she isn't deaf if she can hear noise. Even if they did play the piano loudly, it still wouldn't cause deafness." Jack just wanted the conversation to end.

"I'm going to call the doctor first thing in the morning. Something isn't right."

Jack turned and walked out of the bedroom, glad to be away from his wife.

Katie remembered how Nan always picked on her and Jonathan, and now Barbara, about the house each time she was released from the loony bin. She now figured her mother was trying to find something wrong with the way Aunt Madge took care of Carrie. She couldn't believe how her mother could get sick, go away for a year or months at a time, and then criticize the people who kept her family together once she was home. She decided then and there that her mother was a *malcontent*, a new word she had learned in school. She was never satisfied with anything. She wished again, as she had so many times in the past, that her mother had never come home. How could these so-called doctors at the hospital keep letting her come home to have more babies and cause more problems? She certainly wasn't impressed with the medical profession; as far as it related to her mother, she would give them a big fat failure for a grade.

Sometime later, Katie overheard Nan telling Jack the doctor told her sometimes babies favor one side more than another. Still, Nan persisted in blaming her sister for Carrie's nonexistent problem. Katie only half-listened to her anymore; she was tired of her constant complaints.

Katie despised the first few weeks her mother was home because they were always periods of uncertainty as to what to expect in the way of behavior from her. It was becoming painfully obvious to the maturing Katie that each time her mother was released from the hospital she was more incompetent and less able to take care of her family.

In direct contrast to the way she felt when she was home, Katie was comfortable and very much in control of her life in the school environment. She was very cunning when it came to adapting her personality to suit a given situation, having done it most of her life. When friends came to her with their problems, she was able to offer them consolation and solutions, which was very easy for her after the issues she had been facing at home since she was six years old. Another plus was she was able to distance herself emotionally from her classmates' problems, even as she was sympathizing with them. She worked hard to achieve high grades but was very humble about her successes, which endeared her to all of her peers.

Everyone in school liked Katie, and her popularity soared. Unfortunately, she was not content with all of her achievements. Like a junkie looking for a fix, she was constantly searching for more things to conquer. An A in a course, a perfect score on a State exam, acceptance into the Honor Society, the nomination for treasurer of her tenth grade class—all were not enough. The opportunities the public school system provided to a young person who was eager to take advantage of them were endless, and Katie quickly found herself in the position of wanting to try everything. The new learning environment was like nothing she had ever experienced before, and she was bound and determined to make up for the years of frustration she had felt attending parochial school. What Katie was too immature to realize was those eight tough years in Catholic school had given her a great education, which allowed her to excel in many skills, such as reading, writing, spelling, and mathematics. She didn't see that she was having an easier time of it than her classmates because of the many years of intense learning she experienced prior to entering public high school.

In addition to her extracurricular activities and schoolwork, Katie was also in demand as a babysitter. Watching the neighborhood children was often very discouraging because many times she didn't get paid for her services. Money was very important to Katie; it was a scarce commodity in her family, and she always daydreamed about how great it would be to have more of it. She agonized over unpaid babysitting bills and despised the people who cheated her out of her well-earned cash. One family, in particular, was slobs and their house was always filthy when she arrived. After the kids went to bed, she would clean the house. She kept babysitting for them, hoping they would eventually pay her. Sometimes they did, sometimes they didn't.

Even though Katie succeeded somewhat in separating herself from her domicile after her mother came home from the hospital, she was still very much a part of it mentally, worrying all the time about Nan's health. Her mother looked very haggard, and she was definitely becoming much less active on a daily basis. She was smoking more than ever and that, in combination with the antidepressant drug, was taking its toll on her overall health. Also, with the birth of each child, she put on quite a bit of weight and was at least fifty to sixty pounds overweight for her five foot, three inch frame. Nan was barely getting through each day.

It was a blessing that the house was small, as it didn't require much upkeep. Even though Nan felt isolated and out of her element living on Long Island, the younger children at least had a backyard to play in and thus were able to leave the house without Nan having to supervise them. They also had good neighbors like Anna, who were constantly vigilant and attentive to Nan and the children. Anna became the ears for Nan's complaints after Katie distanced herself from her mother. It was a blessing that all of the children were healthy and well behaved, for it was apparent that Nan couldn't cope with anything but the simple day-to-day issues of running the house.

Katie, now a hormonal teenager, was becoming more and more concerned with her own well being and giving less and less consideration to the problems of the family. She was resentful of the hardships connected with her home life—the embarrassing too-small house, the lack of material things, the sick mother, the distant father, and the unhappiness within the family unit. She absorbed herself totally in school-related activities in order to expend the boundless energy she possessed and receive the accolades such deeds brought and she so desperately craved. The problem was nothing seemed to satisfy Katie's quest for contentment—nothing! One thing, however, didn't change. No matter how often Katie delayed going home with after-school activities, there still came a time when she had to get off the bus and open up the portal to hell. The feeling she experienced every time she entered her house had not changed since her mother was released from the first mental institution in 1954. The nervousness and anticipation of what might be occurring behind the door was always with Katie and once her fingers were on the doorknob, her breathing stopped, her heart beat faster, and her stomach hurt more until she was inside and could determine that her mother's eyes were okay and nothing out of the ordinary was going on. Whether the situation would last for a minute or a year was uncertain; Katie was always in flight-or-fight mode.

Before long, another summer was upon Katie, and it was spent like so many summers before it: hanging around. There was no money for a vacation, so trips to the local beaches were the extent of the family outings. Katie and Elaine sunbathed every day, ending up beat red and sometimes with sun poisoning. It was the early sixties and they were totally oblivious to the damage the sun could do. The girls even applied baby oil to their skin to help the sun cook them.

On Nan's really good days, she would suggest they give each other facials or manicures. When she was younger, Katie was thrilled, but now just the thought of touching her mother repulsed her, and she always turned her down. The damage to their relationship was too severe to survive Katie's puberty issues, as well as Nan's continuing mental challenges. On most days, Katie wished her mother out of her life.

Every day, Katie met Elaine and Maria, and they hung out at Maria's house, sitting on the stoop, looking up at the sky for interesting stars, and talking about their daydreams and awakening sexual desires and fantasies. The kids stayed up late each night watching television and languished in bed for most of the morning.

The house was gorgeous. Everyone had their own room. She had spent the day cleaning the already spotless house and cooking a gourmet dinner. The two beautiful children, a boy and a girl, had been scrubbed clean and placed happily in their beds. As she lay in her own magnificent bed with a sexy white nightgown on, her husband came to her. It brought shivers to her spine as he made love to her.

Katie did a lot of daydreaming during those lazy summer mornings in bed. She was reluctant to get up and face the real world; her imaginary world was so much better. Everything in it was perfect—the perfect husband, the perfect house, the perfect children. When she and her handsome husband made love and he touched her all over, just the way Maria described it to her and Elaine during their summer evening talk sessions, it brought her to such ecstasy that she could hardly stand it. Her fantasies made her feel so good.

When school started, Katie was like a top, wound up so tightly that she couldn't stop spinning. She found her sophomore year very difficult and had to spend more time studying. That, coupled with the many extracurricular activities to which she had obligated herself, created problems.

Unfortunately, there was still no sense of accomplishment for Katie; she was constantly on to the next thing and the next and the next, not stopping for a moment to revel in any of it. Her stomach hurt most of the time, but she had long before accepted it as part of her life. At home, she spent hours confined to the bedroom she shared with her three sisters, working into a state of anxiety to finish projects and study for upcoming tests. Even though she was aware her help was needed around the house, she rushed to complete household chores she couldn't avoid and didn't go out of her way to do any more than that. She even ignored the look in Nan's eyes, except, for some reason, her sleep was haunted by those eyes. Many times during the night, she awoke with a jolt, reaching quickly under her mattress for the knife that wasn't there anymore.

"Katie, come with me. I want to talk to you."

Mrs. Curley's authoritative tone scared Katie as she reluctantly followed the tall blonde into her office. School had only been in session for one week. The kids nicknamed this teacher Betty Boop because of her hairstyle, which was short with spit curls on either side of her cheeks. She was blonde, tall, perfectly proportioned, and had the face of an angel.

"Sit down."

Katie fixed her eyes on the whistle around Mrs. Curley's neck. She was sure she was going to catch heck over her dismal swimming session earlier that morning. Even though she had spent many hours in the water at the beaches on Long Island, it was impossible to learn to swim in the high waves and surf. The first time Katie was ever in a swimming pool was when she started high school, and she couldn't swim a lick.

"You know I'm the faculty sponsor for the cheerleaders, don't you, Katie."

Diane Curley stretched her long legs until they were comfortably propped up on a chair. She sensed Katie's apprehension; Katie reminded her of herself when she was younger. She remembered those awful teen years vividly, the insecurity over matters that seemed so significant at the time, like how one looked, how much money one had, who had boyfriends, who had their period, who was popular, and on and on. She had decided long ago that she would never want to relive that time in her life again. She knew Katie had serious problems at home and her mother was mentally ill.

She continued. "I guess you're wondering why I wanted to talk to you, Katie? I'd like to encourage you to try out for the cheerleading squad."

As she lifted her head to look at Mrs. Curley, Katie's eyes widened in surprise at her statement. She had such a beautiful face—big eyes the color of the sky on the most perfect day and pure white silky skin with just a hint of color, like that of a pink rose, on each check. Katie would have given anything to look like her; she couldn't see that there was actually a strong resemblance between this teacher and herself.

"Katie, did you hear me?"

"What? Oh, yes. Gee, I don't know. I mean...I've thought about it and I'd love to be a cheerleader, but I really don't think I have the...you know...ability to make it. Isn't there a lot of gymnastics involved?"

"No...not too much. If you can jump or do a decent split, that's about all you need."

"Well, in that case, I'd love to. It's really nice of you to ask me." Katie instantly wondered why Mrs. Curley was doing this. *She must like me*, she thought. She knew there was no way she could compete with the other girls, but if Mrs. Curley thought she could, she would give it a try. She idolized this teacher.

"Okay, good. We start practice next week. You'll have to come every day after school for a couple of weeks. The varsity cheerleaders will teach you a routine, and then you'll use it for the tryouts. Here's a late pass for you. Now hurry along to class."

"Thanks...thanks a lot. I really appreciate it." There was a noticeable bounce in Katie's step as she left the office.

So many things worried Katie during those weeks of training. She hated the gym; it was hot and smelly. She knew she would never be able to jump high enough or remember the routine. She thought all the other girls were prettier than she was, and she was absolutely positive there was no way she was going to make it as a cheerleader. Only nine girls would be chosen and there were at least fifty of them auditioning. Without blinking an eye, she saw twenty girls who were better than she was.

Katie was sitting on the edge of the bleachers, praying the cramps that began to envelop her intestines would go away before her number was called. She had picked unlucky number thirteen. She was told it wasn't good to be at the beginning of the competition, as the judges tended to score lower and forget about the earlier performances by the end. At this point, she just wanted the whole experience to be over with. It wasn't long before her number was called and when she stood up, she panicked. Her legs felt like rubber underneath her. She knew she had to get control of herself or she would blow this chance.

As she took her place in the center of the gymnasium, Katie's eyes searched frantically until she found the one friendly face among the judges, the one with the smile showing teeth the color of pearls. It was Betty Boop. She reminded herself to yell loudly so everyone could hear her and jump high. She was doing it all for her, and she couldn't let her down.

She started the routing exactly in time with the music, which none of the other girls before her had managed to do. She was enjoying herself, and her wide smile reflected it. As the adrenaline kicked in, she felt she had boundless energy and her required jump was huge. She even added an optional jump just before the split, which would end the program. Both the second jump and split were flawless. When the music stopped, Katie ran as fast as her feet would take her into the locker room. She reached the toilet just in time to throw up. She didn't get to enjoy the enthusiastic applause that followed her performance.

"Attention, attention." Assistant Principal Nott's nasally voice sounded over the intercom throughout the school the next day. "Mrs. Curley would like to announce the names of the junior varsity cheerleading squad for next year."

Katie rubbed at the goosebumps on her arm, trying to act nonchalant in front of her classmates as she heard Mrs. Curley's soothing voice.

"Only nine girls could be chosen for this year's junior varsity squad. I must say the young ladies who participated in the tryouts were so fantastic that it made the job of the judges extremely difficult. The following girls will make up the junior varsity cheerleading squad."

Thump, thump, thump.

Katie's hand slid across her palpitating heart. As she heard each name, she kept count. That's one, two, three, four, five...only four more names to go. She prayed she would be one of them. No, it would be okay if she wasn't chosen; she really was too busy, anyway. Six names, seven names...only two more. Eight names...only one left. It didn't matter; it would give her more time to work on her grades. She had to make sure she remained in the National Honor Society.

"Katie Ramie."

Had her name been called, or did she just imagine it? A loud bell sounded in her ears.

"Congratulations, Katie. Are you just going to sit there all day?"

It was Katie's homeroom friend, tugging at her arm to get her to move. The girl's name was also Katie and, coincidentally, her last name was Ramey, pronounced the same as Katie's last name but spelled differently. They couldn't have been more different in looks; Katie Ramey was a dark-haired beauty as opposed to Katie Ramie, who was blonde. Despite their different looks, having the same name still caused lots of confusion.

"Come on. You'll be late for first period."

As she followed the other Katie out the door, she realized it must be true.

"Did she really call my name?" Katie asked, as she saw Elaine in the hallway.

"Of course, you nerd. Weren't you listening."

"I can't believe it. How did I do it?"

Later that day, as she rode the activities bus home, she watched the passing cars from her seat like a cat that had just swallowed a canary. She was enjoying every single glorious minute of exhilaration over her latest victory.

In one day, she had become twice as popular as she was before. It was unbelievable.

"Katie, don't you think you are overextending yourself?"

She'd expected hearty congratulations from Nan, not sour words of warning.

"No, I don't. I think I can handle it."

Her flippant reply irritated Nan. Katie was already taking the late bus home every day.

"Listen, you are spending too much time at school. You don't get home anymore until well after five, and then you spend the rest of the evening doing homework. I need your help around here, you know."

"I do the dishes at night and other things." Katie felt the need to defend herself; she was upset that all Nan was concerned about was that she wasn't helping around the house as much as she used to. She felt her mother didn't care one bit that she was a straight "A" student and one of the most popular girls in her class.

"I'm just saying you need to back off on some school things. I need your help; I can't do it all by myself."

Katie turned her back on Nan and shrugged her shoulders as she left the room. She stuck her tongue out at Barbara, who had been eavesdropping on the conversation, as she walked into the bedroom and slammed the door shut.

Katie loved seeing her name on the posters. "YOU CAN DEPEND ON HER. VOTE KATIE RAMIE. VICE PRESIDENT, SOPHOMORE CLASS."

"You're a shoe-in, Katie. Don't worry about it."

"Thanks, thanks so much. I appreciate your support." Katie loved campaigning; she wished it would never end.

She won the election, of course. She was now the vice president of the sophomore class, treasurer of the Student Council, a member of the junior varsity cheerleading squad, a member of the National Honor Society, a member of the Distributive Education Program, and a member of the Audiovisual Program.

"Here's your Honor Society pin, Katie. We are expecting you to maintain your excellent academic record so you will continue as a member of the society throughout high school," the faculty advisor warned.

"It's unanimous, Katie. You've been elected as treasurer of the Student Council. Remember, folks, meetings are twice a month, and you are expected to be here. Take a schedule before you leave."

Katie rushed out of the room to make it to the audiovisual lab, where she would spend two hours working before she took the bus home. Every day was busier than the one before it, with two or three meetings scheduled, including cheerleading practice or actual football and basketball games to cheer for.

"Gosh, Katie. Look at your schedule." Elaine was flabbergasted. "You're in all honors classes. Holy smoke. I wouldn't want to be in your shoes."

"I'm not worried about it."

Katie shrugged off Elaine's concerns, but at night she tossed and turned for hours, unable to get to sleep. She wondered what was wrong with her; she hated not being able to fall asleep quickly, but she had too much on her mind. When she heard the front door open and her dad come in the house from work, she became even more anxious, knowing she had already been in bed for two hours without sleep. She just couldn't relax.

One night, she woke up suddenly and peered through the darkness to see if one of the other children in the room was awake. She had definitely heard noises, and before long she realized they were coming from the living room. She soon recognized what they were. She pulled the covers over her head in disgust so she wouldn't have to hear her parents making love—for it meant just one thing, and that was the possibility of another brother or sister. She never did get back to sleep that night.

Even though Katie was very popular in school, she didn't socialize with any of the kids in school. She was embarrassed about where she lived and wasn't about to invite anyone to her home.

Katie looked disgustedly at herself in the mirror: She would be sixteen years old in a few weeks. She tried to smooth down her thick, unruly ash-blonde hair. She thought she was a complete mess. She hated her hair; it was so oily, it never looked clean. Her face didn't please her any better, and she abhorred her freckles with a passion. Staring back at her were big ocean-blue eyes, but Katie overlooked them and concentrated only on what she believed were her faults. Reaching for a piece of toilet paper, she dabbed at a pimple on her chin, which she had attacked the night before and massacred until it dominated her face in an unsightly mess. To make matters worse, the septum in her left nostril was still swollen and tender from one of her frequent colds. She touched it and an instant, stinging pain made her eyes water. She was thankful at least it didn't get infected this time.

She was five feet, five inches tall and weighed one hundred fifteen pounds and was built like her father, who was over six feet tall, long legged, and well-proportioned. Katie thought she was ugly and was always comparing herself to her female classmates. She definitely had no self-esteem when it came to her appearance.

As she emerged from the bathroom and glanced at the clock in the kitchen, she knew she had just enough time to walk to school if she left right away. It was already getting dark outside and with butterflies in her stomach she looked out the living room window for any signs of life at Buddy's house. She had to hurry up or she would be late, but she didn't have the guts to ask someone to drive her. She wished they would only play football games during the day; the night games were very inconvenient for Katie. She wouldn't admit to Mrs. Curley that she had no transportation. It was fairly safe to walk the twenty-minutes to school during the day, but at night it was a different story. With much trepidation, she put on her coat and quietly left the house.

"I'm sorry, Katie, but my husband isn't here right now, and Butch is still working, so I'm afraid there's nobody around to drive you." There was sympathy in Buddy's mother's deep brown eyes. "You're not going to walk to the school by yourself, are you?"

As she quickly departed, Katie pretended she hadn't heard her neighbor's question. Keeping her head down and her neck buried in her shoulders, Katie ran through the dark streets, clutching her pompoms to her chest. By the time she reached the school, she was panting heavily and felt sick to her stomach.

"Katie, I held up the bus waiting for you. You have to be on time for the games; otherwise, you will lose your place on the squad!"

Mrs. Curley was angrier than Katie had ever seen her. She wanted to crawl into a hole and die.

"I'm so sorry. I couldn't get a ride!"

She found an empty seat quickly and sat forlornly during the remainder of the trip, already worrying about how she was going to get home. She ended up running home that night assuring her teacher she had a ride and disappearing down the dark street as soon as Mrs. Curley turned her back. She would rather risk getting hurt during the dangerous trip home alone than to ask anyone to give her a lift and see where she lived.

"Hey, Katie, wait up."

She turned to watch the tall, lanky boy running toward her. He looked kind of familiar, but she couldn't remember where she had seen him before.

"Hi. Thanks for stopping. Whew, I thought I was going to miss you again."

Looking confused as his breathless words fell upon her ears, Katie's expression registered her bewilderment to him.

"You do know who I am, don't you?" His cheeks turned bright red with embarrassment, making the acne that covered them more prominent. "How dumb of me. I'm Robbie Herk. I play football here at the school."

"Oh, yes, hi. I didn't recognize you out of uniform." She felt stupid, hoping she didn't hurt his feelings and he would believe her excuse.

"Are you coming to the game next Saturday?"

"Yes, I have to cheer."

"Oh, that's good. Uh, well, there's a party afterwards at Rhonda's. Will you go with me?" His smile was broad and genuine

"Gee, I don't know. I'll have to think about it."

The invitation came as a complete surprise; she never expected any boy would invite her anywhere. All of a sudden, she was staring into his big brown eyes, trying to decide what to say to him.

"Well, okay. I'm sure it will be all right."

Upon hearing her answer, his face brightened considerably. "Great. I'll meet you after the game. Thanks. Thanks so much." He turned and took giant steps with his long legs, disappearing onto his bus.

"Who is he?" Pam whispered to one of the cheerleaders as they hovered around the fence during halftime of the football game on Saturday, all eyes focused on the new football player.

"His name is Ben, and he just moved here from the city. He's in my English class," Ellen continued, reveling in the attention her information brought her. "He's a real hunk and not one bit shy, either. Had everyone in the class falling all over him on his first day."

The other girls listened to every word Ellen said.

"I'll introduce him to all of you as soon as I get the chance…and if I feel like it." Holding her head up in the air, the conceited Ellen played up her association with Ben for all it was worth.

During the second half of the game, Katie caught a glimpse of the new boy, but her eyes were mainly on Robbie. He was doing exceptionally well, and each time he came off the field, he winked at her.

"I think we better let Katie cheer for Robbie, girls."

Katie wished Pam would mind her own business; she was so nosey, she never missed a thing. She ignored Pam's sarcastic comment and thought only about meeting him after the game.

"Congratulations, Robbie. You did great today."

Watching his cheeks flush again like they did the other day, she realized he definitely wasn't one bit conceited. She thought he was really cute, too.

"I'm sorry, Katie. We are going to have to walk to the party. I couldn't get my dad's car today. It's in the shop, and he's using my mother's car for work."

"That's okay. I'm used to walking, and it's a beautiful day, anyway. Do you know where Rhonda lives?"

"Yes. It's not too far from here. Come on. Let's get going."

As he reached for her hand, she recoiled so he immediately put his hand back in the pocket of his pants. He waited a while before he broke the silence.

"So I hear you have a big family?"

"Yes. I have three sisters and three brothers."

"Wow. That's a full house."

Yeah, especially in four rooms, she thought.

She wished she knew him well enough to speak what was on her mind. She was too embarrassed to talk about her family, and as they walked the strange streets, she began to worry about how she was going to get home.

"Gee, I think I'm lost. I'll never find my way home after the party." Katie was happy to change the subject.

"Don't worry about it. I'll make sure you get home safely."

She didn't want him to walk her home; if he saw where she lived, she would just die.

As they entered Rhonda's basement, the party was in full swing, and they bumped into one of the other football players.

"Hey, Robbie....What do we have here? Well, if it isn't the famous Katie Ramie. You finally decided to grace us with your presence."

"Don't listen to him, Katie. He's a jerk." He turned her in the opposite direction, pulling her away from the rude remark, but the damage was already done.

She couldn't believe they thought she deliberately stayed away from their parties; this was the first time she had been invited to any of them. The room was swarming with mostly seniors, and the only other people she actually knew were the other cheerleaders.

"I had no idea you were coming, darling." Ellen walked toward Katie, exaggerating her words in movie-star style.

Following her closely was the new boy. He was shorter than Robbie but about thirty pounds heavier. His hair was dark, and his eyes were blue. He reminded Katie of Elvis Presley.

"Oh, I almost forgot. This is Ben O'Riley. Ben, this is Katie Ramie, and you know Robbie already, don't you?" But before giving Ben time to answer, Ellen grabbed his arm and pushed him toward another introduction.

"I swear she's something else. She makes me nervous whenever she's around." Robbie shook his head back and forth as he leaned toward Katie.

"I feel the same way when I'm around her. I'm glad somebody else thinks so."

They giggled together, kindred spirits.

After an hour of standing around, Katie began to worry about getting home. "Robbie, I think I'd better be on my way. It's probably getting dark, and I have a long walk home."

"Good idea. I'm ready to split too."

"Robbie, are you leaving already?"

They both turned around in unison as the new boy approached.

"Yeah, I'm going to walk Katie home. It's getting kind of late."

"Good. I'm leaving myself now. Mind if I join you two?"

"Well...uh...are you going our way? I mean, I don't know which way we're going, either." Robbie's reluctance to have Ben along was obvious.

"Please, both of you. I can walk home by myself. Robbie, if you will take me back to the school, I'll be fine from there." Katie panicked. That's all that she needed, she mused, to have the two of them walk her home. But each time her eyes met Ben's Elvis-like face, she couldn't stop the wonderful feeling of excitement that shot through her.

As the threesome exited outside, she realized it had gotten much colder as night fell and wished she had gone right home after the game. She couldn't believe it—last week she was walking home by herself, and this week she had two boys who wanted to walk her home. She wondered where this Ben guy came from and why he wanted to walk with her and Robbie.

"Are you cold, Katie? Do you want my jacket?"

"Oh, no, Robbie. Please keep it yourself. I'm not cold," Katie lied.

Robbie was no match for the confident and handsome boy who had interrupted his date with Katie, and she could sense he was upset. On the other hand, Katie was herself agonizing over what was ahead. What was going to happen when she walked into the house with two boys? It was already dark. How were the boys going to get home? If her dad was home, he would have to drive them, and she knew he wasn't going to be very happy about that. He didn't even like driving her places, let alone two complete strangers. She was certain as soon as they saw where she lived they would turn around and run.

"Gee, you do live further than I thought you did."

"I told you not to walk me home, Robbie."

"Oh, no. I would have been worried about you. After all, I did ask you to the party." Robbie said it loud enough so Ben realized Katie was his date, but the new boy retaliated.

"Well, now she has two of us to protect her, and I think she will need protection in this neighborhood."

"It's really gone downhill in the last year." Katie tried to make excuses for Ben's cocky statement about her neighborhood. She was mortified.

When the three of them approached her house, Katie was relieved to see her father's car was not in the driveway, but when the boys made no effort to leave once they were at her front door, she was forced to invite them in.

"Mom, this is Robbie, and this is Ben." Katie's mind was spinning, and she hoped she had pointed to the right person when she introduced them. The kids were running around the house; it was a zoo as usual. For the first time in her life, Katie was glad for her mother's presence as she proceeded to play the perfect hostess.

"Hello, boys. I'm glad to meet you. Are you hungry?"

"Hungry, I'm starved."

Katie's eyed widened at Ben's reply. He was really something; he was a perfect stranger in a strange house, and he was acting as if he owned the place.

"I can make you a sandwich."

"Oh, that will be great, just great." Again, it was Ben who did all the talking.

Katie watched in astonishment as he gulped down two baloney sandwiches and a giant glass of milk before Robbie even finished half of his first sandwich. Katie was so nervous that she couldn't think of putting a thing in her mouth. She thanked God her dad wasn't there; if he saw what Ben was eating, he'd have a fit.

Just then, Jonathan came into the kitchen and rolled his eyes at Katie.

"This is my brother, Jonathan. I think he wants to meet you two."

"You're both football players, aren't you?" Jonathan was impressed to meet not one, but two of the high school football players.

As Ben stared at Katie intently, Robbie continued to nibble on his sandwich while he talked football with Jonathan.

"Hey mom, where's dad?"

"He went to the store, Jonathan, but he should be back shortly."

Katie hoped they would leave before her dad got back. She was so engrossed in worrying about how they were going to get home that she was barely paying attention to the small talk going on between her mother and the boys.

"So you were born in Ireland. I never would have guessed it; you don't have an Irish brogue at all."

While Robbie sat quietly in the background, Nan and Ben exchanged words.

"This sure is a busy house. Where do you put all these people?"

While Katie felt like crawling under the table, Nan laughed at Ben's comment. Just then, Jack strolled into the kitchen, and Nan introduced him to Ben and Robbie.

"Hon, I think the boys are going to need a ride home."

Only Katie saw the annoyed look on Jack's face. She knew he was angry; he didn't even like driving his own family anywhere.

"Can I go, mom?"

Katie was glad Jonathan insisted on coming along. At least he would do some of the talking. Katie started to relax somewhat once they were in the car and on their way.

When they approached Ben's beautiful neighborhood with at least an acre of land around each house, Jonathan mentioned something about spears coming out of the woods, which made Robbie and Katie crack up. Katie caught a glimpse of Ben's house when they let him out of the car, and it looked beautiful. Later, as they approached Robbie's house, Katie's heart sank. It looked like a mansion. She was now positive neither boy would bother with her again.

"Goodnight, Katie. I had a great time. See you on Monday."

"Goodnight, Robbie. Thank you for everything. I had a great time, too."

It was uncomfortably quiet in the car once the boys were gone. Even though Katie sensed Jack was not happy about driving the guys home, she didn't really care. It had been one of the best and worst days of her life, and she was emotionally drained.

Much to Katie's surprise, both boys continued to pursue her, but unfortunately, it just wasn't acceptable to date two boys at one time. Katie had to make a choice between Robbie and Ben. She liked Robbie. She felt very comfortable with him, he was gentle, unassuming, and extremely quiet. On the other hand, Ben was cocky and conceited, but he was so good looking, he made her heart beat faster whenever she saw him. So she made her choice based on Ben's looks and magnetic personality.

"I'm sorry, Robbie. I feel terrible about all this. You're really a sweet person, and I like you a lot.

"Yeah, I understand. Don't worry about it."

He bowed his head dejectedly as he walked away from her, and Katie felt like crying. If only he was as good looking as Ben and made her heart flutter like Ben, he'd be the one. She was disappointed he hadn't put up more of a stink, but he wasn't that way. She should have known he wouldn't get mad; he was a real gentleman. She was already second-guessing her decision.

"Katie, how would you like to come to my house for dinner Friday night?" As she boarded the late bus, Ben rushed to catch up with her.

"Sure, I'd love it." Her pulse raced with excitement.

"Great. I'll talk to you about it tonight when I call." His calls were infrequent and short at first, but lately they were spending hours on the phone each night talking, but mainly just listening to each other breathe.

When Friday night finally came, Katie was a bundle of nerves.

"So this is Katie. I'm Ted, Ben's dad."

"Hi, I'm glad to meet you."

Extending her clammy hand as Ben's father gripped it enthusiastically, Katie wasn't prepared for the thick Irish accent, which made it difficult to understand what his dad said when he spoke.

During dinner, Katie observed quietly as the O'Riley family talked continually, arguing with each other one minute and cracking jokes the next. They were all very opinionated. When Ben's parents spoke directly to her, she nodded uncomfortably as everyone around the table laughed, knowing she didn't understand a word they said to her.

"Don't worry, Katie. You'll get used to the way they talk when you're around them more often. Just tell them when you don't understand what they are saying." Ben was trying to ease Katie's nerves. He couldn't possibly understand how different his family was from hers.

At the end of the night, Katie felt slightly depressed. Somehow she just didn't seem to fit in. She didn't feel good enough for Ben's kind of life.

After that night, Ben occasionally escorted Katie home from the football games, but most of the time, she walked to and from the school by herself. On the way home, she lingered, lost in her thoughts about how her life had changed in just a couple of weeks.

The next weekend, after the football game, Ben came running toward Katie, picked her up, and swung her around. "Katie, guess what? I got my license." He was ecstatic, and Katie was instantly jealous and ashamed of herself for being so green-eyed.

"That's great, Ben. Wow! I didn't even know you were trying." She forced herself to sound enthusiastic.

"Come on. My dad's here. He's going to let me drive home. We'll drop you off."

"No, I don't want to put you out. It's in the opposite direction." The last thing she wanted was for Ben's dad to see where she lived.

"Don't be stubborn. I want you to see for yourself what a great driver I am."

Katie wished she had Ben's self-esteem.

Nan and Katie were washing and drying the dishes later that night when Nan asked her what she wanted for her birthday. *What did it matter?* she thought. She wasn't going to get what she asked for, anyway. Pitying herself as she remembered all of the unhappy birthdays she had spent, she hoped everyone would just forget it so she could be totally miserable. Her birthday had always been a day of unfulfilled expectations, and Katie didn't see any reason for that to change. Then the wheels started to turn. She knew exactly what she wanted for her birthday.

Suddenly, filled with enthusiasm, Katie blurted out her answer to Nan's question. "What I'd really like is for dad to take me to get my learner's permit on my birthday. Do you think he would do that?"

"Gee, I guess it could be arranged." A request such as Katie's seemed simple enough to Nan. She didn't have a clue about any of the details involved in getting a learner's permit.

"Great! I'm going to call Ben and get the book. I'll start studying right away." Katie couldn't remember being so happy.

Because she didn't think about the repercussions of the commitments she made on behalf of Jack, herself, or the kids, Nan many times made promises that couldn't be kept. She existed in a world where tomorrow was too far off to worry about and lived only one day at a time; that was all she could cope with. Any obligations made during one day were quickly forgotten by the next day.

Still a child, Katie based her life for the next two weeks on Nan's implied promise. She studied the motor vehicle guidebook inside and out. All she could think about was that she was going to get her learner's permit on her birthday. She called the Motor Vehicle Bureau to get an appointment to take the test. The clerk reminded her that she had to be accompanied by a licensed adult and told her to be there at 2 P.M. on November 2, her birthday. Katie gave Nan all the details and assumed her mother was communicating everything to Jack.

The weekend before her birthday, Ben invited Katie for a ride. His father was convinced that he had enough experience to drive by himself, and Katie had to admit he was very confident behind the wheel, even though he had a tendency to drive too fast for her liking.

"Ben, can I drive?" Katie had butterflies in her stomach.

"What, are you crazy? My father would kill me!"

"Not on the road. Let's go to Smith's Point. It's a deserted road. Please?"

"No, we can't. I have to get home."

"What do you mean? It's Saturday night. What's wrong?" Searching Ben's face, which was partially turned away from her, Katie sensed something was up.

"Well, I have to do something for my dad." His reply was even less convincing than his facial expression, and Katie became sullen as her suspicions mounted.

"Okay, forget it. I don't want to drive. Why don't you just take me home right now?"

"No. We have a little while yet before I have to go home. I'll let you drive as soon as we find the right place." In a gesture of reconciliation, he put his hand on her leg, but Katie was too far gone.

"I said no! Just take me home, and you can go do what you have to do."

But Ben drove around without any apparent destination in mind until nightfall, with Katie sitting in confused silence beside him.

Katie's house was dark when Ben drove up. Quickly, she opened the car door and slammed it behind her, instantly regretting the fact that she did not have the nerve to tell Ben she thought it was horrible of him not to tell her in advance that he couldn't spend the entire evening with her. She momentarily wondered why the house was dark as she knocked on the front door, but she was so upset with Ben that she didn't dwell on it. She also missed seeing the many cars parked in front of Elaine's house.

"SURPRISE! HAPPY BIRTHDAY!"

When Katie opened the door and saw all of the people standing in the living room, she couldn't believe it. Immediately, her initial astonishment gave way to guilt at the way she had treated Ben. And she was feeling something else also: complete and utter humiliation. Even though Ben's smile as he made his way over to her indicated all was forgiven, Katie still felt bad. She needed something to feel bad about, as this surprise was too much to cope with.

"I'm sorry, Ben, for the way I acted. I just didn't think it was anything like this. You should have told me."

"And spoil your mom's big surprise?"

"I would rather have known about it, anyway."

"Happy Birthday, Katie. Come on, Ben. You get to talk to her all the time."

As their discussion was interrupted, Katie turned to face Annie and Ted Magilly.

"Annie and Ted, thanks so much for coming." Katie felt like she was in the middle of a nightmare.

"We wouldn't have missed it for the world. You know, Katie, we had a heck of a time finding your house. I thought you said you lived on the next block over."

Feeling the heat on her face and ears, Katie shifted uncomfortably at Annie's statement. "No, no, you must have misunderstood."

"I'm positive you used to point to the next block when I asked you where you lived. Oh, well. I'm just glad we found it, anyway."

Annie was right. Katie had fibbed about where she lived. The homes were much bigger and nicer on the street that was closest to the hospital, and she used to tell everyone she lived there. Now here they were; all the people she had lied to standing in the small house she hated. She wished they would go away so she could crawl into a hole somewhere. She figured they all pitied her now that they knew where she lived.

It was Nan's idea to stage the surprise party for Katie and, with Ben's help, she had pulled it off. As she carried Katie's cake into the living room, glowing with sixteen candles on it, Nan held her head up high, proud of herself that the party seemed to be a huge success. It had been hard work arranging for all of the little ones to be someplace else and shopping for party supplies, but it appeared everyone was enjoying themselves. Because Katie smiled widely when she approached her, Nan assumed the birthday girl was also enjoying herself. Little did she know that Katie was mortified inside. If only she hadn't lied to her friends about where she lived. If only she lived in a bigger house. If only they weren't poor.

When it came time to open her gifts, Katie smiled until she thought her face would crack. She didn't think she deserved any gifts at all; she didn't want a party and didn't need their gifts. It was all her mother's fault. Why couldn't she just ignore this birthday like she did all the others? Ben should have told her what was going on. Then she wouldn't have gotten mad at him.

When she went to bed that night, Katie sang to herself the lyrics of a popular song that was out at the time titled, "It's My Party and I'll Cry if I Want To." It seemed very appropriate for her misery. Ironically, her friends had a great time.

What would it take to make this wretched child content? Why was she tearing herself apart? Had the seeds of self-destruction been planted too early in her development to be destroyed so that even when things were going well, she was bent on creating aggravation and grief in her life? What was it that made her want to be ignored on her birthday so she could be miserable about it? What was it that caused her to ache for closeness from the human beings in her life but push them away if they came too close? What was it that motivated this complicated human being?

Outwardly, she was a popular and likable person, always assuming responsibilities other people veered away from and helping everyone with their problems. She was forever smiling as if she hadn't a care in the world. Inwardly, however, she was pathetically insecure, unsure of herself, and destructively bitter about her life. Her bouts with depression were well hidden, and other people would have been shocked to know she was ever down emotionally.

On her birthday, Katie enthusiastically got ready for school. Because Nan was sleeping, Katie left her a note reminding her to tell Jack to pick her up at school by 1:00 P.M. for the appointment to get her permit.

As she watched the clock constantly during each class, Katie was unable to think about anything else. When the time arrived, she knew it would be only a matter of minutes before the wall phone in the classroom sounded, summoning her to the office. When 1:15 came and went, she collected her books and readied herself to leave. But by 1:30, she began to panic. If he came right now, she reasoned, they would have enough time to get there. At 1:33, a black cloud of doom began to form in Katie's mind, and at 1:45, it began to rain in her heart. Even when the clock struck 2:00 P.M., a part of her still hoped he would come. She was sure they would let her take the test if they got there a little late, but her dad never showed up. When the school day was over, Katie was reluctant to get on the activity bus. She contemplated walking home so she could delay facing the inevitable, but it was already dark.

Once in the house, Katie walked in long strides to her room and slammed the door as hard as she could. She threw herself down on the bed and tried to cry, but the tears wouldn't come. She spit on her hands and rubbed the liquid around her eyes. Wondering if it did the job, she got up and looked at herself in the mirror, spitting again in her hands and placing it around her eyes until they appeared wet. She wished she could get to the bathroom; she needed to look like she had been crying. It was important.

When Jack opened the bedroom door, Katie was lying on her side, contemplating her problems. As soon as she realized he was in the room, she wished she could cry big, fat crocodile tears and bunches of sobbing sounds that would make him feel bad.

"Katie, we have a gift for you...your mother and I do."

Katie could tell he felt very awkward talking to her. "I don't want a gift. I wanted you to take me for my permit today. How come you didn't come?" It was definitely more words than she had ever spoken to her father at one time in her entire life.

"Your mom didn't tell me until a few minutes ago that you wanted me to take you to get your permit today. I had to change the oil in the car today. Here, take this. It's for your birthday from your mother and me." After letting the small box in his hand fall on the bed next to Katie, Jack quietly left the room.

She hated them. They had ruined her birthday, just like all the others.

The black velvet box caught Katie's eye, and she opened it to reveal a heart-shaped topaz birthstone ring. It was beautiful. Carefully, she slipped it on her finger and was disappointed that it was too big for her. It did fit better on her middle finger, and she raised her hand to admire it. She shouldn't have been so awful, but all she wanted was her driver's permit.

Later, when Nan called her to dinner, Katie entered the kitchen and mumbled her thanks to them for the present. Katie said not a word all through dinner, and after cleaning up, she retreated to her room, where she spent the rest of the evening studying and brooding.

Nan and Jack didn't notice the ring they brought Katie was too big for her; if they did, they ignored it. She ended up putting scotch tape around it so it would fit her finger properly. Jack didn't offer to help Katie learn how to drive or take her for her permit. As a matter of fact, the subject of Katie learning to drive was never mentioned again by either Nan or Jack.

Ben and Katie were definitely a twosome; he gave her an anklet bracelet for her birthday, which indicated they were going steady.

And the dreaded holidays were again quickly approaching.

It started out gradually. Katie noticed it first. Nan began to spend more time reading the paper, more time complaining about the sad state of the world, more time calling her sisters to complain about Jack and the kids. She stopped doing all but the bare necessities when it came to taking care of the house and the kids. A cloud of doom hung overhead and, of course, it was the dreaded month of December.

"Look, just get their coats on, quick! I've been cooped up in this house long enough. We're going for a ride to see Santa Claus." The whites of Nan's eyes pierced through Katie.

"No, mom it's too cold out, and how are we going to get there? Dad's at work. Let's wait until he comes home." Pangs of anxiety once again attacked Katie's vital organs.

"No, he'll spoil it. I don't want him to come along. We'll go by ourselves. I've already called a cab."

Jonathan shot Katie a wary glance, and she realized she was at a loss as to how to stop Nan from going through with her crazy idea. All day long, she talked about taking the kids to see Santa, and she was so obsessed with the idea that Katie didn't think anything short of knocking her out was going to change her mind.

The baby showed his irritation at being jammed into his snowsuit by whimpering.

"Shush up, George. Be a good boy, and don't cry. You'll just make things worse."

He was the only one of the younger Ramie children who was unhappy, however. Sammy, Barbara, and Amy, of course, seemed to think it was a great idea to see Santa Claus and anxiously got into their coats without Katie's help.

"Well, I'm not going, and that's final!" Folding his hands across his chest, Jonathan stared hard at Katie.

"Listen to me, you brat. If she starts acting up, I'm going to need your help with the kids. So get your coat on."

"Jeez, I don't believe this!" As he stomped out of the bedroom, Jonathan added in a whisper, "I say we just hit her over the head. Why don't you call dad?"

Just then, Nan yelled to them, "The cab's here! Come on, everyone!" Nan walked out to the waiting car without bothering to put on her coat.

Katie herded the kids out to the car and crammed them into the cab. She realized too late that what she should have done was lock Nan out of the house and call the police, or at least her dad.

"Take us to see Santa Claus...ho, ho, ho."

The cab driver turned around to face Nan, scowling at her. "Merry Christmas to you, too, lady, but you have to be more specific about where you want to go." The man was becoming more irritated as each minute passed.

"Hawaii, actually. It's too cold here. I'll get my grass skirt and be on my way. What do you say, kids? Want to go to Hawaii?"

"Look, lady, what are you, daffy? I can't take you to Hawaii. The meter is running, so you might as well tell me where it is you want to go."

"Walworths, Walworths!"

The frustrated cabbie spun his wheels as he started down the street, following Nan's loud request. He was only halfway down the block when Nan opened her mouth again.

"Do you know your cab is filthy? Filthy! How do you expect anyone to enjoy their ride in this dirty car?"

The cabbie shrugged his shoulders. Actually, it was dark in the cab and impossible to determine whether it was clean or not. Jonathan and Barbara were sitting in the front of the cab. George was sitting on Jonathan's lap and Sammy on Barbara's lap. In the back seat, Katie was holding Carrie, and Amy sat next to Nan.

Nan lit up a cigarette, and Katie thought she was going to get sick from the smoke and the lack of air in the crowded cab. To add insult to injury, George began to scream at the top of his lungs. He was uncomfortable in his snowsuit in the stifling cab and was letting everyone know it, and poor Jonathan had no idea how to comfort him.

What a mess we are in, Katie thought.

While she was thinking about telling the driver to bring them back home, the cab pulled up to the store. Katie heard Nan cough and before anyone realized what she was doing, she opened her mouth and spit on the floor of the cab.

"Hey, what do you think you're doing, you crazy broad? You have no right to do that."

Clearing her throat, Nan spit again, this time on the back seat. She then threw her head back and let out an exuberant laugh.

Katie opened the back door of the cab and exited it quickly with Carrie in her arms. She grabbed Amy's arm and flung her out of the cab. Jonathan and Barbara, with Sammy and George in their arms, were already out of the cab and standing on the curb, wide-eyed, as they listened to the furious cab driver cursing at Nan.

"Now give me my ten bucks, bitch, and get your ass out of my cab! You are the craziest nut I've ever had in this cab, and I mean to tell you that's no compliment."

Still laughing, Nan responded loudly, "I'm not paying you for this ride. Your cab is too dirty." With that, she got out and slammed the back door shut.

Katie thought she was going to faint right there on the spot.

"Lady, I'm calling the police right now. I've had enough of you. You owe me."

As he left the cab, he closed the door with such fierceness that Katie thought it was going to fly off of its hinges, and she thought Nan was lucky he didn't attack her. He looked like he could have killed her if he wanted to.

"Come on. What are we waiting for? Let's go see Santa!"

The last thing Katie saw as Nan led them all into Walworth's to find Santa Claus was the cab driver running up to the pay phone in front of the store. Katie took a deep breath and motioned for the kids to follow Nan into the store. As Nan walked haphazardly ahead of the kids, brushing into an occasional shopper and ignoring their indignant reactions, Katie and the children fell further behind.

"Where's Santa? Where's Santa?" In a shrill and childlike voice, Nan's question resounded through the store, which was packed with people in a hurry to get their Christmas presents and be on their way.

Finally, Santa appeared, sitting on a chair in the middle of the children's department, surrounded by Christmas decorations and boxes of Santa coloring books. The little ones went crazy when they saw him and began jumping up and down.

"Can we sit on his lap, Katie? Can we, please?"

"Okay. Go stand on line. Jonathan, stay with them."

He gave Katie a look of disgust as he joined them at the back of the queue.

While watching the kids get in line, Katie lost track of Nan for a few moments until she heard shouting over by the chair where Santa was sitting. As she turned her head, Katie heard the familiar voice and crazy dialogue— all coming from the sick lady who was her mother.

"You're filthy! You're not going to touch my kids. Don't you ever wash your suit? Is everybody around here filthy? What's this world coming to?" Nan puckered up her mouth and spit directly on Santa's beard, sending him flying from his seat, his hand raised in the air, ready to come down hard on Nan.

A young man in a brown suit and tie quickly jumped over the velvet rope and stepped between Santa and Nan as mothers scurried away from the scene with crying children in their arms. From the corner of her eye, Katie saw her brothers and sisters cowering behind a counter, which had been set up to take pictures of the happy children with Santa. The man in the brown suit grabbed Nan by the arm and flung her from the platform, pulling her toward a small dressing room located across from Santa's area. Mortified, Katie buried her head in Carrie's blanket and prayed she wouldn't have to get involved. Just then, the cabbie appeared on the scene, followed by a burly policeman.

"There's one of the fruitcake's kids. She's got to be around here somewhere!"

As the cab driver's finger pointed directly at Katie, she suddenly wished the ground would open up and swallow her and Carrie.

"Where's the lady who was with you, girlie? I got me a cop here like I said I would."

"Don't be afraid, honey."

The policeman stepped in front of the cab driver as Katie cowered away from him in fright.

"This man says you used his cab but didn't pay him for the ride. I'd just like to talk to the lady about it, so why don't you tell me where she is?"

"She's over there."

As she said the words and pointed to the dressing room, Katie's voice cracked. A lot of people were looking at her, some with pity and some with disgust, and she wished she could vanish right then and there.

As they hurried toward the dressing room, the cabbie continued to talk to the policeman. "I'm telling you this is one crazy broad. You'll see for yourself. Mark my words!"

They were met by the manager of the store, who immediately started explaining to the policeman what Nan had done to Santa.

"Well, it's up to you both. If you want to press charges, I'll arrest her."

"I don't know. I checked with Santa, and he's willing to forget the whole thing. He found out she has a whole bunch of kids, and he spent some time talking to a few of them. We think she needs some help." He pointed a finger at his head to indicate psychiatric problems as he continued. "Looks like a breakdown of some type."

As the store manager rubbed his chin, pondering the policeman's question regarding filing charges, the cabbie spoke up again.

"I will press charges if I don't get my money. I want twenty dollars now for all the time this has cost me. If I had kept my meter running, she would owe me a bundle. Yes, arrest her or give me my money." His face grew ruddier with every word, and the veins in his neck were brilliant purple streaks against his pink neck.

"Okay buddy, okay. Calm down. You don't want to have a heart attack. We'll get you your money. Where's the little girl?"

As he spotted the familiar face of the terrified teenager still standing rigid in the same spot he had last seen her, the policeman waved for her to join them. She tentatively walked toward them, holding the baby tightly in her arms.

"Honey, what's your name?"

"Katie...Katie Ramie."

"Is that your mother in there?" He pointed toward the dressing room.

"Yes."

"Do you know where your father is?"

"Yes."

"Can I call him?"

"Yes, but I don't know his number by heart. He works at the mental hospital."

"Oh, that's an easy enough number to get. What's his first name?"

"Jack."

"Thanks sweetheart. Now you go over there and sit down. The baby must be heavy in your arms."

He's such a nice man, Katie thought.

Her mouth was so dry; she wished she could get a drink of water. As she got closer to the place where they were holding Nan, she could hear her ranting on about everything that was bothering her. Katie wished she could punch her in the mouth. She vowed she would never again let her mother put her in a situation like this, no matter what it took to stop her.

Jack was shocked when he received the call from the police asking him to pick up his family at the shopping center. He wondered first how they got there and, secondly, what had happened. The policeman informed him over the phone that nobody was hurt, so he was thankful for that.

When Jack arrived at the store, Officer Delaney met him.

"Hello, Mr. Ramie. Sorry about all this, but your wife created quite a disturbance here today and could have gotten herself in some serious trouble. I see you have a big family." The policeman was very sympathetic and felt sorry for Jack and the kids; he'd seen Nan's kind before and knew it was no picnic living with someone like that. "Anyway, the store manager has decided not to press charges against her for the attack on Santa; however, the cab driver wants his money or he will swear out a complaint and I will have to take your wife in. It's up to you. Do you want to pay the fare?"

"How much is it?"

Jack was already fumbling in the pocket of his pants for his wallet as Katie watched closely. She knew he was going to be mad, having to part with his money.

"Twenty dollars, sir." When the policeman finished exchanging the money between Jack and the hyper cab driver, he turned once again to Jack. "I suggest you get your wife to a hospital, Mr. Ramie. She seems very high strung and could be dangerous. Three of the store's security guards are in with her now."

Rubbing his hand across his chin, Jack silently reflected on the policeman's words. Nodding as he passed the officer, Jack went into the dressing room to collect his deranged wife.

When they emerged a few minutes later, Jack had his arm around Nan's shoulders, and her face was pressed against his chest as she shuffled along. As Jack passed her, Katie felt his cold look penetrate her entire body, a wordless stare meant to say, how could you let this happen? She never hated either of her parents more than she did at that moment.

Not one word was spoken by anyone in the car on the way home. Uncanny as it was, even George sensed the importance of staying quiet as he solemnly stared at his big sister. Carrie had been a dream during the entire ordeal, sleeping on and off in Katie's arms.

When Jack stopped the car in the driveway, the kids made a mad dash for the front door, anxious to get in out of the cold, but they had to wait there, with the wind biting at their small bodies as Jack talked Nan into getting out of the car. Finally, after what seemed like an eternity, he pulled on her arms a few times and she swung her legs around and placed them on the ground, shuffling toward them slowly.

Once inside the house, Nan lit a cigarette and sat passively on the couch in the living room. Katie busied herself preparing the kids for bed as they bitterly complained about being hungry.

"As soon as everyone is ready for bed, I'll make you grilled cheese sandwiches."

The gnawing knot in her own stomach was giving her fits. As Katie left the boys' bedroom to cook some food, she ran into Jack standing in the hallway, his legs straddling the heater grate.

"I'm going back to work now."

Katie couldn't believe what she had just heard. "You're taking mom with you?"

Her reply was muttered, just as Jack's previous statement had been. It was difficult to talk to Jack under normal circumstances, let alone at strained times like this.

"I think she should be okay now."

Dumbfounded at his unbelievable assessment of Nan, Katie put her hand on her forehead, thinking to herself that he was just as crazy as Nan was. Why was she such a coward? Why couldn't she scream at him not to leave her alone with them, to take her with him to the hospital, where she belonged? Why was she so afraid to tell him what she thought?

While Katie was involved with her thoughts, Jack began to leave his position in the hallway.

"No, I don't think she's really okay!"

The words fell out of the side of Katie's mouth, so low and inarticulate that they barely reached Jack's ears. She watched the back of him as he disappeared into the living room and out the front door, slamming it shut.

When Katie peered around the corner, Nan was still sitting on the pullout couch, smoking another cigarette and staring into space. She couldn't believe he had walked out and left her there with them. It was painfully obvious to her that he didn't care what happened to them.

Katie quickly made grilled cheese sandwiches for the kids while Jonathan and Barbara kept an eye on their mother. It was way past the little ones' bedtime, and they were practically falling asleep in their tomato soup and sandwiches. As soon as Katie got them settled in bed, Jonathan and Barbara attacked their dinner while Katie took her turn watching Nan.

Katie asked her mother if she wanted something to eat, and she took a bowl of tomato soup from Katie. She had only put two spoonfuls of the hot liquid in her mouth when she threw the bowl onto the floor. Nan's eyelids began to flutter up and down uncontrollably as Katie prepared for the worst.

Nan rocked back and forth wildly as she said over and over again, "Why won't he listen to me?"

It wasn't clear to Katie to whom her mother was referring, as she often had conversations with people who definitely were present only in her own mind.

Between dry, sobbing sounds, Nan talked to her imaginary counterpart. "He doesn't understand me. He doesn't care. He doesn't even know this place is too small for us. I need a place where I can walk to everything. I can't go on like this any longer." Nan began making animal-like noises when the monotonous repetitive statements ended, only to be followed by words sputtered in anger and unrecognizable for the most part except for a few here and there, like father, daddy, Martin, small, and car.

Cautiously, Katie approached Nan, stretching her arms in front of her for protection. "Okay, mom, let's pull out the couch. Come on. You can lie down on the bed, and I'll give you a backrub. Won't that be nice? Then everything will be okay. You're just tired—that's all. As soon as you get some sleep, you'll be as good as new."

Katie waited patiently until Nan stopped flailing her arms and lifted her bulk off of the couch so she could pull it out. Katie then led Nan by the hand from the chair she had quickly settled in and guided her down on the bed. When her head hit the pillow, Nan started crying real tears this time, and a look of desperation crossed her anguished face.

"Shh, shh," Katie repeated over and over again. "Everything will be all right!" She wished she would go to sleep; she couldn't take it much longer. Katie's head ached, and her mouth felt like it was full of cotton balls. The thought of murder crossed her mind again, frightening even her with its intensity. She had to stop thinking like this—it wasn't right. She despised her parents so much, she wished they would die. They would be better off without them.

Even though she hated touching her mother, Katie gently put her hands on Nan's face, stroking her as she said the usual comforting words. "I know what you are going through, but try not to think about it. Try to relax. Try to go to sleep."

All the while, Katie was thinking how she detested even touching her and she couldn't stand the lies any longer. Her only goal was to get her mother to sleep. She prayed to God to prevent her from hurting her mother—or at least thinking about hurting her. She prayed he would stop her from doing what she really wanted to do to her. What was she thinking? No one out there was listening to her, especially not God.

Katie had mastered the technique of deception very well, knowing her mother had to be fooled into believing she had a right to act the way she did. When she was challenged or there was no one to talk her out of her paranoia or the voices in her head giving her direction, she turned violent. And so it had to be done—and Katie would tell her anything she wanted to hear or do anything to calm her down, even give her a soothing back rub when she would rather strangle her instead.

Jack was working from three in the afternoon to eleven at night but usually didn't make it home until midnight. Sitting at the kitchen table, Katie stared tiredly at Nan who was sipping slowly on a cup of tea she had made for her. She hadn't fallen asleep as Katie had hoped she would and, on the contrary, appeared wide awake and ready for action when she arose from the couch after her backrub.

As soon as Jack came in the door, Katie got up from the table and went into the bathroom to get ready for bed. It was the first time she had left Nan's side since she put the kids to bed, and her body ached all over. When she left the bathroom after washing her face and brushing her teeth, she went directly to her room without looking into the kitchen. She immediately got into bed and pulled the covers up over her head.

"Santa! Santa!" Sammy shouted as he ran up the red velvet carpet, arms outstretched, a wide grin on his happy little face. "I want a train for Christmas. Can I have it? Can I?"

As the child was about to sit on Santa's lap, Nan stepped between them, facing Santa. "This will teach you to touch my child, you dirty man!"

Taking a shiny object out of her pocket, Nan swung it at Santa's rotund stomach, and he immediately fell over as blood trickled onto the floor. Nan ran out into the street, but the injured Santa began to chase her with his sleigh. While she was running down the middle of the street to escape from Santa, a cab suddenly appeared from a side street and ran Nan over. As she lay dead in the street, Santa got off of his sleigh and spit in her face repeatedly.

From the time she put her head on the pillow until she woke up the next morning, Katie didn't remember a thing, except for the dream. It was strange, but she could remember it very vividly—all the details, including being very happy about the ending.

It was the last day of school before the Christmas holidays, and Katie quietly dressed to get out of the house before anyone woke up and prevented her from escaping to her only place of refuge. As she gently closed the kitchen door, not daring to go through the living room, where her parents slept, she breathed a sigh of relief that she was free. She knew her mom would probably sleep all day and be ready to act up by the time she got home. She was like Dracula, and Katie was not looking forward to it.

Later that day, as the activities bus unloaded the students, Katie noticed police cars in front of Pat's Tavern. Out of the corner of her eye, she saw a woman who looked like she was naked being put into the back of one of the police cars. Katie wondered what was going on; it was definitely too early in the day for any trouble in the bar. Everybody, including the bus driver, strained their necks to see what was going on. They had all seen the naked woman for sure but were unable to determine who it was in the back seat.

When Katie got off the bus at Maria's house, she lingered on the corner, talking to her friends. Unlike the rest of the girls, who were excited about beginning their Christmas vacation, Katie dreaded the very thought of it.

As she turned the corner toward home, Katie saw a crowd of people in front of her house and recognized Jonathan among them. As soon as he saw her, he ran toward her like he was on fire.

"Yo-you know wh-what mommy did?"

As she took a deep breath, waiting for Jonathan to continue, Katie felt like her heart had stopped beating.

"She wa-was all the way do-down to the tavern before someone st-stopped her."

Katie interrupted her brother at this point. She was painfully aware from his stuttering that he was very upset and tried to calm him down. "Jonathan, slow down. I can barely understand you. You're stuttering again." She was surprised because he was doing less and less of it as he got older; she actually hadn't heard him stutter in a long time. "Come here and sit down on the curb and relax for a second. Talk slowly and start from the beginning." Katie wasn't sure she really wanted to hear what was sure to be bad news.

"Mom walked out of the ho-house naked. Can you believe it? She went down the middle of the ro-road." His words came in breathless, panting sounds, and nothing was going to slow him down until he had it all out. "Naked, Ka-Katie. I swear, everyone saw her. All my fr-friends saw her." He was like a wind-up doll as he jumped up from the curb and walked around in circles in front of Katie. "Anyway, dad co-couldn't catch her, so she got all the way do-down to the bar. Someone called the police because they came right away."

"Keep going, Jonathan. You're not stuttering as much now." She was dying to hear the end of the story and encouraged Jonathan to continue.

"We-well, she went into the bar and tried to scratch some poor guy's eyes out because he tr-tried to cover her up with his coat. When the police got there, they brought her home for a talk with dad. They ju-just took her to the hospital; dad fo-followed them in his car."

She realized then it had been her naked mother they were putting in the squad car when the bus passed the tavern. It was the answer to her prayers. Katie felt like jumping up in the air, throwing her books over her head, and yelling at the top of her lungs. She was ecstatic that her mother was gone from the house even though she wasn't sure for how long, but at least she wouldn't have to deal with her that night. The prospect of spending her vacation watching the kids didn't bother her as much as trying to keep Nan from doing any harm to them. There was one thing Katie knew for sure—it was easier to take care of the kids without Nan around than it was when she was in the throes of a nervous breakdown.

Jack didn't go home after he filled out the health insurance paperwork for Nan's admittance. Instead, he began his shift at the hospital. He didn't call home to see how the children were doing. Katie really didn't expect him to, nor did she care whether she ever heard from either of her parents again.

It was Christmas Eve before Jack was able to focus on the holiday. He found a tree somewhere and dragged it into the house. The kids were thrilled to decorate it. As he always did, Jack had gifts under the tree for each child on Christmas morning. The little ones were excited to see the toys, and Katie wished she was their age again—anything before that dreadful age of six.

A couple of Jack's sisters and brothers and their families stopped by the house on Christmas Day, bringing food and drinks and lots of good humor. Katie was grateful for their visit, the one bright spot in an otherwise dreary day.

The next day, Aunt Madge and her family stopped by briefly with a box of clothing—hand-me-downs for whomever they fit. Katie couldn't wait until they left so she could go through them. She spent the Christmas vacation refereeing arguments among Jonathan, Barbara, and Amy, looking after the younger children, cleaning the house, doing laundry, and sulking. What time she did have to herself she spent on school assignments.

As they fluttered around the kitchen, trying to keep out of Nan's way, Jonathan and Katie shot glaring glances at each other. It was mid-January, and Nan was home for a visit.

"This place is a disgusting mess. I don't understand it. It's only four rooms, and you can't keep it clean."

Nan was furious as she threw a dish towel on the floor. She continued yelling, but Katie tuned her out by engrossing herself deeply in thought. What nerve she had walking into the house after sitting on her behind for a month in the hospital and criticizing them because she didn't like the way things looked! The place was much cleaner than it was when she was supposedly taking care of it; it didn't smell like cigarette smoke all the time, either. She hated the fact that Nan always had to have something to complain about. It didn't seem to phase her at all that her older children were built-in babysitters and housekeepers every time she got sick. She was so self-centered that she was totally incapable of recognizing that fact and throwing some thanks their way.

But Katie wouldn't say a word to defend herself, afraid that Nan would get sick again and she would be responsible for it. Still, to hear her moan and groan about a spot of dirt here or there made Katie livid with anger. Even though she thought she couldn't despise her mother any more than she already did, times like this proved to her there was a lot more room for animosity.

When Jack opened the front door and escorted Nan to the car to take her back to the hospital, Katie breathed a sigh of relief. They were free of her for at least another week.

Because Jack now owned a home, he was not eligible for the kind of social services aid he had received during Nan's previous hospitalizations. They would not send someone to watch the children without receiving some remuneration, based on Jack's salary. Because of this, Jack did not pursue any welfare arrangements, relying instead on neighbors who were willing to watch George, Carrie, and Sammy for the couple of hours during the time he left for work and the older kids got home from school. After that, the children were on their own to get dinner and schoolwork done before bedtime.

"When is mommy coming home? I like her much better than you!" Amy was in tears, venting her anger at Katie because she told her she had to go to bed.

"Shut up, Amy. I'm tired of your tantrums. I don't know when your precious mother is coming home. She'll just show up some day with her suitcase and that will be it."

Katie tried to concentrate on her homework, but she was trembling with anger. Nan's last visit home kept interfering with her thoughts. In a way, Katie hoped Nan never came back, but then again she couldn't continue on this way for much longer. The first few weeks back in school after the Christmas holidays were quiet, but basketball season was just about to begin and, with it, the cheerleading season would be in full swing.

Katie knew after Nan's one-day visits began, it wouldn't be long before she was released, and such was the case with this most recent hospitalization.

Meanwhile, at Pehlam State, Nan bided her time by sleeping, knitting, smoking, and waiting for the medications she was now taking regularly to kick in so she would eventually be liberated. She wasn't in a hurry to get home; being in the hospital was a nice break from the pressure of raising the kids and cleaning the house. The doctors had all kinds of questions, the same ones she had heard a million times before. The drill was always the same, and she made sure her answers were the same also.

Chapter Six: A Decade Passes, but the Pain Remains

As long as Katie could remember, she hadn't really loved anyone without hating them in the end: her mother, father, grandmother, aunts, uncles, cousins, brothers, and sisters—even June Reynolds. As close as she came to knowingly loving someone was with June, but in the end even June had rejected her, or so Katie thought, and she hated her for it. There had been no role models in Katie's life who could show her unconditional love. From the day she was born, she had never experienced acceptance of herself through thick and thin in a secure, solid environment. Katie was needed and used by her family but not loved or appreciated enough to make her secure. Every system in place for the treatment of people with mental problems, from the judicial to the medical, had let her down by not dealing with her mentally ill mother and the ramifications of her illness on her family. By the time she was a teenager, Katie knew the treatment of mental illness consisted of Band-Aiding it and hoping the Band-Aid didn't fall off too quickly.

As she grew into puberty and thrived in the public school environment, Katie felt awkward and even upset when her teachers praised her, yet she continued to do the kinds of things that demanded recognition. She wanted it, but she couldn't handle it when it came her way. Because of all of the years of controlling and manipulating her feelings in her relationships with the people in her life in order to survive, Katie eventually lacked emotion. She had became a master at placating and agreeing with her mother, despite what she really felt, and she was eventually able to do that in all of her relationships. She thus gave the appearance of being on everybody's side. In short, she stifled her personality in order to satisfy an urgent need within her to be accepted by everyone at all costs. She was a deeply unhappy person despite all of her accomplishments; she was disconnected.

"I got it, Katie! I got my period!"

As she hit Katie on the arm, Elaine jumped up and down excitedly. Elaine's nasty habit of slapping her when she told her something irritated Katie, but she was even more upset by this particular news. She wondered when she was going to get hers—probably never, as she was still sure there was something very wrong with her.

"Now everyone, listen to me. You are to stay together when the parade ends. I mean it. The bus will be waiting to take us back to the school. It's freezing out there, so keep moving. Good luck." Mrs. Curley departed from the bus and disappeared into the crowd as the color guard and cheerleaders lined up at the starting place designated for the school.

When she awoke that morning feeling sick, the excitement of participating in the St. Patrick's Day Parade turned to worry, and she still wasn't any better by the time the group was signaled to begin their march down Fifth Avenue. Katie was miserable; she had terrible cramps, and her fingers were frozen before the parade even began.

"Katie, you're out of line. Speed it up."

Mrs. C. was upset with her, but she was doing the best she could under the circumstances. She had awful cramps; they were different from her usual stomach pain. With each step, she hoped the cramps would go away and prayed she wouldn't get sick in the middle of the street. Suddenly, something was dripping out of her. She had to keep her legs together, stay in line, and not fall down. She had to keep going, not slow down, and not disappoint Mrs. C.

When she arrived home, Katie immediately ran into the bathroom. At first, the bloodstains on her pants scared her to death, but then she was relieved. It had finally come. She wasn't a freak after all, but she wondered what she was supposed to do now.

Katie left the bathroom, found a safety pin in Nan's sewing basket, grabbed a clean pair of underpants from her bureau drawer, and rushed back in before anyone else did. She swirled toilet paper around her hand until it was a thick wad. She then stuck the safety pin through the mound of paper and attached it to her underpants. It felt really weird with the big lump of paper between her legs.

"Mom, I think I started my period."

Nan was alone in the kitchen ironing when Katie meekly approached her. "When?"

As Nan looked up at her, Katie thought she saw a flicker of disgust in her eyes. "Today, during the parade. It's not too bad, though."

Appearing annoyed, Nan turned off the iron and brushed past Katie into the master bedroom, where she opened the top dresser drawer that belonged to her and pulled out a white pad from a bright pink box. "Here, use this," Nan said abruptly as she dropped the white napkin in Katie's outstretched hands. "You can pin it on until we get you a belt. You know where the clean ones are. Try not to use too many, though. They are very expensive."

Nan returned to her ironing, obviously finished with the conversation, and Katie disappointedly went to her room. She placed the clean white sanitary napkin in her bureau drawer underneath her one remaining pair of underpants. She had already scrubbed the soiled pair and hung them up on the towel rack to dry. She decided she would continue to use the toilet paper and save the napkin until absolutely necessary; she didn't want to use up her mother's precious supply and make her mad.

Katie hoped her mother was going to have a talk with her about what it meant to get her period. Elaine said she and her mother discussed it for a long time. Katie's thoughts went back to when they lived in the city and how she hated walking to the drugstore to get Nan her box of sanitary napkins. They wrapped them in brown paper and tied them with a string, so everyone knew what they were. She knew what happened to her that day had something to do with having a baby and that she could now get pregnant. Elaine and Maria had discussed it vaguely during one of their talk sessions but didn't go into detail because they knew Katie hadn't gotten her period yet. She would have to find out more from Elaine as soon as she could.

Katie decided she would use her own money for sanitary napkins, and she and Elaine walked the two miles into town one day for that purpose. She was overwhelmed that they now came in a dozen different varieties and they didn't wrap them in brown paper anymore. Katie's face was on fire by the time she decided on a box and thought she was going to die from embarrassment when she placed it on the counter and the druggist eyed it intently as he rung up her purchase.

"I can't believe it, Elaine. I was so mortified. That dirty old man kept looking at me."

"Oh, it's just your imagination. He doesn't care." Elaine was certainly much less affected than Katie and couldn't share in her friend's humiliation over the incident.

"I'm never going back there again." Katie shook her head defiantly.

"You'd better get used to it, kiddo. It's the same everywhere you go."

"Hey, Elaine, I've been meaning to ask you. What did your mom actually tell you when you got your period?"

"Oh, lots of things."

"Can you be more specific? I really need to know."

"Didn't your mom tell you?"

"No." Katie's voice filled with bitterness.

"Gee, I'm surprised. With all those kids and all, I thought she'd have a lot to say."

"No one has a lot to say in my family."

"That sure isn't the problem in mine. We all talk too much."

"That's all right, Elaine. It's a lot better that way—believe me. At least you know where you stand with your mom and dad."

"And my sister—don't forget my big sister. Boy, she sure lets me know how she feels. I think she is really over the moon with this new boyfriend of hers. Maybe I'll get the room to myself finally."

"You're lucky you only have to share it with one person. Come on, El. Tell me what your mom said about your period."

"Well, it's like this. Getting your period means you are a woman. You drop little eggs every month that can be fertilized by a man and bingo, you're pregnant. If you get pregnant, the blood sticks around to nourish the baby. If you aren't pregnant, you get your period. My mom says I better get my period every month until I get married or I'll be in big trouble."

"What about the man?"

"Oh, no. She wasn't too specific about that. She said I'd find out in good time. I think it has something to do with liquid coming out of his penis when he gets hard and has it in you."

"Elaine!"

Katie was totally caught off-guard by her friend's frank and surprising revelation. She burst into uncontrollable giggling, with Elaine following suit, and they continued laughing all the way home.

It was April 1963, exactly ten years from the day Nan killed little Kevin and Martin. April was always a bad month for Katie. Some years, she thought a lot about what happened; during others, she didn't think about it at all. Katie received her Confirmation during one tense April, when she was fifteen years old. It almost didn't happen; she challenged all of the doctrines she needed to embrace to receive this sacrament and almost got thrown out of CCD class. The only reason she went through with it was because she was desperate to have the middle name Theresa. She had read the book about St. Theresa, known as "The Little Flower," three times, and she felt totally connected to her. It had been very traumatic, covering up her true feelings about some of the teachings of the Church in order to receive this sacred rite.

There was no doubt that Nan's mental and physical health had diminished seriously since her last hospitalization. The family learned to survive with Nan's limited functioning, accepting it as a fact of life. They knew there was nothing that was going to make her any better; they just hoped she wouldn't get any worse. Since the incident with Carrie, however, Katie was convinced Nan was indeed capable of killing again. The attacks of diarrhea were becoming more frequent and violent than ever before, and many times the bathroom was occupied when the attacks came. She was often so desperate that she grabbed a brown paper bag and went in it, carrying it outside quickly to the trashcan, hoping no one would find it.

Tenth grade was almost over. Katie held onto her straight-A average, was elected president of the Junior Class, won a spot on the varsity cheerleading squad, and received an invitation to participate in the Work Study Program in her junior year, which meant she would have a job in the Audiovisual Department, working a couple of hours each day after school and during the summer. She and Ben were also dating regularly.

That summer, Katie was even more obsessed with sunning herself than she had been in the past, and for hours at a time, both she and Elaine sweated under the intense heat until they were beet red. The heat and light made Katie feel less depressed. But by nightfall, both girls were swollen and miserable with sun poisoning. It didn't deter them because they still continued to sunbathe in Katie's backyard for long periods of time.

Jack returned to the day shift at the hospital but occasionally dropped the family off at the beach for the day, coming back at the end of his shift to take them home. One day, as Katie lifted herself from baking under the hot sun, she noticed her father approaching them, followed by three other people. She wondered what he was doing back at the beach so soon; it was only noon. As the group got closer, Katie sprung up from the blanket like a rocket. She couldn't believe what she was seeing. Jack was leading some of his patients toward them.

Feeling as if everyone on the crowded beach was staring directly at her, Katie walked down to the water, frantically searching for Jonathan, running quickly toward him as soon as she spotted him. "Jonathan, I'll watch the kids now."

"But it's not your turn, Katie. I still have fifteen minutes to go."

"No, that's okay. You do what you want to do. I don't feel like sitting on the blanket anymore. Go ahead. I'll watch them."

Shaking his head at his sister's surprising generosity, Jonathan made a mad dash for the water and freedom.

"Amy, you're out too far! Get back in here before you drown! Don't you dare splash me, Sammy! That water is cold! I'll kill you, I mean it!" She absorbed herself in watching her brothers and sisters, ignoring what was going on behind her and praying her dad would not venture down to the water with his charges.

Pehlam State Hospital had instituted a new program involving outings for certain patients, and Jack was authorized to take several of his patients on shopping trips and other kinds of outings. He thought nothing of bringing his three charges to the same area of the beach where his family was. Now, as Katie turned around, she watched the three misshapen figures in their saggy bathing suits walking toward her, her dad following closely behind. One of them was carrying a pail and shovel, and kept stopping to blabber incoherently to the people around him. Katie began to panic as the men, women, and children around her covered their faces to hide their laughter at the antics of the three mental patients. She would drop dead if her dad brought them over and everyone thought they were with her.

She ran into the ocean, using it as an escape, letting the cold waves hit her hard. When Sammy yelled to her that he had to go to the bathroom, she felt like kissing him.

"Barbara, come on. Get out of the water and watch George and Amy while I take Sammy to the bathroom. Come on. Hurry up!" She screamed at the top of her lungs to get Barbara's attention as she frolicked with Jonathan in the water. She was anxious to leave the scene.

After that day, Katie didn't accompany her family to the beach on the few occasions they did go. She preferred to stay behind even if it meant watching the baby and George all day. She thought it was bad enough that her own mother didn't act right, but to deliberately subject them to more crazy people was just too much for her to take. She was bitter and thought it unfair that the only place she could go to have some fun was now messed up. It proved to be a very long, hot, miserable summer for Katie.

Because of all of her activities, Katie's junior year in high school was twice as busy and stressful as her sophomore year had been. She knew college was out of the question for her and didn't think about it very much. In the early sixties, females were not encouraged to pursue academic courses leading to college unless their parents could afford to send them. There were very few scholarships awarded to girls to further their education, and the process for achieving one was complicated and fraught with paperwork. A few of her teachers advised her to pursue college preparatory courses, but she honestly felt it was pointless for her to do so. There was no way her parents could afford to send her to a university.

Katie naturally went for a business diploma, taking Typing I, Shorthand I and Business Math I, along with the required academic courses of English, History and Science. But during her first week in typing class, Katie was ready to give up her goal of becoming a secretary.

"I'll never get my fingers straightened out enough to do this, Mrs. Roberts. I might as well quit right now."

"Katie, listen to me. You're too much of a perfectionist. Typing isn't something you learn in one week. It takes months of training and years of practice before you can reach top speeds. Now calm down and concentrate. I don't want to hear any more talk of quitting."

As her teacher predicted, in a couple of months, she was typing remarkably well.

Katie turned seventeen on the day she was called into the counselor's office. She thought the worst and wondered what she had done wrong.

"Katie, the Audiovisual Department has an opening. They need someone to help Mrs. Better for a couple of hours each day. Are you interested? They will be paying you for the hours you work."

"Are you kidding? When do I start?"

It was her best birthday present ever. She had worked for them for free just to get the experience, and now they were rewarding her with a paying job. Despite the fact that this additional commitment put more pressure on Katie, she worked even harder to meet her daily responsibilities and was delighted at the opportunity to earn some much-needed money. She wouldn't have to rely on the occasional neighborhood babysitting jobs and be at the mercy of those deadbeat parents who didn't pay her enough, not at all, or weeks later.

There was one thing that never changed; however, at some point, the school day ended and Katie had to go home.

Nan was never happy with her life, but when she was in crisis, the vocalizations became more frequent and more unrealistic. She had been in a delicate condition for a long time, and complete deterioration was not far away—neither were the holidays. As Nan became less and less able to cope with the family responsibilities, Jack, Katie, and the older children pitched in and took care of them. For a while, it looked like maybe she would pull through this latest episode. Jack made sure she was well supplied with tranquilizers, and even though they made her tired and withdrawn, they did keep her under control. But as Christmas approached, Nan appeared consistently morose, preferring to sit and smoke for much of the day. Christmas Day that year was one of the worst ever. Jack went to work, and Nan remained in a comatose-like state as the kids took turns watching her.

When Katie answered the knock on the door to find Ben standing on the stoop, a silly grin on his face, her depression lifted somewhat. "My goodness, what are you doing here? I didn't expect to see you today."

"Well, I thought I'd make like Santa Claus and drop your gift off myself." He beamed as he handed her a small box.

"What is this? You shouldn't have. Oh my goodness!"

She was shocked and embarrassed by the gold Christmas charm Ben had given her. Katie immediately regretted not getting him a more expensive gift. She wished he had given her something cheaper—a bottle of perfume instead or, for that matter, nothing. She would have felt better if he hadn't gotten her anything.

"Gee, Ben, thank you so much. This is really too much!" What was she going to do with a charm? She didn't even have a bracelet or chain to wear with it. It would just sit in the box.

She had invited Ben into the living room.

"Wait here. I have something for you."

She dashed into the bedroom, pulled a carefully wrapped package from her drawer, and quickly returned to the living room.

"Here, Ben. I'm sorry it isn't much."

She noticed he was intently watching Nan, who was sitting stoically on the couch, staring into thin air.

"Hey, thanks. This is just what I needed. It's my third bottle today."

"Oh, no. I'm so sorry. Let me have it. I'll take it back and get you something else." Katie felt her face flush with embarrassment.

"No, really. Old Spice is my favorite, especially this bottle." Lowering his voice, he drew closer to Katie. "What's the matter with your mom? She looks sick." Once again, his eyes focused on Nan's immobile body.

"She's not feeling too well, and the holidays are bad for her."

"How come she didn't recognize me? I mean, she's seen me a half-dozen times at least, but when I said hello, she looked at me as if I was a stranger."

In a whisper, Katie painfully told him what was wrong. "Well, when she gets like this her memory goes a little. Ben, she's more than just physically ill—it's mental—and usually she has to be hospitalized." Katie wished Ben would just leave. She knew it was over for them. Who would want to date someone whose mother was nuts.

"How many times has she done this?"

"Too many to even count, but she's pretty good this time compared to her other breakdowns." She wondered what she was doing, why she didn't shut up. He didn't need to know everything. Why was she jeopardizing their relationship? The last thing Katie wanted was for Ben to feel sorry for her. She already felt beneath him in so many other regards and now this.

"Well, I'd better get going. I promised my parents I wouldn't stay long. We have company at home." Glancing nervously at his watch, Ben backed out of the door, but it wasn't Katie he was looking at when he left.

"Thank you so much for the beautiful gift! It was very generous of you!" Katie shouted at him as he ran down the path to his car.

"Ah, it was nothing. I hope you enjoy it. I'll talk to you sometime soon."

It was the way he said it that sent Katie running into her room, where she fell miserably on the bed. She didn't care who was watching Nan. Only much later when Barbara shouted to her that she had a phone call, did Katie leave the room.

She gripped the phone and took a deep breath before she recognized his voice.

"Hi, there."

"Is that you, Ben?"

"Yeah. Who did you expect?"

"I'm just, well, surprised, that's all." She hadn't expected to ever hear from him again, but he'd barely been gone an hour and already he had called. "To tell you the truth, I didn't expect you to call."

"Why not?"

"Well, I though maybe you got scared away."

"Scared of what?"

"Oh, things."

"You mean your mom?"

"I guess so."

"She doesn't have some contagious disease I might get, does she?"

"No." For the first time in a long while, Katie allowed herself a small giggle.

"Then don't worry about it."

"You know, Ben, you're the only person who knows how I feel about my mom and where I live."

"Wait a minute. I don't remember you telling me how you feel."

"You know, very embarrassed. I really do!"

"Shucks, Katie. It's not your fault that you live in a small house and your mother is sick."

"I know, but it still bothers me a lot." Afraid that her conversation might be overheard, Katie leaned closer to the phone.

"Yeah, I guess it would bother me too if my mother acted the way your mom did tonight. And that house you live in, it's a cracker box, all right. I know it would drive me crazy, too." Ben laughed heartily as he continued. "Get it? Drive me crazy."

"You're right, Ben. It's enough to make me sick." Katie's reply was filled with bitterness.

"Hey, let's drop the subject and talk about something more upbeat, like the fact that I finally got rid of my provisional permit. I can now drive by myself legally. No more walking for us."

"Oh, but I like walking places together." Katie reminisced about the long walks from the school to her house, holding hands, sharing his coat, stopping to kiss on a dark street. She marveled at how different it was compared to walking those same streets alone.

"Yeah, but you have to admit it will be a lot easier driving places. Think of all the time we'll have for other things." As he made loud tapping noises with his teeth, Ben sounded eager and happy.

"I envy you. It must be nice to be so sure of everything."

"What do you mean, Katie?"

"You never seem to worry. No matter what you do, you are sure it is going to work out fine."

"I don't understand Katie. Don't you think it's good to be optimistic about things?"

"Yeah, I guess so. You're right. It's just that in my life, things seem to go wrong all the time."

"Ah, you worry too much for your own good. Listen, I've got to go. I'm getting dirty looks for tying up the phone. I'll call you tomorrow."

"Goodbye, Ben. I'm sorry."

She was disgusted with herself, what a dud she was. Ben probably couldn't wait to get rid of her with all that gloom-and-doom talk. She just knew something bad was going to happen to their relationship. It couldn't last—it was too good to be true. The dial tone sounded in her ear for a long time before she hung up the phone. So much for the happy holidays!

A couple of weeks later, as she entered the house, Katie heard Nan's awful high-pitched voice, the one that always meant trouble.

"Stay away from me! I mean it!"

Because they had gotten through the holidays without Nan requiring hospitalization, and because there was no new baby in the house, Katie hoped Nan wouldn't get any worse. Now her dream of stability faded as she entered the living room. Four-year-old George sat on the couch, red-faced and crying. Amy put her arm protectively around his neck as she consoled him. Barbara was holding sixteen-month-old Carrie, shaking her up and down to keep her quiet, and Jonathan stood against the wall with his ear up to it, biting his nails. Katie tiptoed over to George and put her hand on his head, which felt sticky and wet. She looked at Amy and shrugged her shoulders for an explanation.

"Mommy poured milk all over George's head."

Putting her finger to her lips, Katie signaled Amy to lower her voice.

"He wouldn't drink his milk, and she opened his mouth and poured it down his throat until he was choking. Then she took the whole carton of milk and dumped it over his head." Amy's eyes were wide with excitement, and she stopped for a moment to catch her breath.

"Daddy was in here taking a nap when it happened," Barbara interjected. "I woke him up, and he's been in the kitchen with her ever since. She's nuts, Katie!"

"Shut up all of you! I'm missing it." Waving his hand in annoyance, Jonathan moved his ear closer to the wall.

Instantly, Katie looked around for something to defend them with, as past experience proved to her that Jack wasn't the best at protecting them from Nan. Picking up a couple of knitting needles from her mother's sewing basket, Katie held them firmly in her grasp. From the sounds in the kitchen, Nan's emotions were reaching the hysterical stage, and it appeared Jack certainly didn't have control over her.

"I'm telling you to get out of here! I don't need you! I'm perfectly okay! It's you who's sick—everyone knows that! You're the one who causes me to get this way. If you left me alone, everything would be all right!"

"Nan, look. Let's sit down. Put that knife away!"

What the heck was Jack talking about? Did she have a knife in her hand? How did that happen? Katie stood paralyzed, afraid for her life. She knew they shouldn't be in the house—it was too dangerous. Like the Pied Piper, Katie motioned the children toward the front door and led them to the neighbor's house.

The instant she saw Katie at the door with the children, Anna's black eyes looked worried as she chewed on her lip. "What can I do to help?"

"Nothing right now, Anna; just watch the kids for me. If it gets worse, I'll come over and let you know. My dad's trying to calm her down, but I just didn't want to take any chances with the kids. She has a knife, and you know how she gets. She already tried to hurt George."

"Come here, sweetheart. Everything's going to be okay." Gathering the sobbing child in her arms, Anna comforted him. "Let's get some cookies and milk."

As Katie watched the group disappear into Anna's warm house, she felt good about her decision to get them out of the house. As she turned to leave, Jonathan tugged on her arm. He wouldn't hear of staying at Anna's and stole across the front lawn like a deer with Katie in pursuit. Once inside the house, their fears returned as they stood motionless in the middle of the living room, huddling as close to each other as possible. Again, Katie reached for the knitting needles, which she left on the top of the television. She wasn't taking any chances.

The teakettle whistled away.

"Why don't they turn it off, Katie? Oh, goodness. Maybe they're both dead."

They hadn't heard any voices since coming in the house.

"Don't be stupid. Of course they aren't dead," Katie whispered to Jonathan. But the thought did cross her mind also.

It was awfully quiet, and the teakettle was still whistling away. Just as Katie thought they would have to investigate, the deathly silence was broken by Nan.

"Leave my arm alone! You hurt me, and I don't want to sit here any-more!"

Katie hoped Jack had gotten the knife away from her. Nan sounded like she was crying, but Katie was willing to bet there wasn't a tear in her eyes.

"Stay there, I mean it, or I'm going to do worse!"

Katie had never heard her father speak with such authority.

"Damn, we missed it!" Putting his hand over his mouth at the profanity that slipped out, Jonathan's eyes widened in surprise for a moment before he continued. "Well, we did miss it, Katie. Dad must have floored her one, and we missed it. You and your big ideas! Get the kids out of the house." Looking defiantly at Katie as he mimicked her, Jonathan went on. "Dad can handle her—don't worry."

Katie was just about to speak in defense of her actions when the sounds of a struggle ensued from the kitchen—a chair falling to the floor, the kettle whistling, a shrill scream from Nan, feet stomping against the floor, the table slamming against the wall, the kettle whistling, broken glass, skin being slapped, then sudden quiet. No more whistling noise, replaced instead by a masculine cry of pain. And without thinking, Katie darted into the kitchen just in time to see Jack bent over in agony, holding his hand. Rocking on its side on the floor in front of him was the teakettle, spilling steaming water from its spout.

Nan was pacing back and forth in front of the stove and staring nervously at the exit through the kitchen, into the hallway and the living room, which was blocked by Katie and Jack. She looked like a wild animal. Instinctively, Katie threw up her hands and made stabbing motions in the air with the knitting needles, quietly warning her mother not to come near her. Moving her bulky body around, Nan ran for the kitchen door leading out to the backyard and tugged on the knob like a child. She forgot it had to be turned in order to open it. She kicked the door in frustration and then whirled around to face Jack and Katie, who remained frozen in place, blocking her only other means of escape. Seeing this, she turned back toward the door and, with a much calmer demeanor the second time, succeeded in opening it.

Katie ran to the kitchen window, and the last she saw of her mother she was crouched next to one of the bushes at the far end of the yard. Jack walked slowly from the kitchen into the bathroom, clutching his hand, his face drained of color, as Katie continued to look out the window. It was a bitter cold day, and Nan was wearing only a light blouse and slacks. Katie figured if she stayed out there long enough, she would freeze to death. She guessed her dad wasn't going to do anything about it, and she certainly wasn't going after her.

Jonathan appeared beside Katie at the sink. "What are we going to do?" Canvassing the yard, he looked for his mother. "It must be cold out there. She's probably frozen by now. Let's call the police. Dad's hurt and we can't go after her. I know the number."

With excited enthusiasm, Jonathan reached for the phone. "Hello, hello? You have to get some police to my house. My father is hurt, and my mother is out in the backyard. Oh, yeah, I forgot. My name is Jonathan Ramie, and I live at 801 St. Paul's Drive. Hey, how soon will they be here? This is an emergency. Okay, thanks."

When he hung up, he looked as proud as a peacock as he turned to smile at Katie. "She said they would be here in a couple of minutes." He was bursting at the seams that he had taken care of the situation. He didn't realize how serious things were, how his life was in danger living with Nan.

She knew once the police arrived, everyone in the neighborhood would know they were having trouble again. She almost regretted that she let Jonathan call the police; she wouldn't mind if her mother did freeze to death out there. She felt instantly guilty and shook her head to get rid of the evil thoughts lurking there. She wondered how her dad was doing, but she couldn't feel too sympathetic about his injury. She hoped that maybe after this, he would be more careful about getting her out of the house before she hurt someone. She knew, however, she was only kidding herself, as things were never going to change. As long as she lived in their house, she would always need to keep those knives and knitting needles handy because it was survival of the fittest in the Ramie household.

"Gosh darn. I was hoping they would turn on the sirens."

As he ran from his place in the hall where he had been watching for the arrival of the police, Jonathan didn't notice the dirty look Katie gave him. He bolted to open the door just as Jack left the bathroom and watched in silence as the policeman entered the house. When Katie joined them in the living room, she noticed Jack's hand was swollen and bright red. She still couldn't feel sorry for him; she knew it must hurt badly, but she didn't care. It was his fault that it happened; Nan should have been in the hospital weeks ago.

"She's out back!"

"Okay, son, calm down. My partner is on his way around the other side of the house." Looking directly at Jack, he continued. "I'm Officer Leighton. Are you hurt, sir?"

"Yes. I burned my hand."

"Well, we called for an ambulance when we got the word from the dispatcher. She mentioned someone being hurt. Let me see your hand."

In his eagerness to see what was going on outside, Jonathan ran from window to window. Katie wanted to wring his neck. He thought it was a lousy game. She knew she had to get hold of herself; it wasn't Jonathan's fault. He was probably just as terrified as Katie, only he wanted to help— really help. Katie chastised herself for doing nothing.

"That looks like a second-degree burn at least, sir. How did it happen?"

As the policeman searched the children's faces for the answer he had not gotten from Jack, Jonathan shrugged his shoulders and Katie stared at him blankly. He had a feeling that whoever was outside of the house might be the culprit, so he radioed his partner to be on the lookout for someone who was most likely dangerous.

"I think you'll need to go to the hospital for this injury, sir. Is there anyone else hurt? The caller spoke of a person being outside. Who is that?"

"That's my mom. I'm the caller. She's outside without a coat on, and she's having a nervous breakdown."

Mortified at Jonathan's statement, Katie cringed. Sometimes he had such a big mouth.

"I'm going outside. Where did you see her last?" The cop directed his question to the three of them.

"I'll show you." Katie felt guilty that she hadn't been of any assistance and showed the police officer the bush she had last seen Nan hiding in from the kitchen window.

"Okay, thanks. Anything else you want to tell me that would help?"

Mustering all of the courage she could find, Katie replied, "Yeah. She's very dangerous."

"Thanks."

When the young policeman joined his partner, the two of them made their way over the back of the fence and through the vacant lot behind the house.

Meanwhile, Katie was bending over the kitchen sink in pain, clutching her stomach with her sweaty hands. Her jaw muscles hurt, and she had trouble swallowing. She just wanted the ordeal to end, to be over with quickly. Running her tongue along the outside of her mouth to wet the dried, cracked skin on her lips, Katie made a conscious effort not to embed her teeth in them, but the painful stinging and the taste of blood in her mouth confirmed she had already done damage to her lips. Despite that, she bit down on them again when she looked out the window to see three struggling figures emerge from the woods on the other side of the vacant lot in back of their house. One of the officers, now coatless, worked hard to keep hold of Nan's waist while the other one held both of her legs as they dragged her across the ground. She was acting like an animal. Katie wondered what was going on inside her mother's mind that could be so bad, that would cause her to be so out of control. Everybody had problems and dealt with them. Why couldn't she be strong? She wished they hadn't found her, and was pretty sure her dad felt the same way. What else would explain why he didn't go after her or call the police himself?

All hope faded as Katie watched them approach the kitchen door. Reluctantly, she opened it for them and observed with shame their efforts to get the frantic woman back in the house. The officer who had given up his coat for Nan to wear was bleeding from a scratch on his face.

"Has the ambulance come yet, young lady?" He was panting.

"I don't know. I'll check."

At the living room window, Katie saw Jonathan waving his hands at the red-and-white ambulance pulling up behind the police car and shuddered at the familiar faces of her neighbors gathering in front of the house. Returning quickly to the kitchen, she informed the police officer that the ambulance was there.

"Took their time, Jeff. Glad it wasn't a life-or-death situation." His tone was as sardonic as the grin he threw his partner, but then he turned toward Katie with a different expression on his face.

She hated that look. Everyone looked at her like that—her relatives, the neighbors, her teachers, even Ben. It was a look of mixed sympathy and relief. They were silently saying to her, "Gee, I'm sorry, kid. Thank goodness it's your mother and not mine." She reminded herself that she couldn't blame the policeman. He was just doing his job.

From her squatting position on the floor, a policeman's hands pressed firmly on either side of her shoulders, Nan made incoherent sounds. A young man in white appeared in the hallway, and Katie stepped aside to let him into the kitchen.

"What took you so long?" The policeman seemed annoyed.

The attendant was so young that his voice still squeaked when he talked. "This has been some hell of a day, I'll tell you. What's going on here?"

"This woman is having some mental problems, son. Be careful!" As he looked at Nan warily, the boy shook his head.

"We aren't supposed to get involved with these kinds of things. You should call Pehlam, and they will send an ambulance.

"Look, we're not asking you to treat the lady, just help us get her to the hospital. It's right around the corner, guys. How hard is that?" The other attendant entered the kitchen, and Katie began to worry they wouldn't take Nan with them.

"The man in there says he'll take himself to the hospital. He has a bad burn and should see a doctor immediately, but he doesn't want to go in the ambulance. Is there anybody else hurt?"

"Yeah, her, but it's a little different problem."

The young boy whistled to his partner, obviously a special warning signal they had established between them, and then spoke up. "Uh, I guess we aren't needed her any longer. I'm sorry we can't help you out, but we have to follow orders." He noticed the scratch on the officer's face. "Can I get you a Band-Aid for that cut?"

The policemen exchanged disgusted glances upon hearing the attendant's words. They were not willing to give up their hold on the struggling woman.

"I don't know, Jeff. Maybe we had better let this man take his wife there himself. Goodness knows when they will get around to sending an ambulance from that zoo over there!"

"Yeah, you're right."

"You don't need anything else from us, then."

As the two medics brushed their way past Katie, making a hasty retreat from the house, she knew she had to say something. If she didn't, Jack might talk the policemen into letting Nan go.

"Please, can I say something?" Her vocal chords remained still as she spoke softly so as not to be overheard. "You have to take her to the hospital." Pointing accusingly to the pot lying on the floor, Katie continued in a whisper. "She threw the kettle of boiling water at my father. Earlier, she tried to hurt my little brother. You can't leave her here with us. The rest of the kids are with the neighbor next door. I took them over there so they would be safe. Please believe me. She's very dangerous. If you leave her here, she'll hurt someone again. She can kill people."

Officer Leighton watched the tormented face of the girl as she told her story. He'd never seen such terror in the eyes of someone so young.

"That does it, Jeff. Let's get her into the car."

As she was led kicking and biting to the waiting vehicle, Nan spit out more throaty syllables, all of which were not in the least decipherable.

"Come on, sir. We think it's best that we help you get your wife to the hospital. She is too messed up for you to handle by yourself, especially with your injury. Please come with us."

"Can I follow you in my car?" Staggering up from the couch, Jack moaned.

"Can you drive okay with that hand the way it is?"

"I can manage. I'd just rather take my own car."

From her place in the hallway, Katie listened. She couldn't believe her father was already thinking ahead, even at a time like this. She didn't care— she just wanted them all gone. She couldn't stand it another minute longer and breathed a sigh of relief when they were all finally out of the house. She peered out the window, watching the policemen struggling to get Nan into the car as the neighbors witnessed the latest Ramie sideshow. She was so relieved it was all over that she didn't care what they thought.

After the police car left and the neighbors went their way, Katie limply collected the kids from Anna and began the all-too-familiar ritual of restoring order back into their lives.

This time, however, the breakdown was different from the others; there was no feasible explanation for it. There was nothing to blame, no new baby to care for, and the holidays were long gone. Thinking about the future and more altercations like the one that day sent Katie into a state of depression. And then there was the matter of the kids. If Jack came back without Nan, and that was not a certainty, she would once again be faced with additional unwelcome responsibilities. Later, some of the aunts and uncles arrived, but this time even the visit from them didn't ease the pain Katie felt.

It was two days before things straightened out and Katie could return to school. Jack watched the little ones during the day until he had to go to work, and Anna came to the rescue again, taking care of them until Katie or Jonathan got home from school.

Katie adjusted her schedule so she would be home immediately after school on most days, as she didn't want to take advantage of Anna's kindness. She worked in the Audiovisual Department during her lunch and study periods and cancelled as many of her after-school activities as she could, except for cheerleading practice, which she attended once a week.

As she quickly ran a brush through her hair, Katie got that sinking feeling she experienced when she knew she was in trouble. When she walked into the living room, Sammy, who was sprawled out in front of the television, looked up.

"Where are you going, Katie?"

"To a basketball game. I have to cheer. Did Jonathan or Barbara say where they were going?"

"No."

"I told them not to leave the house."

Katie was pacing back and forth across the thin rug, wringing her hands together. She avoided looking at the clock on the wall, which was ticking the time away. She actually toyed with the idea of leaving the children with Amy.

She was eight, older than Katie had been when she was left alone, but she knew Amy couldn't handle watching the other children. No, she couldn't justify leaving the kids by themselves, and anyway, there was still the problem of a ride. She pulled the living room curtain aside and strained her eyes to see through the darkness to Bud's house, but her hopes for a solution to her problem faded when she saw there weren't any cars in their driveway and the house was completely dark. Even if she started walking to school at that moment, she would be late, and she didn't have the nerve to ask any of the other neighbors for a ride. When Katie responded to Carrie's cries, she noticed she was flushed and her forehead felt warm. After giving Carrie a baby aspirin, she reached for the phone and called the school.

"Hello, my name is Katie Ramie. I'm one of the cheerleaders. Can you get a message to Mrs. Curley, please?"

"Hold on. I'll see if I can locate her."

Recognizing the voice as belonging to the nice maintenance man, Katie prayed he wouldn't find her. She preferred to leave a message rather than talk to Mrs. Curley directly.

"Sorry. I don't see her anywhere. What's your name?"

"Katie…Katie Ramie. Please tell her I'm sick and can't make the game. Please don't forget to tell her I called. Thanks so much."

About a half-hour later, Katie attacked Jonathan as he came through the door.

"I asked you to stick around tonight. I'm in big trouble now. There was a game tonight at the school, and I missed it because there was no one here to take care of the kids."

"Shut up, grouch." Turning his attention to the television, Jonathan ignored his sister's plight.

"She's been yelling all night long." Amy stuck her tongue out at Katie as she escaped the room before Katie could smack her.

"Oh, I swear, I hate you all."

Throwing her hands up in the air, Katie stomped into the bedroom and slammed the door, startling little Carrie, who had just fallen asleep. Hurling herself on her bed, she remained there in misery until she had to get up and yell at the kids to get ready for bed. As she was removing her cheerleading uniform and preparing for bed, she thought about how much she hated her life. She wished again that she had never been born. And the next morning wasn't any better than the night before had been.

"I want to talk to you, Katie."

As she followed the bouncy Mrs. Curley into her office, she tried her best to look as sick as she felt. As her teacher straddled one of the chairs in her office, she motioned to Katie to take a seat opposite her.

"Your mom's back in the hospital again, isn't she?" Mrs. Curley's unexpected question caught Katie off-guard.

"Uh, yes."

"Why didn't you tell me?" Leaning forward so that her whistle struck the chair, Mrs. Curley gave Katie that look—the pity look she hated.

"I...I just didn't think about it. I...I hoped I could take care of it without anyone knowing."

Softening her tone a little, Mrs. Curley continued. "Well, you can't, honey. It's obvious that things are going to suffer because of the added pressures at home. I would rather know about them than be surprised, like I was last night. Do you understand?"

"Yes. I'm sorry. I really tried to get here, but it just didn't work out. I even had my uniform on, but the baby was sick and I didn't have a ride." It surprised her when tears started falling down her cheeks, but she instantly felt like a giant burden was lifted from her.

"I've been thinking about it, Katie, and it might be a good idea for you to take a couple of weeks off from cheerleading. This would allow you to look after your brothers and sisters and not have to worry about getting to the games."

Katie started to cry harder. No one understood how much she loved cheerleading. She didn't want to be given a reprieve from the things she adored. She wanted to stay away from her house, not be forced to be there more.

"But if I miss practices and games, won't that mean I will be thrown off the squad?"

"No." Mrs. Curley smiled. "I'm giving you a leave of absence, kiddo. That's different. I expect you to come back the minute your mother comes home."

She thanked Mrs. Curley between sobs. Why did she have to sacrifice the things she liked to do? She didn't want to give up cheerleading; it was so much fun. She didn't want to miss work, either; she needed the money. It just wasn't fair. She could feel the hate eating away at her insides, but she managed a smile for Mrs. Curley.

"You have a beautiful smile, Katie. You should show it more often. Now, go on. Get out there and play some volleyball before gym period is over; and don't forget to let me know how things are going at home."

Nan was home in less than three weeks, supposedly sane, but Katie knew better.

Katie and Ben were still going strong. They kissed a lot without coming up for air, watched movies at the drive-in, and parked and necked on deserted streets.

Then a dream come true. She and Ben were voted king and queen of the Junior Cotillion. It was a glorious night, and Katie felt beautiful in her first cocktail dress, a silk number with a Kelly green balloon-shaped skirt and white sequined bodice. She spent a good chunk of her hard-earned money working in the Distributive Education Program on the outfit and even had her shoes dyed to match the dress. Sitting next to Ben on the throne in the gymnasium, she felt just like a real queen, but the dream turned into a nightmare just a few days later.

Katie put the ankle bracelet Ben had given her in an envelope and placed it angrily in her notebook. The pain was still with her, anguish that began on Saturday night, when he didn't call her like he was supposed to and which heightened considerably by Sunday evening. Three people had called to inform her that her boyfriend was seen on Saturday night with Dina Larose, the school's beautiful brunette majorette who had a reputation for her flirting and tongue-kissing.

In the past few weeks, Katie felt pressured by Ben to go a little further each time they made out. She was already feeling guilty because she let him touch her in places she shouldn't have. Katie was beginning to weaken, and it frightened her. There were two incidents of pregnancy in the school she knew of. In once case, the boyfriend denied he was the father and skipped town and, in the other case, the girl was forced to marry the guy even though she didn't want to. Up to that point, Katie had refused to give into Ben, and now she guessed he decided she was a lost cause.

Seeing Ben in the lunch room, she defiantly passed him the envelope and rushed away before he had a chance to say anything. Later, as she walked to the activities bus, she heard his familiar voice.

"Hey, wait up, Katie. Why wouldn't you talk to me at lunch? Why are you giving me back the bracelet?"

"Don't tell me you don't know why."

"I guess you know about my date?" He acted as if it was no big deal.

"Yeah, I know! Boy, do I know! Now leave me alone!"

As she turned from him to catch her bus, he grabbed her arm.

"You're causing a scene, Ben."

"I don't care. I don't want you to break up with me. I'm telling you I made a mistake. I needed to see someone else—well, I thought I needed it—but I still like you the best."

"Well, maybe I should make sure if I like you the best, Ben. Is that what's going to happen every time you think you're not sure? I don't know, maybe you have the right idea. Maybe we should date other people. With the way it's been with us lately, getting so serious, I don't know."

"No, don't say that. It won't happen again. I promise you."

Katie melted at his reassuring words and decided to take him back, but the next time they were alone in his car, she insisted on talking about his date with Dina.

"I swear, Katie, when she kissed me, I felt like I was being swallowed up. It was disgusting!"

"Yeah, I'll just bet." Sarcasm laced Katie's words.

"Anyway, let's get on with our own business, if you know what I mean." Ben's arm went around Katie's shoulders, and his hand came to rest on her breast.

"Stop that, Ben. Please don't touch me there." As she turned her head away from him, she moved his hand away.

"It's okay. I won't touch the princess." Abruptly he took his arm from her shoulder.

"Look, I'm sorry, but I have a problem with us like this." She found it hard to come up with the right words to explain her feelings and so she mumbled.

"I'm really scared, you know. It feels so good when you touch me or kiss me, but then I start to think about what kind of problems it would cause if we...well, if we did anything. I know you would break off with me."

"You're crazy, Katie, I wouldn't do that." His low laugh irritated her. "Do you think I would desert you if you were in trouble? You're so pessimistic; you always think the worst about everything."

"Well, I'm really sorry, but I don't have any reason to believe otherwise."

Nonetheless each time they were alone together, their petting sessions grew a little more passionate, resulting in many arguments between them.

"I got the job, can you believe it? I'm going to be a lifeguard!" It was hard for Katie to congratulate Ben with enthusiasm, knowing he would be spending the summer at the beach watching all kinds of pretty girls.

"That's nice, Ben. I can't wait to spend the summer in that stuffy audio-visual office. Mrs. Better offered to pick me up in the morning so I don't have to walk to work. I think it's pretty nice of her; it is out of her way." She was deliberately trying to avoid talking about Ben's new lifeguard job.

"Maybe you should start learning how to drive? I'll tell you what, why don't I give you some lessons the next time we are out? We know plenty of places where we can go." As he brushed her arm with his elbow, Ben gave her a sensuous smile.

"That sounds great." Forgetting about her misery over his new job Katie relaxed somewhat. She was deliriously happy; she was going to learn how to drive and she was sure everything would be different for her once she could drive.

Even though Ben was the center of Katie's existence and she depended on him for everything in her life that was enjoyable, she still wasn't happy with the relationship. On most days she felt like she didn't deserve him and that eventually he would smarten up and dump her. On other days, however, she grew restless and yearned for different boys to date; other people to relate to so she wouldn't be alone when the inevitable happened. She was convinced she had nothing to offer Ben and wondered why he even spent time with her; she was sure he would break up with her eventually.

Her summer job labeling slides was boring and the office was stifling, as the school was not air conditioned; still Katie was grateful for the work. It gave her the opportunity to save a little money out of her paycheck to buy a car. Some of what she made went to Nan, who informed her as soon as she started working that she was expected to contribute something to the house. Even though Mrs. Better picked her up each morning Katie walked home from her summer job each day. She spent this time dwelling on her situation. She figured she'd never save enough money to buy a car—it was hopeless, she would always be poor. It was around this time that her bouts with depression started becoming more serious, lasting three or four days at a time. During these times she was moody and became totally silent.

"I'm really getting sick and tired of asking you what's wrong. It seems like you're always in a bad mood." Ben's frustration was evident in his voice and Katie just looked at him, quietly shrugging her shoulders because she really didn't know what was wrong with her. There had always been problems in Katie's life…maybe, just maybe when things were going smoothly and there were no serious issues facing her, she had a tendency, a real need, to create problems for herself. After all, the apple doesn't fall too far from the tree. One thing was for certain—her mind and body were exhausted from all of the drama in her short life.

A few days later Ben and Katie were out driving. "Why don't you spend the day at the beach with me this Saturday?" Ben was happy and it showed. He also looked good with his glowing tan.

"No, I don't think so." Katie was in the midst of another one of her blue moods. She was definitely feeling sorry for herself.

"Why not?"

"Well, you'll be busy working and I'll spend the whole day sitting on the blanket."

"I'll get a couple of breaks and a lunch hour, and you can spread your blanket right near my chair."

"I don't think so." Still she hoped he would continue to pursue it. She needed to be asked again and again. She didn't count on Ben giving up. After a few minutes of dejected silence Katie spoke.

"You know the last time I went to the beach with you, I felt like a third wheel."

"What do you mean?"

"Well, some of the girls hanging around you…I mean, they are really something; those skimpy bathing suits and all. I just feel…well, inferior. Even that Marla, the older lady…you know, your supervisor's wife, looks good. She's so tan."

"What's your problem, Katie? You look just as good as any of them. I don't know why you do this to yourself. Look, if it makes you feel uncomfortable I understand. Don't come." She wanted him to ask again, convince her that he really wanted her there just one more time. But Ben's emphatic comment decided it for Katie. Unfortunately, her insecurities were so deep rooted that no amount of pleading on Ben's part would be reassurance enough for her. So that Saturday instead of accompanying him to the beach, Katie toasted herself under the blazing sun in the privacy of her own backyard. When Ben picked her up for a date that night, she was sick from sun poisoning. She was miserable during the entire date; her eyelids were so swollen, she could barely see the movie and each time Ben touched her, she screamed out in pain. Just before he dropped her off, Ben told her about the beach party planned for the next Saturday.

"This is the only party we're having and I'm not going to miss it. I'm inviting you because I want you to be there. If that's not enough for you then forget it." He ended his statement on an abrasive note and Katie immediately was defensive. More often lately he didn't argue with her if she refused to go someplace with him and it bothered her tremendously. However, she was deathly afraid of being with the beach people; they were so much more sophisticated than she believed herself to be, and thus she initially reacted unfavorably to Ben's request that she join him. Now she thought that he really didn't want her to go and she cringed.

"I guess I'll go." The reluctance in her reply made Ben upset.

"Don't do me any favors, Katie. If you can't be happy about it forget about going. I mean it." Why couldn't she just come out and tell him she really wanted to go, but she was scared? She figured he wouldn't understand that feeling at all; he was comfortable in any situation. It appeared to Katie that the crisis she expected was getting closer and closer, but what she didn't realize was that she was bringing it all on herself.

It rained the day of the beach party, but by the time they were ready to take the boat over to the island where Ben worked the skies had cleared. Katie was upset at having to take the ferry because she knew her hair would be a limp mess as soon as the humidity hit it; and she was right. Earlier in the day she had walked in the rain to a small boutique in town that sold ladies clothing to buy something new for the party, but the cheapest thing she could find was a flowered blouse in a size that was too big for her. Because she was desperate for something different to wear to the beach, she bought it anyway. By the time they disembarked from the boat, she was feeling very unattractive and disheveled. When she got a look at the other girls heading for the party, it confirmed her fears that she was indeed the ugly duckling. She wished she could dig a hole in the sand and bury herself in it.

"Hey, Katie, get something to drink. I'll be right back." As Katie watched Ben disappear she couldn't believe he was leaving her to fend for herself in a crowd of strangers. She helped herself to a glass of soda and found a place to sit in a dark corner, glad she had something to hold onto. The breeze from the ocean gave her chills as she watched the party feeling like a spectator rather than a participant. The jumbled conversation, the laughter, the mingling, the flirting, the drinking, the smoking—all convinced her she didn't belong there, and then a familiar voice startled her back to reality.

"Come on, Katie, what the hell are you doing over there by yourself? Come join us." As she timidly walked toward Ben, she noticed a beer in his hand. That explained why he sounded so different. "This is Bill and Greta, and you know Jim, my boss, and his wife Marla, don't you? This is Katie, everyone."

Katie nodded at the strange faces, but her eyes focused on Marla. The end of the summer had left her with a gorgeous tan that enhanced her strong, slender body. When Katie first met Marla, Ben told her she was over thirty years old, but Katie thought she really looked fantastic for her age and felt insignificant standing next to her. They were all drinking beer and having a good time laughing at nothing. Soon Jim and Marla departed from the group and two very drunk young men replaced them.

"Hey, Ben, where did you find that little girl?" As they slurred their words Katie felt her face grow hot.

"Oh, shut up." With the help of the beer Ben's Irish temper surfaced.

"Touchy, touchy, aren't we? We can't help it if you like babies." Moving swiftly, Ben pushed his elbow as hard as he could into the offender's stomach. A large plastic cup flew out of the big mouth's hand as he staggered from the blow, and the liquid in it attacked Katie from all sides, soaking her new blouse and permeating her with the smell of beer. Ben's two fellow lifeguards staggered away and Ben retrieved his windbreaker from the lifeguard station, wrapping it around Katie's shivering shoulders.

"I'm sorry about all this, Katie. You were right; I shouldn't have brought you here." A familiar sinking feeling overtook her at Ben's pronouncement.

"Yeah, I just don't belong." She was surprised as tears threatened to blur her vision as she waved him away. "I'll just sit here until the ferry is ready to go; I don't want to go back there."

When she was alone she thought more tears would come, but neither the hurt nor the wetness surfaced. The tears were still there deep inside, tearing her apart, making her head hurt, her jaws stiff from grinding her teeth, and her heart ache, and she never felt so alone in her whole life. No, not really...what was she thinking...she had felt this way many times before—many, many times before. She sat there for a good hour before Ben came for her and they caught the ferry back to the mainland.

When Ben dropped her off at home she was disappointed that the house was dark and her parents were not there. She wanted them to see her the way she was...wet and miserable. The stench of beer on her clothes filled her nostrils but she dared not wash herself. She lay down on the couch instead to wait for Jack and Nan to get home. But the longer she remained there the more she realized how silly it was for her to think they would really care. It was already well past midnight, and for all they knew she was still out.

Normally, if she wasn't home when they got there, they would simply leave the door open and go to bed, not caring how late she came in.

With acrimony she lifted herself up from the couch and stomped into the bathroom. Tugging at the stained blouse she threw it into the small sink, washing away the stench and stains by hand, and then jumped into the shower and allowed the water to flow on her sticky hair and body. She wished she could stay in it all night and use up all the precious water her father was always worrying about. But Katie was a creature of habit and so she resisted the impulse to take a nice, long shower, afraid Jack would come home and get mad at her for using too much water. As she exited the bathroom a sleepy-eyed Jonathan bumped into Katie. "What's going on?"

"Oh, nothing. I just had a bunch of beer spilled on me tonight."

"Sounds like fun. Were you drinking?" Before Katie could respond her brother brushed past her and closed the door to the bathroom, obviously uninterested in her answer. She fell asleep as soon as her aching head hit the pillow.

She watched him as he made love to the strange girl; she wanted to run away but her legs wouldn't move. "I told you. I told you so," her mother's voice kept chanting. "You're so stupid. It's too late now...he has someone else." Katie tried to get her mother's attention but Nan moved further away from her until she was running frantically to avoid any contact with Katie. "Please help me; I need to talk to you. I'm scared, please come back." Something grabbed at Katie's legs as she screamed for her mother and she wrenched her head around to see what it was, but there was nothing there. Still it kept pulling at her legs, bringing her down. Suddenly a hole appeared in the ground and she was being buried in it, sinking gradually as the mysterious force pulled her down. Just before her eyes were buried in the brown muck that smelled of beer, she looked up to see Nan and Ben looking down and laughing at her. She could hear their low laughter as blackness crept in around her and she gasped for air.

Katie woke up sucking in air through her mouth. It was still dark outside and she stumbled to the bathroom, not daring to turn on any lights for fear of waking up her family. She was getting another cold and grabbed a huge piece of toilet paper to catch the liquid flowing from her nose, unrolling more of it to take with her back to the bedroom. She reached for the jar of Vicks vapor rub hidden in her dresser drawer and scooped some of it out with her fingers, rubbing the ointment on her chest and then sticking her fingers in each nostril of her nose, breathing in the welcome vapors. Once she was settled back in bed she took more of the Vicks out of the jar, applied it to the toilet paper, and placed it against her nose. When she awoke again a couple of hours later struggling to breathe, she repeated the same process. All night long she slept fitfully, unable to rid herself of the feeling that she was suffocating. She also couldn't forget about the awful nightmare.

Because Katie had a deviated septum, something she didn't even realize she had, every time she got a cold it would linger for weeks. The nostril on the side with the deviated septum would swell and close off the entire sinus cavity. Fluid would build up and she would end up with an upper respiratory infection or a bad cough as it settled in her chest. She got these terrible colds two or three times a year and was totally miserable.

As the summer progressed, Katie's virulent moods became more prolonged. Even though she looked forward to her dates with Ben more than anything else that happened to her, as soon as she was with him she closed down, giving him the silent treatment or being short with him when she did talk.

"I'm staying overnight at the beach Sunday. It's my turn." When Katie didn't react Ben whistled to himself to break the silence.

"What's wrong with you tonight?" When the tight-lipped, unhappy girl beside him didn't answer, he went on angrily. "I just don't know how to deal with you anymore; you act like there's something wrong all the time, but when I ask you what it is you won't answer me. What the hell is your problem?" Again, dead silence. "Okay, excuse me for asking. I swear; this stinks."

Katie was worried she was pushing Ben too far, and struggled for some way to break the ice. "Do you like staying the night at the beach?"

"Yeah, it's okay; but lonely, you know, with no one around."

"I'll bet. You mean no one stays with you?" She had heard different stories about the lifeguard overnights and her question was serious, but Ben chuckled increasing her antagonism.

"I was serious. I heard some of the lifeguards have company. Forget it if you think it's so funny!" Wrapping her icy fingers around her wrist; she moved further away from him.

"You're so suspicious, Katie. You make yourself miserable over nothing."

"Right, like I have no reason to worry."

"Damn it, you don't…and you know this whole thing with you isn't fun anymore. Do you want me to take you home?" The sudden stop he made with the car flung her forward in her seat, and when she didn't respond, he turned his automobile around with such vehemence that it scared her.

Katie's stomach was in knots by the time he brought his car to a screeching halt in front of her house. As she opened the car door and got out, Ben stared straight ahead, not acknowledging her departure. His car was gone from the street by the time she entered the house. She wished she was dead; Ben had finally given up on her.

Only one week remained before the start of school and each day she did not hear from Ben was like a nightmare for Katie. By the end of the week she was totally despondent. To make matters worse, Mrs. Better took her vacation that week, and Katie had to walk to and from work. The weather was hot and humid all week long. Now she finally had something definite to be wretched and desolate about…and she was. She missed Ben terribly; she reached for the phone on a number of occasions but pride prevented her from dialing his number.

She received her last summer paycheck on Thursday and stopped by the bank in town to cash it before going home. During the long walk, she thought about the money she had stashed away in a sock in her drawer—almost a hundred dollars—and about the course in driver education she would be taking the first semester of her senior year. She felt very lucky to have gotten into the first class. If she passed the test she would be able to get her license sooner. It was out of the question that her dad would help her learn to drive and with Ben gone, she decided to ask Mrs. Better for help when she got back from her vacation. She was the only one with a car who she knew might be willing to help her.

Thinking about the complications of her life at that moment depressed Katie even more, and by the time she got home she was in a sorry state. When she was alone in her bedroom she opened her drawer and reached for the white knee sock hidden under her clothes. It felt strangely light when she gripped it and she was horrified to discover it was empty. Her heart almost stopped beating. She couldn't believe it. At first she thought maybe she put the money somewhere else and forgot about it or maybe it fell out. In a state of shock she pulled apart the entire drawer, and her consternation mounted as she realized the money was definitely gone.

She sat down heavily on the bed, pondering her predicament. Her first thought was to storm out of the room and accuse everyone of stealing her money until she found the guilty party. She hadn't really wanted anyone to know she was saving money, feeling it would be taken away. She recalled her mother's all too frequent pleas even after giving her money from her paycheck every week. "We need it for food." "I'm out of cigarettes and we need bread." "Just a couple of dollars for now." She began to add it all up.

Furious, she slapped her fists against the bed as she realized slowly but surely Nan took the money. With the empty sock clutched tightly in her hand she left the room. Nan was sitting at the kitchen table busily knitting a doily; it was supposed to be good therapy for her and they had a hundred of them around the house in all shapes and colors. Katie didn't waste a minute confronting her.

"Do you know anything about the money that was in this sock?" Katie's voice quivered as she dangled the limp sock in front of Nan. As Katie asked her question, Nan's serene look turned sour and she cleared her throat.

"Yes, I came across it while I was putting some stuff away in your drawer." She was lying. She didn't need to put anything away in her drawer; she was snooping. Katie had the urge to shout at her, call her a liar, tell her she didn't believe she just happened to come across it, tell her she thought she was looking for it—looking for easy money.

"What happened to the money?" Katie kept her eyes on the knitting needles as her insides did leap frogs. She was unable to look at her mother directly.

"Well, I thought it was strange you would just have money lying around like that especially when you know we need all the help we can get, so I...I borrowed it!"

"Borrowed it?" Incredulous Katie went on. "Aren't you supposed to ask a person's permission before you borrow something?" As Nan continued to count stitches in her needlework, ignoring her daughter's question, Katie pursued the issue.

"Are you going to pay it back then?"

"Gee, I don't know if that's possible." She couldn't believe her mother was sitting there as calm as you please knowing she stole her money; she felt like killing her. At this point Katie completely lost the respectful tone she knew she should have for her elders.

"Then if you don't plan to pay it back, it means you just stole it...took it, I mean. That was money I was saving for a car. You had no right to do that." Katie's animosity caused Nan's temper to flare.

"Young lady, you better be careful about the way you are talking to me. I had every right to that money. You're living in this house and if it wasn't for us, you wouldn't have a place to sleep. Anyway you don't even have your license yet. There's plenty of time to worry about getting a car."

Not content to let Nan have the last word, Katie shouted back.

"I worry about getting a car plenty right now. I'm tired of walking everywhere I go. In case you hadn't noticed I do plenty of walking at night, too, and I could get hurt."

"Don't get fresh with me." The familiar grinding sound of Nan's teeth warned Katie her mother was reaching the end of her tolerance, but she didn't care.

"Am I going to get my money back?"

"It isn't really your money anymore. It belongs to the family; this is a family. You haven't been contributing your fair share lately; the least you can do is help out financially now that you are working."

"But I do. I give you money every week. What more do you want; you want my whole paycheck?"

"I told you not to raise your voice at me. It's enough you go around here like a queen bee most of the time ignoring things that need to be done...." Katie cut Nan off with a furious reply.

"But I work now! You can't expect me to do that and take care of the house and the kids, too. That's your job. Why don't you try doing it yourself for a change? You call me a queen bee; you've got to be kidding! How about all your little vacations from us every time things get a little too rough for you?" As soon as the hasty words left her mouth Katie regretted them. It seemed to her it all happened in slow motion—Nan pushing back the chair as she let go of her knitting needles unraveling some of her previous work, and with one motion extending her hand, her fist closed, until it made contact with the left side of Katie's face. Then as her head bobbed up and down slowly from the impact of the blow, everything happened quickly.

"Go ahead, hit me some more! I don't care. You stole my money and I don't have anything now. Nothing!" Katie's face was stinging and she was livid from all the years of abuse.

"You think that lousy old bed in there, one small drawer, and a stinking quarter of a closet...and those lousy canned meals you cook are worth paying for? Why don't you and dad pay me for all those times I took care of the kids while you were off getting a rest from your family? Is that why you had me—to be your live in babysitter and housekeeper...and now to take my hard earned money?" Before Nan could retaliate with another blow to her Katie bound out of the kitchen and kept on going until she was standing in the breezeway leading into Buddy's house, where she leaned her shaking body against the screen, wondering what to do next. Soon Buddy's mom appeared at the door. She was a little Italian woman about four and a half feet tall who lived to take care of her family. She hardly ever left the house; she spent most of her time cooking.

"What's the matter, Katie? You look sick."

"Oh, nothing." Trying to sound matter-of-fact, she asked, "Is Bud here?"

Looking at Katie suspiciously, she shook her head. "No, he's out tonight; I don't expect him until later." The foul smell of cat litter permeated the air in the passageway and Katie felt herself getting nauseous.

"Tell him I came by to see him." Gagging as she opened her mouth to say thanks Katie turned on her heels and stepped quickly outside, breathing in the fresh air. With no place to go and no real friends she cared to talk to, she ended up sitting under the oak tree in the backyard of her house contemplating suicide. She knew it wasn't fair to seek out Bud just because she was having problems. For some reason, at that point she remembered with fondness how Bud had taught her and Jonathan to ride a two-wheeler. He couldn't believe two kids as old as Jonathan and Katie didn't know how to ride a bicycle. He didn't understand that in New York City most of the kids didn't have bikes; it was too dangerous to maneuver them on the crowded streets.

She revisited the thought of killing herself, but knew it wouldn't have any impact on anyone. The only thing they would miss was her money. Katie dug in the pocket of her pants and pulled out the money she had gotten when she cashed her check at the bank what seemed like a lifetime ago. She would have to keep her money with her at all times, and vowed to herself she would not give Nan another penny.

On the way back to her backyard from Bud's, she passed right by Elaine's house. She and Elaine had not been close since her sophomore year, when she got involved in so many activities that she didn't have time for friends. It was kind of ironic, but even though Katie was a friend to everyone in the school, she had no close friends of her own. She no longer had time to spend on fostering a relationship with individual people, so Elaine and Maria eventually gave up on Katie.

As darkness fell and the neighbors retired for the night, she again seriously contemplated ending her life, but she didn't have a clue how to do it. She knew from all the warnings on her mother's pills that if a person took too many they could cause death, and that definitely seemed like the easiest way to go. Her mother had enough pills in the medicine cabinet to kill an elephant.

Much later when there were no lights on in the back of her house, she slipped in the side door then tiptoed through the kitchen and into her bedroom where she fell into bed. She had seen the glare of the television lights as she passed the living room indicating her mother was probably still awake watching a show, but she didn't acknowledge Katie's return.

After a fitful night of sleep and wearing the same clothes she had worn the day before and slept in, including the money in her pocket, she left an hour earlier than usual to walk to work. This day she actually hoped she would be attacked by someone or something, but she was not bothered by man or beast.

Her boss was in a bad mood that day without Mrs. Better, and it was stifling hot in the audiovisual lab so as the day progressed, killing herself was looking better and better to Katie. By the time she reached the outside of the school gates on her trek homeward that evening, she decided she would definitely commit suicide that weekend.

She was halfway home when she heard the sound of a horn and looked up to see Ben's car following her. She deflected her gaze quickly back to the ground, but a surge of hope mounted inside her and her whole body tingled with excitement. Still, as his car slowly followed her up the road, she refused to acknowledge it was there. Ben stuck his head out the window and waved to her.

"Do you want a ride home?" As her eyes continued to search the ground, Katie shook her head.

"No thanks. I'd rather walk."

"Don't be silly; get in. It's only a ride." Without looking at him she reached for the door handle and let herself in the car, breathing in the familiar smell of it.

"How have you been?"

"Oh, okay, I guess." She blinked away a sudden flood of tears, surprised beyond belief that she was crying. She thought about all those times when she wanted to cry and couldn't. Now the one time she wanted to be strong, look what was happening.

"Hey, are you crying? Did I say something wrong? Or maybe you're crying because you're happy to see me?" Waving her hand at Ben as the tears trickled down her face, Katie sobbed.

"It's just been a terrible week...I...I...." She struggled to find the right words to tell him how much she missed him without actually having to say it. "I've been so lonely. I had to walk to work every day. Mrs. Better took her vacation this week."

Ben interrupted Katie's flow of words. "I was hoping maybe you missed me. Was I right?" It was suddenly easy to blurt out an answer to his question knowing he wanted her to say it.

"Yes, I did, very much." As he drove her home, Katie told him about the incident with Nan, and he agreed her mother shouldn't have taken her money. All ideas about suicide faded as soon as Ben invited her to the movies that night.

Later that evening when Ben arrived for their date, Nan received him warmly, offering him a glass of milk and some pie which he gulped down in short order. The atmosphere was certainly different from the night before, and it appeared to Katie that Nan completely dismissed or forgot about the incident the previous night. She knew she would never get her money back, but she didn't care as much about that as she had the night before. In just a few short hours Katie had risen from the pits of despair to the top of the world and she still couldn't believe it as she climbed into Ben's car.

"We have some time before the movie; do you want to practice driving or have you decided to give it up?" When he patted the side of the seat, Katie slid over next to him.

"Are you kidding? I'd love to."

"Okay, I know a good place to teach you. Did you know you will have to get a permit?" As Katie wrinkled her nose at him Ben continued. "Don't get excited, all you have to do is take a written test for it; remember, I gave you the book after I got my license. You need the permit to take driver education anyway, so you better start studying."

"I'm so excited I can hardly stand it." Putting her hand on Ben's leg Katie squeezed her fingers around his knee."

"Don't be too anxious. You probably won't get much driving in this evening. If you get the hang of starting and stopping the car, it will be good enough." When Ben turned the engine off on the deserted beach road, Katie ran around to the driver's side not wasting a minute of time.

"Okay, first lesson...this is the key." Waving it in front of her nose, Ben smiled.

"Funny, Ben, really funny!"

"Here, then start her up." As Katie fumbled with the keys, Ben roared with laughter.

"I don't see what you find so hysterical. Why don't you help me instead of laughing?"

"I thought you didn't need any help, big shot."

"I'm sorry, I guess I do. I didn't realize there was so much to learn." As Ben reached over to show her the mechanics of starting the car, Katie sighed.

"There, now you have the hang of it. You're doing just fine. Start it up again and then you can drive it up the road."

"Oh goody!"

"Easy now, give it a little gas or it will stall. Now keep your foot steady on the pedal. Good, you're doing great. Pull over up there; easy on the brake." Only after she turned off the ignition did Katie relax, beaming proudly at Ben.

"You did fine for the first time. Come on, crawl over me and we can get going. It's getting dark." With her hand on the door, Katie grinned at him.

"No problem, I'll just get out and walk around."

"What are you afraid of, Katie? I won't bite."

"I'm not afraid; it's just dumb to climb over each other when we can do it a lot easier the other way." But she was grateful for his driving lesson and felt bad when he looked at her with disappointment.

"Oh, what the heck…okay…if it will make you happy." Swinging her left leg out from under the wheel she put it over Ben's knees in an awkward attempt to get to the other side of the car.

"Hey, you're pretty good at this, aren't you?" Wrapping his arms around Katie's waist Ben pressed her against him.

"I knew what was on your mind all along, you sneak!" As he forced her straddling body against his, a fire started deep within her and continued as he smothered her face with tiny kisses that fueled the flame which erupted in her loins.

"Oh, Katie, doesn't this feel great?" As his hand inched its way along her lower back he began toying with the waistband of her pants with his other hand. Squirming as he reached under her clothing and touched her bare skin, Katie's fidgeting only caused him to grow more excited. As he gripped her more firmly, molding her to his body, she felt a sudden thickness against her groin that wasn't there previously, and found it increasingly hard to concentrate on anything but the incredible feeling of warmth that possessed her, making her feel like a butterfly still in its cocoon. As his mouth covered hers, the distinct aroma that was his invaded her nostrils, bringing her back to the reality of the moment.

"No, Ben, no more." Using her elbows against his chest to pry herself away, Katie rocked back on her haunches so their bodies were no longer entwined. She rubbed at her knees which ached from the pressure of her weight and avoided looking at Ben. There was really no need to as his head was flung back against the seat, his eyes tightly closed. Carefully she lifted her body from his, and busied herself tucking her blouse back in her pants, until she was settled and could avoid him no longer.

"Are you okay, Ben?" Still she couldn't bring herself to face him. "Aren't you going to answer me?"

"I can't; I don't feel like holding a conversation right now." Ben looked like he was in agony and Katie felt badly. She didn't know what she was going to do; it felt so good. She didn't know if she could stop herself the next time…if there was a next time. What a mess; she was sure he was really mad at her. As Katie was absorbed in her own thoughts, Ben started the car and headed for the movies, remaining unresponsive for the rest of their date.

When he dropped her off at home, Katie turned to him and grabbed his arm. "I'm sorry, Ben, I really am. I wish you could understand that even though it felt really good…we, I mean I just can't take the chance of giving up school if I get in trouble. Plus, I'm positive you would lose your respect for me, no matter what you say."

Throwing up his hands, Ben dismissed her with a kiss on the cheek. "Don't worry about it, okay? I'll call you tomorrow." But he didn't.

The first few weeks of school were so uncomfortably hot that Katie found herself wishing she was at the beach and regretted all those missed opportunities to spend time in the coolness of the ocean water. On one particularly hot Saturday afternoon shortly after school began Barbara appeared at the door, panting heavily as she excitedly delivered her news. "Something terrible has happened up the street!"

"What happened, what is it?" Katie yelled as she ran to the door

"I don't know, but it must be awful. Mrs. Galado came screaming out of the backyard; something about Janie in the pool."

"Oh, my God, I knew something would happen to them one of these days." As she approached their house Katie thought about all the times she came close to saying something to Lana about the fact that she didn't watch her kids closely enough…but she always chickened out in the end. She was sure they didn't want to hear from some teenager that they were not taking proper care of their kids. Katie sensed impending danger when they installed a pool in their backyard, even though it was above ground and one had to climb a ladder in order to get into it. She saw the baby, who was just about two years old, in the yard all alone many times and made a point of telling Janie's older sister to watch her. Because of the pool Katie had been reluctant to accept babysitting jobs from this family during the day; the responsibility of watching three little children around a pool scared her.

Katie reached their house just as the police arrived and worked her way through the crowd of people that had gathered. Once inside the front door she saw Lana Galado sitting at the kitchen table crying, dabbing at her eyes with a cloth diaper.

"What happened?" As Katie leaned against the kitchen sink trying to catch her breath, Candy, Buddy's sister-in-law and a good friend of Lana's, shook her head and closed her eyes. Katie got the message loud and clear without any verbalizations. Hearing hacking sounds coming from the backyard Katie looked out the window and watched in amazement as Jim Galado, Lana's husband, attacked the redwood deck surrounding the pool with an ax.

It was a little late for that she thought. It would have been better to have just kept an eye on the baby.

A policeman gingerly approached Jim and summoned his attention, evidently talking him out of continuing the destruction of the pool. Dropping to the ground at the same time he let go of the ax, Jim covered his face in his hands as his shoulders heaved up and down. It was sad to see all this first-hand, and a tear glistened in Katie's eye as she remembered that moment many years ago when she found out her little brothers were dead, killed by her mother. It was a confusing feeling, that mixture of sorrow and hate, and she was experiencing it again now. She couldn't do anything to help these people, so she let herself out of the house.

She walked slowly across the lawn and stopped abruptly as she saw a tall man carrying a bulky green bag toward a brown truck. It didn't register right away what she was seeing; it was Janie's little body. Then she overheard the man carrying the bag say to the policeman, "Christ, she must have been in the pool for hours; she's completely waterlogged."

All during the funeral Katie watched the grief-stricken parents as they received sympathy and words of comfort from people. They didn't really deserve condolences; they killed her because they weren't watching her properly. Everyone said someone was going to drown in that pool someday and now those same people were comforting them, telling them how sorry they were, how they shouldn't blame themselves. *What bull*, Katie thought.

Sitting close to the casket where Janie's swollen and discolored body lay so stiff in a white silk dress, Katie was lost in thought. She wouldn't be in that casket if they had taken proper care of her. She hoped they suffered forever. No matter what, she couldn't feel sorry for them. Even though her cynicism was well hidden, Katie despised them for killing their daughter, and it renewed the rancor she felt for her own mother.

Watching Lana and Jim made Katie realize something else, too—the loss of little Janie wasn't just a temporary crisis, something to be dealt with quickly, something that would eventually go away and be forgotten. No, the guilt and sorrow over her death was a lifelong pain for her parents. Turning her head slightly to get a glimpse of Nan who was sitting next to her, she saw a look on her mother's face which confirmed what she was thinking. Looking much older than her years Nan stared intently ahead of her, and Katie was sure at that point she never really succeeded in blocking out the death of her two sons from her mind—and it was probably the spark that ignited all of her succeeding breakdowns and a big reason behind her inability to deal effectively with her life.

Turning her attention to Lana, Katie wondered what was in store for her. How would she cope with the culpability she was bound to feel? True, the baby did not die directly at her hands, but rather through indirect delinquency on her part. Katie thought maybe that was the reason why Lana was standing there instead of locked up somewhere in a mental hospital. She wondered if that was the variable that would give peace to her life. Katie didn't know how she could come close to absolving herself of wrongdoing in the death of an innocent child who relied on her parents to protect her. Was Nan better off than Lana in that she had the ability to bury her guilt deep in the confines of her subconscious so it only surfaced occasionally, or was Lana better off because she faced it realistically—attending the funeral, seeing all of the people, talking, even about the incident, discussing Janie's antics while she was alive, at times even laughing through her tears?

Katie thought maybe Lana was in fact guiltier of a crime than her mom was. After all Nan was supposedly out of her mind when she killed or tried to hurt people—so they said—and was unaware of what she was doing. Lana on the other hand was perfectly sane, and yet she let Janie roam around the yard unattended for hours at a time. So, was she really as sane as she appeared to be? Just because Lana appeared to be in control of herself and didn't need shots or pills to get her through the ordeal of losing her baby didn't mean she was mentally sound; on the contrary, she could be just as sick as Nan only she was able to handle it in a more capable way—a way that was more acceptable to society.

Confused and frustrated, Katie abruptly got up and walked outside into the miserably hot, humid air. It hit her like a brick but it still felt better than watching the drama inside.

A few days after Janie's funeral, Katie's life was jolted again when she learned that her fourteen-year-old cousin drowned while swimming at the beach. They suspected he suffered a severe cramp and went down quickly even though he was an excellent swimmer. It was a sad funeral and her heart went out to her aunt and uncle. She thought it wasn't fair that they should have to suffer the loss of a child especially when it wasn't their fault. There was one fact Katie knew for certain—life was very unfair.

It was the first time Katie noticed the small growths on Nan's eyelids as they fluttered; they looked like whiteheads only they were brown. She would find out much later they were skin tags; she thought they were gross. Pressing the bottle of rubbing alcohol into her palm Katie let the cool liquid flow into her hands, and gently rubbed it on Nan's freckled arm which was wet with perspiration.

"Now doesn't that feel better? Just relax; I know you are going to be fine this time. We aren't going to let this thing get to you." Sounding more reassuring than she felt, Katie hoped she could talk Nan out of what seemed like another breakdown.

"Look, it's not going to do you any good to get yourself into such a state that you end up in the hospital. I know you don't want that and neither do we. The kids need you around; if it wasn't for you we wouldn't have anyone to take care of us or to talk to." Hoping Nan was still lucid enough that she could understand what she was saying to her, Katie reiterated her last statement. "Did you hear me? We need you!"

"Do you really think so?" Nan sounded like a little girl who had just been told for the first time that she was pretty. Her glassy eyes penetrated Katie's face as she spoke.

"Of course! Without you things would be a real mess around here. Now you have to stop dwelling on stuff that makes you nervous and concentrate on happy things so you stay healthy for us. Did you take your pills?"

Nan's hand went up to her forehead and she rubbed at it in obvious confusion. "Gee, I don't remember."

"Wait, I'll get them and a glass of water." After the funerals, Katie saw it coming…all that death brought back the haunting memories. She tried to sympathize a little more with what Nan was going through, and how it felt every time the submerged incident of her sons' deaths fought to overtake her conscious state and destroy her mentally. Katie thought how much better it would have been if she had been made to deal with it right away—accept it, talk about it, admit it, whatever it took to bring it out in the open. Instead, the lives of her little brothers had been crushed out like the cigarettes their mother smoked. It was as if they never existed. She thought about how many times she wanted to talk about the whole thing, even listen to Nan's side of the story—find out why she did what she did.

She wanted to know more about the boys; especially the baby as she hardly knew anything about him. She would like to have discussed her dreams, especially the one she had often and which terrified her the most…watching her mother pick up Kevin to throw him out the window as he pleaded with Katie to help him. At first she was sure she hadn't even been in the bedroom when Kevin was killed; lately she wasn't so sure.

She wondered if Nan could tell her what it felt like to have a nervous breakdown. She realized of course that she couldn't ask her mother any of those things. She was certain her continued fragile mental state was due to the fact that she was carrying around the burden of the entire incident hidden somewhere deep inside her. Katie couldn't risk discussing it with her; she would probably crack up for good. She didn't want to have to fill Nan's shoes for even a week or two, especially not now when her life was too busy with other important things. It would be very inconvenient to have to deal with taking care of the house and kids at this time.

With the help of the tranquilizers she resumed taking and Katie's reassuring words, Nan slowly regained enough control of herself so she could function without being hospitalized. With great relief Katie withdrew herself once again from the family problems and charged headlong into her own life.

Each time she and Ben went out Katie talked him into letting her drive.

"Keep the wheel still; don't turn it so much. The car will stay on a straight path that way. Now ease your foot up and down on the gas pedal. That's better. See the difference? The car is riding much smoother. No! You're doing it again. You're still jerking the car. Relax, damn it!" It always ended the same way with Ben yelling and Katie convinced she would never learn to drive.

"It's pointless; I'm never going to get the hang of this." Turning the wheel sharply, Katie brought her foot down too hard on the brake causing the car to come to an abrupt stop.

"Jeez, you almost gave me whiplash." Throwing his head back against the seat of the car, Ben wiped his brow in mock relief. "I told you not to make sharp movements with the wheel. I'm glad I'm still in one piece after that."

"I'm not going to pass the road test," Katie whined as she pulled the car off the road.

"That's what you said about the written test and you aced it. But this car is too hard for you to drive. You need a smaller car with power steering, like the ones in school."

"Yeah, they are easier to drive, but I only practice in them a couple of minutes twice a week and the course is almost over. We haven't even done parallel parking yet. I don't know what I'm going to do."

"Don't worry about it. You have plenty of time to get a license. There's no big rush."

"Maybe you don't think so, but my birthday is in a couple of weeks and I want to get my license as soon as I can." The truth was she was terrified of ending up like her mother, always depending on someone to take her places. She was determined not to be a burden on anyone.

Smiling mischievously, Ben began to play with Katie's arm, causing a prickling sensation in her groin as he bent over to kiss her, invading her mouth with his tongue—something he had obviously learned on his date with Dina, the kissing expert. The last couple of times, instead of keeping her tongue pressed tightly against the base of her mouth, Katie had begun touching his tongue with her own. She was surprised at how good it felt when their tongues met and entwined.

"How do you like French kissing, Katie?"

"Is that what it's called? It's okay, I guess."

"Gee, you could be a little more enthusiastic."

"I'm sorry, Ben. I'm still upset about this driving business. You don't realize how important it is to me. It's more than important; it's vital." The idea that she might not get her license soon, or at all, left Katie feeling totally helpless. She hated relying completely on Ben to practice driving and wished her father would offer to help; of course she hadn't asked him and never would.

The painful throbbing in her mouth started suddenly and persisted all night until she couldn't stand it any longer. Her body ached from a long night of tossing and turning. Twice she had gotten up and crushed an aspirin with a spoon, rubbing the granules on her gums in the area of the pain and gagging from the bitter taste. When the morning light told her it was time to get up for school, she remained in bed holding her swollen cheek.

As she entered the room and picked Carrie up out of the crib Nan noticed Katie was still in bed.

"What's the matter with you, Katie?"

"I have a toothache. I can't stand it a minute longer. Please, can you call a dentist?"

"We really don't know any dentists. Did you take some aspirin?

"Yes, and it didn't help at all." Katie took a deep breath against the onslaught of excruciating pain which began in her mouth and shot up slowly and agonizingly to the top of her head.

"Oh...oh, I mean it. You've got to get me to a doctor. Ohhhhhh... please!" Nan became more alarmed when she saw Katie's face. It was more than her cheek that was swollen—the whole side of her face was distorted.

"I'll see what I can do." A couple of minutes after she left the room Katie heard her mother on the phone.

"Okay, thanks. We'll be there in about an hour. I really appreciate the appointment, especially on such short notice, but I think it really is an emergency." Immediately Nan got back on the phone and asked Anna if she would watch the kids for awhile.

"Katie, get up and get dressed. Anna gave me the name of a dentist and he'll see you in an hour. She's coming over for the children. Hurry...we have to walk into town."

"Oh, thank God!" Once outside, Katie pressed a diaper to her face to prevent the cool fall air from invading her mouth and causing further pain.

"You haven't had a bad toothache like this before, have you?" It was difficult to talk, so Katie only nodded in answer to Nan's question. Her mom obviously didn't remember the time she had her teeth pulled at the hospital and had the terrible dream while she was under anesthesia; maybe she was even in the hospital during that crisis. She wondered if she would have to have a tooth pulled again today. She didn't even care whether she did or how bad the dreams were, as long as she didn't have to suffer anymore.

It was a beautiful fall day even though it was completely lost on Katie. Nan talked about how much she was enjoying the walk and the respite from the kids. Before they left the house, Nan had dutifully taken her pills and was feeling more peaceful with each step she took. The serenity the pills gave her helped ease the constant disappointment of her unhappy life. Even if the euphoria was drug induced it was better than the tension and anxiety she felt without them. When she slipped her hand around Katie's arm in an attempt to draw her closer, she noticed her daughter's arm stiffened instantly at her touch. Nan was undeterred however, and continued to hold onto Katie until they arrived at the dentist's office. By the time she sat in the dental chair, a half hour after arriving at the office, Katie was sick to her stomach and felt like she was dying.

"Young lady, I'm afraid the tooth is going to have to come out."

"Take it out; I don't care. Will the pain go away?"

"Yes, it will…eventually. The tooth is abscessed—that's why your face is so swollen. Because of the infection the extraction will be more painful, but everything should get back to normal once the tooth is out."

"Are you going to do it now?"

"You bet, as soon as I give you a shot."

"You're not going to put me to sleep?"

"No, we don't do that too much anymore."

"What does the shot do?"

"It numbs the mouth so you don't feel the pain. When was the last time you were at the dentist?"

"I've never been to a dentist's office. A long time ago I went to the hospital to get a couple of teeth pulled. It was really terrible."

"I bet it was. Well, this shot will numb you and you can watch me just in case I make any mistakes." She felt a few tugs on her mouth and before she knew it, he told her he was finished.

"No kidding? That didn't hurt at all." He tapped Katie's shoulder affectionately and asked her to stay in the chair while he got her mom.

"Mrs. Ramie, your daughter's mouth is in very bad shape. Without taking x-rays I can see at least three other teeth that probably can't be saved with fillings and need to be removed." As she overheard the conversation taking place outside the door, Katie stiffened.

"She also has at least four teeth that need fillings as soon as possible. After that, she will need bridge work and caps. Right now though, she needs a few weeks to recover from the extraction I did today. I want you to fill this prescription for the infection as soon as possible." The dentist noticed he didn't have the mother's full attention, so he turned his attention back to Katie.

"Now young lady, you should be feeling better as the day goes on. You will experience some pain as the shot wears off but that will go away eventually. Don't drink anything hot or cold for a couple of hours and then only liquids for the rest of the day. Because of the infection I want you to take some pills that should get rid of it. If you feel more pain in the next couple of days, I want you to call me. It could mean the infection is not clearing up. Do you understand?" Through the mound of bloodstained cotton in her mouth Katie unsuccessfully tried to respond to the doctor's question.

"Oh, I'm sorry. Here, let me take that out now. The bleeding seems to have stopped, but I'm going to put a clean piece of cotton over the gum anyway. You may feel a little bit of nausea from the blood you swallowed." As she looked into the doctor's blue eyes Katie fell in love.

"I'll be back," she garbled. "I don't want to get another toothache like that again. Thanks." She and Nan left the office after Nan told the receptionist to send the bill to the house. Even with a diaper wrapped around her head and a wad of blood-soaked cotton stuffed in her mouth Katie felt absolutely wonderful. The pain was gone and in its place she felt only a heavenly numbness. As she walked she thought about the health class the school gave last semester, and how everyone worried about the part of it where they separated the girls and boys and talked about periods and stuff like that. What disturbed Katie more than anything, however, were the pictures of people who had neglected their teeth. Now that the dentist had confirmed her teeth were in bad shape, she worried about losing them and looking ugly like the people in the movie. Later as she drifted into blissful sleep, she vowed to herself she would get her teeth fixed no matter what.

The prescription the doctor gave Nan for Katie went unfilled; luckily Katie's immune system was able to deal with the infection without antibiotics. A few weeks after the extraction, Katie asked Nan if she could go back to the dentist.

"I'm sorry, Katie, here's the bill. I've been meaning to give it to you…its twenty-five dollars. You'll have to pay it. We really can't afford to have you see a dentist."

"You mean I have to wait until I get another toothache like the last one?" There was no sense in arguing; Katie knew what the situation was. She knew there was no extra money for luxuries like the dentist. She vowed that as soon as she had some money she would get her teeth fixed. First, she had to get her driver's license and a car.

Even though Ben was the treasurer of the senior class, it was Katie who devised the plan for collecting the dues and it was Katie who monitored the books. She felt it would be less of a hardship for her fellow classmates to pay their dues in increments rather than in one lump sum. One morning a week the homeroom captains collected installment payments on the dues from their classmates and gave them to Katie, who entered the figures in a log book. She then turned the money over to Mr. Day, the chairman of the Distributive Education program, who deposited the cash in the class bank account. The dues were used for various activities including senior week, which consisted of the prom, a class trip, the senior follies, and an awards ceremony.

It started out as an unacceptable thought in the back of her mind. But as her own monetary pressures increased, it became a justifiable solution to her problems. Why shouldn't she help herself to a few dollars here or there? With all the work she was doing and had done for her class she deserved a little reward. It wasn't like she was spending it on nonsense, and besides, she would pay it back.

Katie made an appointment with the dentist when one of her wisdom teeth started bothering her, and walked to his office by herself one day after school. She paid him ten dollars of her precious savings which she kept with her at all times, and promised to pay him the rest of the money before her next appointment, which was scheduled for a month from that date. She had saved nothing close to the amount of money she needed for a car and insurance. The small amount of money she was making working after school a couple of hours a day didn't go very far, especially now that she had to take care of all the expenses connected with being a senior. She wanted a class ring in the worst way, but it appeared to be entirely out of the question...that is until she decided to borrow some of the senior dues money.

The next time she collected the money from the homeroom captains she entered the correct installments in the log book, counted up the cash, and then removed ten dollars for herself. When she presented the total cash received to Mr. Day, she quoted him the amount that was left after she removed the ten dollars.

As the weeks went by she became more comfortable about taking a couple of dollars, each time the dues were collected. She convinced herself Mr. Day wasn't going to ask for her log book so he could balance it against the actual cash received. She deserved it; she was a hard worker; she did everything for the class. If it wasn't for her they wouldn't even be having a senior week. It if wasn't for her family being so poor she wouldn't have to borrow any money. If it wasn't for all of her brothers and sisters she could afford a class ring. Yes, a ring would be a great gift from her class to her for all of her hard work. She deserved it.

Mr. Day trusted Katie implicitly and nominated her for the outstanding Distributive Education student, an honor which would get her a medal and certificate at the senior awards ceremony. The dues were coming in better than ever thanks to Katie's plan to collect the money in installments. He thought it was a superb idea.

When Ben got a look at Katie in her new red suit, he whistled loudly.

"You have a great chance of being picked, Katie. I just know it, especially in that outfit. You look like a Valentine."

"Are you sure, Ben?"

"Positive."

"Thanks for nominating me. I really would like to be the Varsity Club queen." She was nervous, but she needed to keep her calm while being interviewed by the members of the club which consisted of all of the male athletes in the school. She thought she deserved to buy the new suit for her interview; after all if she was going to be their queen, she would have to dress appropriately.

After the interview was over, Ben joined Katie in the hallway. "You did fantastic, I swear. I'm so proud of you." Ben lifted Katie up off the ground and hugged her tightly. "I just know you're going to win."

A couple of days later while attending a dance, Katie was stunned when another classmate was chosen as queen of the Varsity Club. Ben immediately leaned over and whispered in Katie's ear. "They felt you won too many things; they wanted to give someone else a chance."

Katie saw it differently—it was a defining moment that convinced her God was punishing her for taking the senior dues money for her own purposes. She immediately began to pay back the money she took even though it wiped out most of her savings and eliminated totally her visits to the dentist. She felt much better about herself once the senior log book was balanced.

"I'm so nervous I can't think straight. Wait a minute; I don't have my birth certificate." For the second time she ran back into the house to collect a forgotten item and returned to Ben's car out of breath.

"You're going to do just fine, Katie, don't worry. I'll tell you what. Why don't you drive up to the motor vehicle building? It will be good practice for you."

"Okay, but I sure wish I had your confidence, Ben. I just know I'm going to fail." It was a warm day in November shortly after Katie's seventeenth birthday. Her pants were sticking to the seat of the car, and her perspiring hands slipped as they gripped the wheel. She felt unsure of herself and nervous driving Ben's car.

Three days later, Katie's world was shattered when the official notice that she had failed the driving test arrived. She guessed she had done miserably, but she was hoping for a miracle. She could not be consoled.

"Sometimes they like to fail people on the first try just for the hell of it."

"Oh, Ben, that's not true at all. I just can't drive. I'll never get my license. I'm going to be just like my mother."

"Don't be silly. You can take it again."

"No, I'll probably just mess it up. I must have been three feet away from the curb when I parallel parked, and I'm sure I didn't come to a complete stop at the stop sign. I could scream…I'm so mad." Nobody could understand how important it was to her to get her license. Being able to drive was the key to freedom, something she had to have…and quickly.

"Well, I was talking to my mom about it, and she says you should take the test in a car with power steering like her Lark. It's much easier to park and so small that you can handle it better. She said she would take you out in it to practice if you wanted to."

"You're kidding, Ben…did she really? I can't believe she'd actually do that for me. Why even my own father…" The words were too bitter to relay and she stopped speaking in mid-sentence; besides Ben knew it all anyway. For the first time in days she felt a glimmer of hope.

Unfortunately winter was approaching, and Katie only got a couple of sessions of driving practice with Ben's mother before the weather got bad, and it would be early spring before they resumed.

"I'm really sorry, Katie. I know it doesn't console you much to hear me say I feel helpless and frustrated that I couldn't get you a scholarship so that you could attend college. You're one of the brightest girls to graduate from this school." As Mr. Cummings, the senior guidance counselor, rose from his desk, Katie nodded miserably.

"You see, when you decided to take business courses instead of college preparatory classes, you diminished your chances of receiving a scholarship based on academic grades. So even though your grade point average is outstanding, you don't have the appropriate courses to qualify you for a full scholarship to a college."

Katie had received a PTA scholarship award of $1,000, provided she used it to attend college full-time, and it had brought her to Mr. Cummings to see if it was possible for her to go to college. After filling out some applications, she was accepted at a small upstate New York college, but they did not offer scholarships to females and the cost of tuition was exorbitant.

"Would it be possible for you to attend one of the community colleges in the area full time? I'm sure we could get you some kind of monetary grant for that although it wouldn't be much."

"Gee, Mr. Cummings, I don't know. I'm absolutely positive my parents won't be able to help with money, and I don't think I could attend school full time and work enough hours to pay for school and a car...and anyway—" Katie lowered her head and picked at her skirt.

"Yes, go on Katie. You seem to be bothered by something."

"Well, I'm really nervous about college. I know I don't have the background, so it probably will be more difficult for me to get good grades. My goodness, I spend so much time studying in order to do as well as I do in high school. If I have to go to school full time and work too, I don't think I could do it. I need...I mean...I want to do great if I go, but where am I going to get the money to pay for it and all the other things I need, too? You know I've been offered a job in the front office here and I'm thinking seriously about taking it."

"Yes, I heard. I'm delighted we might be able to keep you around here. There's nobody who works harder than you do, and it would be great to see your smiling face every day."

"Thanks. I really appreciate everything you have done for me. I guess I should have made up my mind about college a lot sooner. I might have had a better chance at a full scholarship."

"Well, Katie, if it will make you feel better not many people get scholarships to college. As a matter of fact we weren't able to get any full scholarships for academic excellence this year, and we have never had a full scholarship offered to a female." Katie's eyes widened at that news.

"Three or four people, including your boyfriend Ben, have managed to get their education completely financed by a university, and that was for athletic achievement. So it would have been almost impossible for you to get a free education no matter how soon in the game you began preparation. Even Walter Zulkowsky—you know him I'm sure, number one in your class—even he has to foot the bill for his education."

"Whew! What a surprise. I just assumed with his brains any university would be glad to have him."

"Oh, sure. He's been accepted to a dozen or more places, but his parents will pay through the nose for his education. Why don't you think about going to school part-time, maybe at night? If you really want to get a college education, you can do it."

"I'll think about it. Thanks, thanks so much." She did think about her situation but all it succeeded in doing was increasing her animosity toward Nan and Jack. She hadn't even discussed the scholarship offer with them. She knew there wasn't a chance they would be able to help her further her education. Not once during high school had they mentioned anything about her going to college, and it was obvious to Katie they weren't the least bit interested in her future. She did have the offer of the job at the school and she was grateful for that.

Thanks to Ben's mother Katie got her driver's license in early spring. She was never more excited in her whole life and she immediately began looking for a car.

"Go ahead, Katie, give it to him." As Katie reluctantly handed the fifty dollars to Tory, Jonathan's eyes glistened with excitement. It was half of what she had saved since paying back the money she took from the senior dues, and she hoped the car she had purchased from a neighbor, with Jonathan's encouragement, was worth the price. A musty smell filled her nostrils as she turned the key to the engine, but it was the most beautifully repugnant odor she had ever inhaled. The exhilaration she felt was almost unbearable as she maneuvered the car down the familiar streets.

A few weeks later, Katie made her first major purchase for the car.

"I don't believe you did that, Katie. You spent more for tires than you did for the car." Ben was laughing hysterically as he held his stomach. "Did you hear that, Jonathan?"

"Why did you do that, stupid? You're not supposed to pay a lot of money for parts for an old car." Jonathan looked annoyingly at his sister as he continued to yell. "Geez…you girls don't know anything. Why didn't you ask before you did a dumb thing like that?"

"I don't know. I thought it was okay. You said I needed new tires badly and I got them. I was kind of shocked when they charged me sixty dollars. Don't you think they look nice, though?"

"Nice? They are the best tires you can buy, but not for a fifty dollar car." As Ben shook his head Katie realized that freedom had a lot of expenses attached to it, and keeping the car repaired and filled with gas was enough to deplete her small earnings. Jack had also made it clear he would carry

Katie on his car insurance policy only until she graduated from school which was just a few months away, and then she would have to pay for car insurance herself. Still, she was grateful for that little bit of assistance from him.

Katie was under stress to save as much as possible for car insurance, and she was discovering much to her dismay that having a car didn't really make much of a difference in her life. As a matter of fact it was causing her quite a few problems financially, and Nan relied on her to run errands all the time which put additional pressure on her already overextended schedule. She now was sure nothing in her life turned out the way she wanted it too—nothing.

"Hi, Katie. Listen, about tonight, I can't pick you up. My boss wants me to work until four-thirty. Can you drive over to my house for dinner, and then we can drop your car off at your house on the way to the movies?"

"Are you sure it's okay for me to eat dinner at your house?"

"Of course. My parents are expecting you." There was always so much activity going on in the O'Riley household that it was an interesting place to visit, and the meals Ben's mom cooked included fresh Italian bread, real butter, and homemade pies—all of Katie's favorites.

Later in her car on the way to Ben's house, she recalled the frightening walks to and from school and cheerleading that were now just bitter memories. She thought if it wasn't for Ben's mom, she would still be walking everywhere. A feeling of contempt for her parents was slowly diminishing her good mood. She tried to concentrate on other things instead of dwelling on the past. As Ben's house came into view, Katie marveled at the beautiful lawn that was a far cry from the dirt and weeds that made up her front yard. How she wished she lived in a house like Ben's. She couldn't imagine what it would be like to be proud of where you lived rather than trying to hide it from everyone. She hoped someday she would have a house like that.

It was just about dusk when they left Ben's house satiated from a wonderful meal, each in their own car. Ben pulled out ahead of Katie and gradually gained a good distance on her, eventually disappearing from sight.

Just as she turned on to one of the back roads leading to her house, Katie's car sputtered and came to a halt. As she pondered what to do, Katie put her head on the steering wheel. She was sure Ben would be there as soon as he realized she was not behind him, but five minutes passed with no sign of him and it was now dark. She continued to search the road frantically for his car, anticipation turning to anger at the realization he had not come looking for her.

Another ten minutes passed, and then through the rearview mirror she caught a glimpse of a vehicle pulling up behind her. Goosebumps appeared on her arm when she realized it was not Ben's car, but a black truck from which a burly man departed heading in her direction. When she realized it was too late to close the window against the rapidly approaching stranger, Katie panicked.

"What's the matter here? Are you okay?" His voice was husky and matched his overall appearance, but he seemed like he really wanted to help.

"I don't really know. My car just died on me."

"Let me see if I can start it. Move over!" Before Katie could think about it, he was in the car, sitting behind the steering wheel, and pumping the gas pedal.

"Looks like you've run out of gas, girlie. Don't you check your gas gage occasionally?" His dark eyes stared menacingly at her sending shivers up and down her spine.

"I've only had the car for a short time. I…I didn't think to look at it. I guess I was lower on gas than I thought."

"You got a couple of bucks? I've got a can. I'll go get you some gas." Immediately Katie fumbled in her purse for money.

"Yes, I do. Oh, how nice of you to do this. I'm sorry to impose on you."

"You better lock your doors until I get back." With that, the good samaritan sauntered back to his truck and took off in a hurry.

In the confines of the car with darkness all around her, Katie wondered furiously where Ben was. He should certainly know by now that something was wrong. Ten minutes later, when the now familiar truck pulled up behind her again, Katie actually breathed a sigh of relief. She thought for sure he might not come back. He could have taken her money and disappeared leaving her stranded. As he attached a nozzle to the gas can and opened the gas tank cap to deposit the liquid into it, he whistled happily.

When he was done, he approached the window on the driver's side and tapped on it with his knuckles. As soon as Katie opened the window halfway to thank him with a big smile on her face, he reached his chubby hand down and unlocked the door. Before Katie could protest his actions, he threw his huge torso in the front seat of the car forcing her to move over.

""I…I really think it will start now. You've been kind enough, but I think I can drive it myself." He ignored her comments and turned the key to the ignition as Katie said a prayer the car would start. It did.

"Oh great, it started. Thank you so much." As Katie faced him directly, her innocent eyes showing the thanks she felt, an alarm sounded within her. The smell had been there all along, but it hadn't registered until that moment. She had been so concerned over the car. As he turned toward her to speak, the pungent odor of alcohol made her flinch.

"Let's make sure this baby doesn't give you any more trouble. I'll drive up here a little ways."

"No!" The word came out much more harshly than she had intended. "Really, it seems to be working just fine now. Thank you so—" Before she got the words out he leaned toward her, his arms outstretched.

"This is the kind of thanks I really want." As his big arms locked around Katie, his fat, ugly lips came down on hers. She was barely able to breath from the horrible stench of alcohol and cigarettes on his breath and the hold he had on her mouth. She tried to push him away but was no match for his strength. Suddenly he stopped kissing her and brought the foul wetness of his mouth down to her throat. When he did that Katie screamed.

"Leave me alone, let me go!" Shoving the attacker with all her might, Katie wondered if she was really making any noise as she screamed again. "My boyfriend should be here any minute. I was following him…and by now he is looking for me!"

"Okay, kid, shut up. That's all I wanted anyway, a nice, big, fat kiss."

As Katie covered her face with her hands he let himself out the door. When she finally had the courage to uncover her eyes he was gone, and she couldn't believe her luck. Frantically she rolled up the window and locked the door, but she was shaking so violently she couldn't get the car out of park and into drive. As her head fell against the steering wheel, she said another prayer for the strength to get out of there. "Calm down, Katie, calm down," she said to herself over and over. "Now get the hell out of here quickly before he comes back."

Lifting her head she looked in the mirror to make sure he wasn't behind her again, and with trance-like movements began driving the car home. She didn't even hear the horns that blared from the aggravated drivers trying to pass her as she crawled along the road at five miles an hour.

As she turned the car into her street, she caught a glimpse of two people standing in front of her house talking to each other. As she edged her car up against the curb, she realized through her haziness that it was Ben talking to Jonathan. She felt so weak she could barely push the door open and put her feet on the ground. She used the car door to support her while she stood up, but the words that sounded in her ear stunned her, sending the adrenaline flowing through her veins.

"Hey, what took you so long? We missed the damn movie, you know." Katie swung her pocketbook wildly as she flung herself at Ben.

"You big idiot! Why didn't you come looking for me?" Both her fist and her pocketbook landed on his chest at the same time, and he and Jonathan listened stoically as she whimpered.

"I almost got raped. My car ran out of gas. Why didn't you come looking for me? What did you think I was doing out there?" Heaving, she turned and ran into the house, but before she reached the bedroom she thought she heard a squealing sound. As Katie's composure returned and she realized she was okay, she began to evaluate the situation. She was sure Ben felt very bad about what happened. He was supposed to protect her, instead he was shooting the bull with Jonathan while she was in trouble. By the time Ben and Jonathan came into the house a half-hour later, Katie was almost fully recovered.

"We couldn't find the creep." Exhibiting his characteristic macho image, Ben popped out his chest as he strode toward Katie.

"How did you expect to find him? You didn't even ask me what he looked like or what kind of car he was driving." Her voice quivered unexpectedly. "I don't understand you at all. I disappear for almost an hour when I'm supposed to be following you home. I'm in an old car and it's pitch black outside, and you don't bother to come looking for me. Don't you care what happens to me?"

"I thought you stopped for gas." As he became defensive, Ben's chin hardened.

"Five minutes maybe; but how could you justify a whole hour to get gas especially when I knew we had to hurry to make the movie as it was?" Suddenly Katie started to laugh.

"You thought I stopped for gas, did you? Well, I did—the hard way." It seemed like a necessary part of the recovery process—she needed to laugh.

"Well, what do you want to do now?" As he spoke, he didn't look as big in stature to her anymore. She wondered if that was because he hadn't come to her rescue. She could feel one of her blue moods coming on. Since her discussion with the school counselor she was even more prone to depression than she was before, basically because she was now certain she had no future.

"I don't feel like going anywhere tonight." Actually she would have preferred it if he stuck around to comfort her, telling her over and over again how sorry he was, but instead he seized the opportunity and was gone before she finished with her own thoughts, leaving her in an extremely pitiable state.

As graduation approached Katie was often in a sullen mood, sulking for days at a time without any explanation, and not understanding the reason for her moroseness except that she felt sorry for herself. In school she put on a brave face, and no one would have guessed she was depressed in any way. What Katie needed, no one could help her with—no one could help her overcome the feelings of insecurity and unhappiness that plagued her. She had to do it herself but she seemed incapable of it, especially now that high school was ending and she was becoming more desperate by the minute about her future.

As she ran to catch the bus Katie's bladder felt like it was going to explode every time her feet touched the ground, and a painful burning sensation began to work its way up to her stomach.

"Come on, Miss Ramie, we're ready to go!" A frown crossed the vice-principal's face as she stood in the doorway of the bus. Katie couldn't believe they were upset about waiting two minutes for her to get the attendance list, especially when she had put the whole event together without any help. Senior week—what a laugh that was. Katie thought it would be a great idea to have a whole week of special activities for the graduates. It was great all right—great for everyone but her.

Once she was seated on the bus, she looked down at her hands which were streaked with blue mimeograph ink from making copies of the list. She felt like a wet dishrag as she huddled her tired body against the seat of the bus and took in a long breath against the pain of neglect she felt in her gut. She should have stopped at the bathroom when she had the chance. She was glad this was the last event with only graduation to go. As she closed her eyes, the past week flashed before her like a movie on a screen. The first image was of Ben driving his car to the beach with Katie sitting next to him.

"Hurry, Ben, or we won't be able to catch up with them. What's the matter?" Katie noticed Ben's car slowing down.

"Christ, there's something wrong with the car." Ben pulled over to the side of the road just as the car died.

"Oh no!" Katie clenched her fists. A caravan of about one-hundred members of the senior class were on their way to a beach party which Katie had arranged, when Ben's car broke down. Katie was incredulous as she watched their friends pass them by and disappear out of sight. She was instantly sorry she had suggested the outing to begin with.

It wasn't until later after Ben miraculously got the car started again and they were back on the road that Katie realized there was no hope of finding the group. They had not decided on an exact place for the beach party. She realized she shouldn't have divided up the food, that she should have kept it all. Maybe someone would have stopped to help them. She didn't even know what they ended up with, but it couldn't be much.

Ben hit his hand hard against the steering wheel in annoyance as he made his third run down the beach searching for familiar cars. "Well, what do you think we should do now?" he moaned.

"I think it's useless to look for them anymore. We could drive up and down the beach like this all day and never find them. This is a big place and for all we know they could even be at another beach." Unable to control her rage, Katie slapped the car seat as she spoke.

"They cheated me. After all the work I did planning this, how could they go off and leave us? All I want to do is go home. No, I really don't want to do that either. Ben, why don't you see what we finally ended up with in the back of the car?" After bringing the car to an abrupt halt and opening up the trunk Ben gave Katie the bad news.

"Some blankets, charcoal, and a box of cookies. Just great. We'll really get far on this stuff, won't we?" As he shoved a cookie in his mouth, he continued. "Let's find a refreshment stand and get some food. I'm starving."

Later as she nibbled on a hot dog, Katie's anger increased. "Oh, I'm so ticked off. I swear, I'd like to kill every last one of them for spoiling our day."

"Ah…let's try to forget it. I feel better now that I've eaten. Why don't we take a walk on the beach?" Ben shoved the last of the three hot dogs he had bought for lunch in his mouth.

"Okay, why not." The turbulent surf roared and Katie felt in union with the ocean as it projected her mood. "My goodness it sure is cold by the water. I didn't realize it would be this chilly." She wrapped her arms around herself trying to keep warm.

"It's a little too early for the beach, but I love it like this when it's isolated. Let's go by those rocks and sit; it won't be as windy." Once they were settled Ben draped one of the blankets he had been carrying around her shoulders, and she welcomed the warmth it instantly provided. She began to feel strangely calm; this alien feeling surprised her.

"Gosh, it's nice just sitting here. Finally I don't feel rushed or pressured." With her feet buried in the sand, arms wrapped around her knees under the protection of the blanket, staring out at the magnificent ocean Katie contentedly enjoyed the isolation. But Ben had other plans as he spread the second blanket he had carried with him behind them and plopped down next to Katie.

"Are you still upset?" In a gesture of affection Ben touched her face as he spoke. It was the only part of her body that was exposed.

"No, not anymore. I feel pretty good as a matter of fact. You know, I think I've worked too hard at being president of the class...and treasurer, too!" As soon as she saw the look on Ben's face she knew she shouldn't have said it.

"I didn't ask you to do my job for me, Katie."

"I know, but it wouldn't have gotten done if I hadn't taken care of it."

"You'd be surprised, Katie. You're not the only one who can do things well you know." He didn't want to talk about it anymore, and Ben made his intentions known by wrapping his arms around Katie. However, she wanted desperately to continue the conversation—it was all she could do to keep from screaming out her hurt to the world, she was so frustrated with her life. She was bitter that she couldn't go to college; that she wasn't enjoying herself like all the other seniors were. She wondered what she was going to do with herself after graduation. She was probably the only one in her class who was going to stay at the high school. What a loser she was. She was smart, popular, not at all lazy, and supposedly everything a great high school student should be. But what did all the hard work get her? Nothing—absolutely nothing.

She was surprised when she felt Ben's lips on hers, and her body stiffened once again as he gently pushed her back onto the blanket. She was enjoying the kiss for awhile until she felt Ben tugging on her clothes.

"Katie, help me. Don't worry, there's nobody around."

"No, Ben, we can't do this. Not here."

"Shit!" Standing up quickly Ben tore off what remained of his clothing until he had stripped to his bathing suit, and darted into the icy water. The serenity Katie had known just minutes before could not be recaptured. It was the story of her life so it seemed…a few brief moments of happiness here and there that were always being taken away from her abruptly and completely.

The pungent odor of diesel fuel from the bus brought Katie back to the present. A tinge of car sickness engulfed her and she shut her eyes again, this time reminiscing about the senior frolics.

The pretty blonde girl angrily approached Katie, dabbing at her eyes with a tissue. "Why didn't you let us perform?"

"I'm sorry, Kathy. The show was running late; they made us stop. Didn't you hear Ms. Novak come back and tell us to end it right away?" Katie felt terrible that three groups did not get to perform. It had been a long night, she was tired, and there was still the dance to contend with, but her classmate continued screaming at her between sobs.

"You got yourself out on stage though, didn't you?" We practiced every day for a whole week for nothing. Do you hear me…for nothing!"

"Look, I know how you feel. I only went out on stage to announce the show was over, and I sang my song as everyone left the auditorium just like we planned. Kathy, if I had let your group perform, the principal would have cut us off altogether, and that wouldn't have been fair to the other acts. Please try to understand."

The throbbing pain in her head was getting worse. She still hadn't recovered from the pie-throwing incident. What a surprise that had been. She agreed to participate in one of the acts, never suspecting her classmates had conspired to throw a pie in her face, mimicking a popular comedic gimmick of the day. The skit had been a huge success, and her classmates roared with laughter watching their class president react in horror to the deluge of shaving cream that covered her from head to foot.

Katie hated the idea of anyone being unhappy about anything she did, and it ruined the night for her. In hindsight she should have had the three remaining groups come on stage and alternate performing while the audience was disbanding, but when she was informed the show had to end immediately, she didn't have time to think about strategy. Well, so much for the senior frolics.

Originally she planned the event with enthusiasm, thinking it would be great fun for members of the class to entertain their fellow classmates on stage, after which there would be a dance with refreshments. She didn't expect it to turn into an anxiety-ridden experience as she dealt with choosing the acts from among her friends, and then contending with rehearsals every day without any previous experience in stage production. It was amazing the show had any semblance of organization when it was finally ready to be presented. The dance was in full swing when Katie entered the gymnasium.

"The show was great, Katie. You did a wonderful job."

"Nice going, Katie. We had a fantastic time. You were hysterical when you got hit with that pie…we loved it!"

"You're a good sport, Katie. Not everyone would still be smiling after getting a pie thrown in their face."

"You sing really nice, Katie. I had no idea."

Even Mrs. Curley joined in the accolades. "Katie, you really surprised us. What a nice voice you have. My goodness, you're just loaded with talent. 'Teenager in Love' is one of my favorite songs, too."

But the praise she received didn't help ease the guilt she felt about the kids who had been shut out of performing that night.

The next day Katie was informed that the red velvet stage curtain had been ruined in the pie throwing incident, and the class would have to pay to get it cleaned. She knew it was her punishment for what happened the night before—for not letting the show continue until the last few acts were done even if it meant getting in trouble with the principal.

Someone on the bus started a sing along, jarring Katie from her thoughts. Fixing her eyes solemnly on the couple necking in the seat across from her, she drifted back in time once again to the senior prom.

"You're going to be sorry, I'm telling you. Don't you know you're not supposed to do anything different with your hair before a big event?" Since Katie started going steady with Ben, Elaine very rarely got to talk to her, and when she did the aloofness was evident in her voice and actions.

"But I'm sick of it like this." She ran her hands through her mousy brown, shoulder-length hair which was hanging limply from the day's activities, and continued speaking in despair. "I need a change, and anyway short hair is really in now."

Despite all the warnings about it, Katie made an appointment for her first ever professional hair cut at a beauty parlor. As soon as she looked in the mirror after she was done, she knew she had made a big mistake. Her hair looked terrible, and there wasn't enough of it left to work with to make it look any better.

"Oh, no! What did you do?" As Katie got in Ben's car his eyes blazed with displeasure, and she was so miserable she couldn't even answer him. All of a sudden she was besieged with an urgency to go to the bathroom, and her eyes rolled around in her head as each wave of pain overtook her. The five-minute trip to her house seemed to take an eternity, and just when she thought she couldn't possibly hold it another minute longer she was home.

"I wish you told me you were getting your hair cut. I certainly would have talked you out of it. I hate to say this, but it looked much better long."

"Okay, Ben. I hear you, and I agree. But right now I'm really feeling sick, and if I don't get in the house quickly, I can't guarantee what's going to happen." Nothing—not even the botched haircut—concerned her at that point as she bid Ben a quick goodbye, waddling carefully into the house and toward the bathroom. Unfortunately as luck would have it, somebody was already in it.

Katie leaned her body against the wall and tried not to move or to think as she cried out. "Could you please hurry up in there...please!" A couple of minutes later she got her turn in the bathroom. After that, it was another hour before the pain subsided enough so she could concentrate on getting ready for the prom.

When Ben arrived to pick her up Katie was still not feeling well. She had wanted to look so good for the dance. She wanted to be gorgeous just this once, but everything had gone wrong and now she looked and felt like crap.

"Are you okay, Katie? You look pale?" Ben look very handsome in his tuxedo as he strutted across the living room with a corsage box in his hand. He exuded confidence and that made Katie feel even more inferior.

"I'm doing a lot better now," she mumbled, not wanting to talk about the frequent attacks of diarrhea and accompanying pain that were so mortifying to her.

"You look so handsome." She was painfully aware he hadn't complimented her on how she looked, as she unhappily accepted the blue flowers that matched her dress and his tuxedo and placed the corsage on her wrist.

"I guess we better head out now." Ben was as anxious to get going as Katie was dreading stepping out the door. She was very wrong when she thought things couldn't get any worse that night. By the time she and Ben sat down at their assigned table Katie saw at least eight other girls wearing her dress: three in pink, two in yellow, one in green, and two in lavender. Mercifully she had not seen it in blue...and prayed she wouldn't before the night was over. She berated herself for not realizing the umpire waist dress advertised as the Jackie Kennedy look would be worn by every other girl attending the prom. The fact that it was the cheapest dress in the store and there were loads of them on the rack should have been a tip-off, but Katie was too naïve in the fashion sense to assess a situation like that.

"That's a popular dress you have on, Katie." She felt like crawling into a hole. It had to be bad if Ben, who didn't have a fashion conscious bone in his body, noticed the dress on just about every other girl.

Wishing the night would end quickly, Katie turned her attention to the bandstand where the class advisor was preparing to make the announcement of king and queen of the prom. Katie and Ben were both finalists for the title, but rumors circulated that Ben didn't have a chance of winning because he belonged to a macho clique that was not widely accepted by the entire class. Katie felt like she had won just about every award and was happy to relinquish this title to another deserving couple.

Interestingly enough her homeroom friend with the same name as hers was also in the running—Katie Ramey. There was constant confusion on the part of their teachers and classmates because both names were pronounced exactly the same way. Katie genuinely liked Katie Ramey, a beautiful brunette, and hoped she would win. Her boyfriend, Everett Reber, a sweet boy, had soared to popularity in his senior year as a basketball star and was thought to be a shoe-in for class king.

It was indeed a sad comedy of errors when Katie Ramie and Everett Reber were announced as the prom's royal couple. Katie remained in her seat convinced after hearing Everettt's name that the other Katie had won, and happily watched as they made their way to the podium. The whole room filled with the buzzing sounds of teenagers until the senior class advisor, Mr. Peperline, announced the name of the queen again.

"Katie Ramie…R-A-M-I-E." He spelled it carefully in his typical English teacher fashion, pointing at Katie who was pointing to herself in consternation.

"Yes, you my dear! Come up here, please." Katie wished she could fall through the floor. The last thing she wanted to do was to take her friend's place on the podium. In a daze, Katie brushed past the other girl to receive the pearl crown and gold charm, both of which she and Mr. Peperline purchased earlier in the week not thinking for a minute they would eventually belong to her.

Her hand went up to her mouth in horror when the prince and princess were announced and Ben, the prince, approached the stage and took his place beside Katie Ramey, the princess. She knew then something definitely must have gone wrong with the voting…her classmates must have gotten the names confused and voted for her by mistake. She felt awful. They should have made some distinction between the two Katies on the ballot…Katie Ramie (the blonde), Katie Ramey (the brunette).

She berated herself for making such a huge mistake on the voting sheet and was convinced the outcome couldn't possibly be the way the class wanted it. She even thought about giving the pearl tiara and charm to Katie Ramey right then and there. However, as Mr. Peperline introduced the prince and princess—Ben O'Riley and Katie Ramey, and the king and queen—Everett Reber and Katie Ramie, the crowd roared. No one in the room except for her, seemed upset with the outcome.

As they made their way to the middle of the floor to begin the first dance of the evening, Katie found herself in the arms of Everett, a tall, handsome blonde, who was completely oblivious of the fact that his Katie was already in the process of munching on Ben's ear as they danced together.

Everett whispered in Katie's ear. "You seem tense tonight."

"Oh, I'm just a little bit surprised, I guess." But she couldn't take her eyes off of Ben and Katie.

"You really have worked hard for the class, Katie, and we all appreciate it. They say we are the best senior class ever and that's obviously because of you. The plaque we presented at the awards ceremony is beautiful, aside from being the first gift a senior class has ever given to the school."

"Why thanks, Ev. That's really sweet of you to say that. I really think there was some kind of mistake in the voting for this king and queen thing though. How's everything going for you?" Trying to distract herself from the flirting going on between Ben and the other Katie, she made a sincere effort to converse with her dance partner.

"Great...just great. I got a partial scholarship for basketball...did you hear?"

"Umm...the counselor mentioned something about an athletic scholarship." She tried not to sound bitter in her reply. It was the way the other Katie was dancing with Ben the next time she looked at them that made her blurt out.

"Well, Ev, all I can say is that you had better be careful." She was stunned that the comment she had only been thinking in her mind came out of her mouth.

"Huh? What the heck do you mean by that?" Ev momentarily lost his step as he distanced himself from Katie so he could look down into her face.

"Oh, nothing. Just watch out. I don't want to see you get hurt." Ev misinterpreted her comment as having something to do with playing basketball and registered a look of confusion before dropping the subject.

When the dance ended Katie turned to join Ben at the table, but was surprised to see him escorting the other Katie back to her table. Everett awkwardly took the initiative and tugged on Katie's arm until she followed him back to her own table. He shrugged as he pulled out one of the metal folding chairs for Katie, grinned, and motioned to her to be seated.

"I guess they want us to sit together for awhile? So you're stuck with me, Miss President!" He bowed, but Katie's eyes were elsewhere. She thought it wasn't the class that wanted them to sit together; it was Ben who took a seat at the other Katie's table on his own initiative. She couldn't really blame him. She knew she looked ugly with the new short hairdo and the dress that everyone else seemed to be wearing, and she hadn't been in the best mood.

"Katie really looks beautiful tonight, Ev!" She pointed to her so that Ev would notice how she and Ben were flirting with each other.

"Yeah, she does look good alright." He stared directly at his girl, but didn't raise so much as an eyebrow at her coquettish behavior.

"Well, Ev, from the looks of it we might as well get used to each other—we may have lost our partners." His silly grin irritated her more than watching the prince and princess enjoying each other.

In contrast to her own blondness, Katie Ramey's hair was stark black and tonight she wore it in an upsweep with pretty ringlets. Her skin was like a baby's—pink and clear—and she was wearing a very feminine, rose-colored gown that was a one-of-a-kind in that there wasn't another dress like it in the room. Katie was jealous.

Only later, after she and Ben were reunited and the prom was over, did Katie let her anger surface as they walked to the car.

"I saw her chewing on your ear, Ben, so don't deny it."

"Don't be ridiculous. It was noisy so she was talking in my ear."

You sure as hell seemed to be enjoying it. You didn't have to follow her back to the table, you know. We were only supposed to start the dancing, not spend the whole night with each other."

"Oh, Katie. Why don't you just drop it...please? I didn't spend the whole night with her; just a couple of minutes after the dance only because she started to tell me something she wanted to finish. It was her suggestion."

"Would you jump off a roof if she told you to?" Here she was, queen of the prom, by far the most popular girl in her class having been awarded every token of approval they could give her, and still she wasn't happy. She was so insecure and paranoid that the sight of another girl with Ben was all she needed to convince herself she might lose him. Katie again succeeded in causing herself unnecessary grief due to the unhealthy way she perceived herself, and she wasn't the least bit aware of her self-destructive behavior.

"Well, I really don't feel like going into the city tonight; it's really late and I'm exhausted."

"Come on, don't spoil it by acting like a baby. Everyone's going. You can't just go home after the prom." As he loosened the tie on his tux, Ben breathed a sigh of relief. "This thing has been strangling me all night long."

"It's really too bad it didn't," Katie muttered under her breath, and then continued to question him further about the proposed trip into New York City.

"Where are we going to meet everyone when we get there?"

"I don't really know."

"What do you mean you don't know? This city is a big place. You must have planned to get together somewhere. Now I'm positive this whole idea is a big mistake. It's just like the beach party all over again—we don't know where anyone is." Despite Katie's misgivings Ben stubbornly continued to drive toward the city. When they were just about halfway there, his car suddenly lurched off the road and narrowly missed the guardrail. Katie's screams echoed through the vehicle.

"Ben, are you falling asleep?"

"No, what's the matter? You scared me." When he looked at Katie it was apparent that he had dozed off; his eyelids were heavy and he seemed dazed.

"I scared you. I can't believe it. The car...you almost ran it off the road. Don't you remember? Take me home...right now!" At the next overpass Ben swerved off the highway and turned in the direction of home.

"Are you satisfied now?"

"Ben, I don't believe you. You almost fell asleep. Don't take it out on me. Don't you see that it's too dangerous to go into the city this late at night? Can you imagine what it would be like on the way home? I'd have to put toothpicks in your eyes to keep them open."

They were silent for the rest of the trip. Later as they neared home, Katie realized by the route he was taking that he had intentions of stopping his car on the deserted back road near her house. Her mind fumbled with different thoughts. She didn't want to stop tonight; she could hardly see straight. On the other hand, she knew nobody was waiting up for her at home. She could walk in at noon the next day, and they probably wouldn't even know she had been gone overnight. Why shouldn't she give him what he wanted? Why was she holding back? Soon he would be leaving to go to college and she probably wouldn't see him again. She knew she was going to lose him whether she gave in to him or not. Katie was still deep in thought when Ben parked the car, turned to her, and flashed his trademark Elvis Presley smile.

"Come over here. Did I tell you how nice you look tonight?"

"Not really, but you don't have to. I know I don't look good. As you said, my hair is a mess, and this dress was on just about everybody." Katie grabbed the material in the skirt of her dress and shook it with disgust.

"I didn't see any guys in it." Ben's attempt at humor was lost on Katie as he continued. "But you still looked better than any other girl there tonight."

"Thanks, but I know you don't really mean that; I know what you have in mind."

"Oh, you do? What are you, a mind reader?" As his big arms went around her and his hand boldly rested on her breast, the last thing she saw before she closed her eyes was his thick brows so Grecian-looking and strong, coming toward her. Hungrily his thin lips nibbled at her face, as her inner turmoil began. She wondered what to do as his hand pressed against her body, guiding her down on the seat until she was lying flat She was aware of his arms lifting her until her head touched the car door...and of the hardness of his anxious body on hers...and of the night air chilling her bare legs as he lifted her long dress and fumbled with her nylons, detaching them ungraciously from the garters.

"Jesus, you might as well be wearing a chastity belt." As his fingers dug into her and clumsily tore at her girdle, his voice was high with frustration. Her mind was telling her not to let this happen, while her body was reveling in the warmth of it all. Nothing in her whole life had ever felt this good.

He lifted himself from her, taking with him the hotness, removing his tongue from deep within her mouth, leaving her face unprotected against the night air. She heard the sound of his zipper coming down. She wanted it, wanted whatever it was that could make her feel so good. As she arched slowly toward him, she squeezed her eyes together tightly as he bore down on her once again. Flesh to flesh now for the first time ever. She was shivering from the coldness that had crept in while he was away from her. The moist flesh of his mouth made contact with her neck. His hand clumsily lifted her back and picked at the zipper of her dress. It seemed forever before his impatient fingers crawled around her shoulders, tugging at her bra until they succeeded in releasing it from her. She prayed he wouldn't see the tissues she had stuffed in the cups, but that fear subsided quickly when she felt his wet lips against her breasts and then a fantastic surge of warmth from within them. Her legs, forced together by underwear and nylons wrapped tightly around her knees, tingled violently as he rubbed himself up and down against her groin. She wondered if this was it; there couldn't be more than this. But as Ben accidentally bit her nipple, so sensitive and tender, Katie jerked in pain.

"Don't do that; it hurts." Her voice sounded distant and different and she wondered if it was really her who had spoken.

"Oh, God, I can't hold it any longer!" As he swallowed her mouth in his, she couldn't feel his lips—just a bitter, salty taste that invaded her tongue, and her breasts ached as if a million pins were sticking in them. Desperately she tried to recapture the ecstasy she had felt just moments before, while something hard began assaulting her thighs...searching, groping frantically. Hands now, pushing against her stiff legs trying to separate them, reaching now for her panties, girdle and nylons, pulling them down further on her legs. She was now resisting, keeping her legs together, and there was too much liquid to swallow. She was having difficulty breathing. The hard thing was again touching her, the black ugliness looming large in her mind as the dirty coat opened and closed to reveal the organ behind it. Was it that same kind of hideousness probing at her now, trying desperately to invade her innermost region? All of a sudden she felt revulsion, and her body became noticeably uncooperative.

"Damn it, Katie...open your legs; help me here." Pinned helplessly against the seat, his weight on her chest making it almost impossible for her to get air into her lungs, Katie's logical mind finally took over. She couldn't let him do this. He would break off with her and then she would have nothing. She was acting crazy. Nobody else cared about her and he wouldn't either if she gave in to him. He would be gone. What if she got pregnant? He'd have to marry her. That wasn't such a bad idea...a good way to get away from her present life. But then she remembered Maria...the boy denied it, and her family sent her back to Puerto Rico.

"Christ, Katie, what's wrong with you?" As Ben spit out the words, Katie gasped for air.

"I can't, Ben. I can't, I'm sorry. I really am, but I just can't right now. I'm so confused." As Ben quietly lifted himself from her, his knee pinched the side of her leg as his weight came down on it. She ran her trembling hand over her compressed chest and bit her lip in silent pain as he got off of her. He shoved her legs roughly out from under him, and she fumbled to rearrange her garments. He sat motionless behind the wheel of the car while she continued to grope in the darkness, dressing herself, totally mortified by the situation.

Through the blackness she caught a glimpse of his strong profile. His jaw line extended and she was suddenly afraid. She tried unsuccessfully to collect herself as her underpants and girdle pinched her, her nylons bagged around her ankles, and her strapless bra cut into her already sensitive bosom.

Her hands searched frantically along the seat and floor of the dark car until they made contact with the softness of the tissue paper. It was crazy, but she couldn't help worrying about finding the tissues she used to stuff her bra, and was relieved when they were finally in her possession.

When Ben unexpectedly turned to her, pointing his finger dangerously close to her eyes, she flinched. "Do you know what they call girls like you? Do you?" As his lips quivered he continued, "A cockteaser...that's right...a cockteaser!" Each time he said it he pounded his fist against the dashboard, and Katie inched a little further away from him. "Why did you stop?"

"I couldn't let it happen. If I did...I would lose you. Don't you understand? I have nothing. You're the only person in this whole world who seems to care about me." She paused and her voice turned bitter as she continued, "Or at least I think so. And you're going away to college, and I'm staying right here and probably will never see you again."

"But I love you, Katie; that's the difference."

"So because you say you love me makes it okay to have sex? Well, not from what I've heard. Once guys get it, then they dump the girl and find someone else. You know it, too, don't you, Ben!"

"You're dead wrong, Katie. I wouldn't do that." The indignation he felt reflected in the icy stare he gave her.

"Maria thought that way, too!" Katie ignored Ben's puzzled look and continued. "Listen, I can't be sure what you would do, but I'm afraid to take that chance. I need more assurance than just your words, and I'm sorry if you think I was teasing you. I had no intention of doing that. I wanted it, too, just as much as you did, until I started thinking about the repercussions."

Throwing his hands up in the air in exasperation, Ben cried. "What do you want to do? What do you want me to do?"

The wheels were turning. She'd thought about it a lot, especially when she realized she wasn't going to be able to go to college.

"Well, if you love me like you say you do, maybe we should get married." As she spoke, she kept her eyes glued to the wilted flowers on the corsage which was still on her wrist.

Clearing his throat, his voice an octave higher than usual, Ben muttered, "Are you crazy? We can't do that."

"Why not, Ben?" Rising in her chest like a wave was all the hurt she had ever felt. She was being rejected again. "Why not...huh? It's okay to tell me you love me and try to mess around, but it's just meaningless words. It's just like I thought, isn't it?"

"That's not it at all. We're not even out of high school yet."

"I don't mean we have to get married right now. I meant after we graduate."

"But I wouldn't be able to go to college if I got married."

"Nonsense. Whatever gave you that idea?" Katie was becoming very edgy with resentment as she continued. "I have a guaranteed job with the school. Either I'll stay here and work, or I could find a job near the university."

"Jeez, I don't know. I guess I just need to think about it." Ben looked away from her as he rubbed his chin nervously.

"Well, I've thought about it a lot, which just goes to prove which one of us is the most serious person in this relationship." She expected some kind of reply from him, but all he did was peer at his watch through the darkness.

She was hurt that he called her that awful name; hurt that he obviously wasn't enthusiastic about marrying her; hurt that he hadn't even thought about where she stood in his future.

"It's late. I'd better get you home. Lord, is that the sun coming up?" As he changed the subject, her heart sank. A few minutes later when he pulled up to her house, she quietly left the car after his halfhearted attempt to kiss her goodnight.

"I'll call you tomorrow some time." She didn't acknowledge his statement as she slammed the door and walked slowly toward the front stoop where she collapsed and watched the sun come up.

For awhile it looked like she could have the world if she wanted it; for awhile it appeared no doors were closed to her, but now she knew better—for all of those doors had shut in her face leaving her trapped in a place she didn't want to be. As she lifted her tired body from the cold concrete and stared disgustedly at the front door of the house, she made a vow to herself she would get away from it one way or the other

"Did you check the list, Katie? Katie, do we have everyone?" The dour sound of the vice principal's voice brought her rudely back to the present.

"Yes, I checked it." There was exhaustion evident in her voice.

"Come on, girl, where's your enthusiasm? You're going on a picnic, you know." Elaine plopped down beside Katie on the seat.

"I'm just tired. I'll be okay once we get there."

"Where's lover boy today?" Elaine bit down on her fingernail, not that she had anything left of it. As a matter of fact, they were all eaten to the quick. Poor Elaine. Katie wondered how she felt about not being asked to the prom. She had called her the morning after the dance to tell her she didn't miss much at all.

"Ben and the other jocks will grace us with their presence later. They had to stay at the school for some kind of meeting."

"Do I detect a problem between the lovebirds?" From the very beginning of their relationship, Elaine had a knack for reading Katie's moods.

"No, nothing serious; just the end-of-high school blues. Oh, here we are. Look, I've got to run. I have to make sure the food and drink is here and all that stuff." Ignoring the hurt in Elaine's green eyes, Katie ran to supervise the day's activities.

As she escaped her friend, Katie thought it ironic that the best summer of her miserable life was the first summer on Long Island with Elaine, Maria, and Bud. She had given up those friendships which provided her with the only carefree days she had ever known…for academic excellence, extracurricular activities, and a boyfriend. In her heart she wasn't at all certain it had been worth it.

Katie wolfed down a frankfurter and soda between organizing the softball game and badminton and volleyball competitions, too busy to participate in them herself because she had to keep the picnic on schedule. A short while later while bending to retrieve a bag of garbage, Ben snuck up behind her and patted her on the rear causing her to jump.

"Oh, my God! You scared me half to death. When did you get here?"

"About a half-hour ago. Hey, this was a great idea and it's a beautiful day. I'll see you later. I'm going to check out the softball game. Don't work too hard." As Katie watched him walk away, her doubts intensified. She was sure he was distancing himself from her; avoiding her. These fears were confirmed when Ben's promise to join her never materialized. He was so involved in the athletic events that he lost track of time.

Katie worked to the very end cleaning up paper plates and soda cans from the grass so there wouldn't be any complaints from the school administrators and park officials who had let them use the site. At the end of the day there were a lot of happy seniors enjoying the day away from school, all except one—Katie.

"Hey, Katie, I can't talk to you now, I'm going to miss my bus. It was a great day. I'll call you tonight." She heard Ben talk but before she actually saw him, he was gone. She walked stiffly to her own bus loathing everything and everyone in her life.

Katie pushed the cap around her head, trying to find an angle that looked appealing, and groaned knowing it was hopeless. She cursed herself again for getting her hair cut. For the hundredth time she rehearsed the speech she had prepared to begin the graduation ceremony, present the gifts to the school, and announce the valedictorian to the crowd. She knew this was the end of it all. After today she would be nothing.

In the few times they were together since the prom, Ben carefully avoided the subject of marriage like it was the plague, and each time Katie saw him or talked to him she grew more despondent. At first she had high hopes because he still called her, but then she realized he probably decided to wait until he left for college to end their relationship. There were many times during those days that she regretted her decision not to have sex with Ben; at least there was the possibility she could have gotten pregnant. He couldn't possibly deny that he was the father; after all, everyone knew they were dating each other exclusively. She still hadn't recovered from the shock of finding out Maria was pregnant and her boyfriend was denying he was the father, and Maria's parents had sent her to Puerto Rico to have the baby.

As she walked toward the place in the hallway where she and Ben had agreed to meet, Katie became more despondent. When she caught a glimpse of him, she realized how handsome he looked in his cap and gown. She regretted the missed opportunity to make him hers with a possible pregnancy, and more importantly, to start a new life.

"Are you nervous?" He blew the tassel on his cap out of his face.

"A little. I hope I don't mess up."

"Are your parents coming?"

As she answered him, Katie tried to keep her voice from quivering. "I don't know. I gave them the announcement, but they didn't tell me whether they were coming."

"Well, I'll meet you in front of the building when we're done. Good luck." He kissed her lightly on the cheek.

"Thanks."

Ben disappeared into his homeroom as she watched him with regret and sadness. After the ceremony she waited on the curb in her yellow eyelet dress, squinting against the brilliance of the sun, searching for Ben. She was shocked to hear the sound of her mother's voice.

"Katie, I thought we would never find you." As she turned around in the direction of the sound, Katie saw Nan approaching her followed closely by Jack.

"Oh, you made it." Katie sounded genuinely surprised.

"Yes, Dad took an early lunch. We didn't get here in time for the whole ceremony, but it was nice anyway." While Katie watched uncomfortably Nan took out a cigarette and lit it up, taking a long drag and blowing out lots of smoke. The trio stood in awkward silence, Katie surveying her father as he shuffled from foot to foot avoiding any eye contact until Ben's parents appeared, obviously excited and happy about their son's graduation. Kisses and handshakes were exchanged as Katie wished to herself that Nan and Jack had not come at all. It was Nan who broke the ensuing silence.

"Well, I guess we had better go. Jack has to get back to work."

"Katie, will you join us for lunch?" The invitation from Ben's mother was a pleasant surprise to Katie.

"Go ahead, we have nothing planned." Nan intently crushed her cigarette out on the sidewalk with her foot and didn't look up as she spoke. "See you later; have a good time." Nan's wet kiss against Katie's cheek felt strange, and a tinge of sadness engulfed her as her parents walked away.

The feeling remained with her despite the cheery mood which prevailed during lunch with Ben's family. She felt like an outsider and wished her own family was celebrating with her instead; however, she knew that daydream was impossible like so many other fantasies she had. The fact that they were not together on this day was a fitting culmination to her childhood.

After paying the check, Ben's father turned to the two graduates. "So what are you two up to for the rest of the day?"

"We're just going to drive into the city and meet a few friends for dinner; maybe stop at Lindey's and get some of their famous cheesecake." Even on a full stomach Ben could enthusiastically talk about food.

"Well, be careful and have a good time." After more kisses and hugs, Katie and Ben were finally alone.

"We did it!" Ben radiated happiness as he got behind the wheel of his car and squealed with joy. Katie wished she could share in his excitement, but she felt so down.

"You look nice in that dress, Katie."

"Thanks. I really think it's kind of babyish though. You know me; I'm always picking the wrong styles."

"Stop that, Katie! When are you going to stop criticizing yourself?" He reached for her hand and pulled her close to him.

"Now, let's not worry about anything tonight and really celebrate. We deserve it, don't we?" She smiled at him and squeezed his hand tightly. He was right. No more unhappy thoughts, at least for the rest of this special day.

Much later as he parked his car in the usual place, Ben grabbed Katie close to him. "Well, what do you think?"

"I had a great time, and I'm totally stuffed." Her heart was racing.

"That's not what I mean." As his lips brushed against her cheek, she tried to block out the uneasy sensation she had when he came near her, knowing the initial revulsion would go away quickly as it had in the past. He began to caress her but soon stopped abruptly, throwing Katie off guard.

"I've got a graduation present for you." He beamed; his face remained close to Katie's.

"You shouldn't have done that. Remember we said no gifts." Presents made her feel obligated and she hated getting them.

"I've been thinking a lot about what you said to me, you know, after the prom. When you first suggested we get married, I thought it was ridiculous. You're absolutely right though. It isn't fair for me to ask you to give yourself to me without a commitment in return. So we'll do whatever you want." As Ben talked, the tingling began in her toes and traveled up the entire length of her body until it made her dizzy.

"One thing though, we need to keep this to ourselves. I can't risk losing my scholarship, and I will if they find out about this. It'll be our secret until I get established at school."

"Okay, I don't care. Whatever way you want it. Oh, my goodness, this is the best present I've ever gotten." She threw her hands around his neck tightly and started to plan for happier days. Things were working out well despite her earlier misgivings.

This time when he started to undress her, she relaxed and let it happen. She finally had her way out; now she needed to work on making sure it would become reality. All she could remember when it was over was the pain, the sweat, the smell, and the fear. She didn't experience any of the wonderful feelings she expected.

They went all the way that night. Katie wasn't one bit disappointed that it didn't feel good...the plan was more important.

Chapter Seven: Time Stands Still

Katie started working as a secretary for her high school principal immediately after graduation and enjoyed the job tremendously. She opened up a bank account so she had somewhere to keep her money safe, and practically every time she and Ben got together they had intercourse. They did it in drive-in movies, on secluded roads, deserted beaches, and in Ben's bedroom in the basement of his house.

"How are you feeling now, Katie? You sure made a pig out of yourself eating all that sweet crap at dinner. I'm surprised you have any teeth left." Sensing the rigidness of her body against his, Ben stroked Katie's arm as he propped himself up on one elbow.

Earlier while Ben dined on pizza, Katie ate three custard filled doughnuts until she was sick to her stomach. She still wasn't feeling well when she crawled in beside him in his small bed, fixing her eyes on the ceiling. She was nervous about what was to come.

"Hey, it's okay. Try to relax." As Ben's flaccid penis grew hard, he began to perspire. His kiss was familiar as was the feel of his body, but that didn't do a thing to ease her tensions. His sweat fell on Katie's chest as he turned his attention to her breasts.

"Please touch it. Please hold it, make it feel good," Ben pleaded. Katie was too sick to even respond, and realizing his request was being ignored Ben mounted Katie and began moving his body up and down. He could feel himself losing control. With each painful thrust Katie squeezed him tightly in an attempt to ease the assault on her body, as the groaning sounds he made echoed through the room. He fumbled wildly for the right entry, but with each unsuccessful attempt Katie grew more rigid until he finally cried out.

"You're driving me crazy; I think I'm going to explode! Relax, for gosh sake. If you do, it will be much better for both of us. Please." It was no use; it hurt too much for her to enjoy it.

"I can't, I can't." So with one stabbing motion, Ben lunged into Katie's dryness, feeling the surge of hotness within him give way to relief. When his body finally relaxed on hers, she felt only searing agony where he had just been and then the weight of his body crushing her.

"Ben, I can't breathe. You'll have to get off of me. You're too heavy, please. Oh, my God, it hurts."

"If you had only taken it easy like I said, it wouldn't have been so bad. Next time it will be better, I promise. Hey, I'm beat. How about you?" Ben kissed her lightly on the cheek and turned his back to her as he pulled the bed sheet over himself.

Katie blinked away tears of anguish. She was too sick, too hurt to move. She was sure it had to be better than what she was experiencing; it had been wonderful in her dreams. Hours later while a fire consumed the lower portion of her body, burning out of control, she finally collapsed into unconsciousness.

She was lying in a pool of water, face down. She couldn't breathe. A man in a dirty overcoat stood over her, his foot pressed against her back so she couldn't get up. "You bad girl. You shouldn't have done that...now I'm going to make you look at it again," he said over and over.

Suddenly she was awake, eyes wide open, pain gripping at her insides. She felt clammy. She moved her hand slowly across her abdomen and down the side of the bed, discovering that the sheets were damp also. *Oh, my God*, she thought to herself, *don't tell me I wet the bed*. But Ben's back was still facing her and her hand accidentally touched it. Moisture from his perspiration covered her hand. He was absolutely drenched. Desperately she tried to get out of the bed, but her body wasn't willing. Instead she moved slowly over to the edge of the mattress searching for dryness, just like she used to when she slept with her sisters. The effort sent shooting pains all through her crotch and up into her throat. As she turned over on her side she lifted her knees up to her stomach, and put a hand over her mouth to muffle the involuntary moans that escaped her every time she moved.

Spending the night together had seemed like a good idea at the time. Ben's family was staying in the city with relatives and would be away from the house for two full days. Now she couldn't believe how badly it had turned out. Hours later, she finally fell back into a fretful sleep just as the sun was coming up.

The next morning Ben tried again, but it ended the same as the night before. It was good for him, but Katie could barely walk and every movement of her legs brought with it such discomfort that she shuffled miserably from one place to the other trying to get dressed.

Ben suggested a movie, and even sitting down did not bring any relief to her misery. They went to two movies that day, and she sat through each one of them in agony. When she urinated the burning was so intense that tears came to her eyes.

After the movie Ben suggested they stop for something to eat, but Katie didn't even order a drink for fear of having to go to the bathroom again. She was feeling queasy even before they finished eating, and by the time she was in the car on the way home she was very ill. She felt alternately clammy and flushed and struggled to stay upright, but eventually slid down until she was lying on the front seat of the car praying whatever was happening to her would go away quickly. She couldn't even answer Ben when he asked her what was wrong. She was afraid if she tried to talk she would definitely lose consciousness. She closed her eyes and tried to get past each wave of the illness by gripping the side of the car seat. She had no idea she had severe cystitis. Later that night when Ben dropped her off at her house, the awful burning pain had been replaced by a manageable stinging sensation which lasted for days.

To make matters worse, every time they were together in the ensuing weeks Ben wanted to have sex.

"Hi, listen, my parents are going into the city again to see some friends. I'll pick you up and we can come back to my house. How does that sound, Katie?"

"Okay, I guess."

"Gee whiz, don't sound so enthusiastic."

"I'm sorry; I've got a lot on my mind."

Two hours later Ben was still trying to keep his penis rigid so he could penetrate her impossible tightness.

"I'm really trying to be patient. Do you know how rough this is on me? We've been at it for a long time and we aren't getting anywhere. What is your problem?" They were in Ben's bedroom, and Katie's ears were perked for any noise which would warn them someone was in the house.

"I don't know. I'm nervous, I guess. It hurt so much last time and I'm worried somebody will catch us."

"They will if we continue like this all day. I told you they won't be home until after dark. Now unless you ease up, we might as well forget it." It was the additional pressure of his last statement that made her even tighter and a few minutes later Ben released her stiff and unyielding body, quietly put on his clothes, and left the room. Relieved, she hurriedly got up from the bed, dressed, and joined him in the recreation room where he was sitting stone-faced watching television.

"I'm really sorry, Ben. I don't know why this is happening. All I can say is I'm scared. I swear it hurt for days last time; all that on top of someone coming in and finding us; I just can't hack it. I'm sorry."

"I don't understand it, Katie. I promised to do whatever you wanted when I got established at school, but it seems you're still not happy."

"I am, but it's so painful every time we do it." As she put her hand on his shoulders, Katie's eyes pleaded with him for understanding.

"I told you it might hurt the first few times, but then it gets better. Christ, it wouldn't hurt at all if you just relaxed a little. Another thing. Why don't you look at me when I'm naked? Am I that ugly?" Katie was surprised at Ben's unexpected questions and nervously giggled.

"No, you definitely are not ugly. It's just that I really don't need to look at it; at you, I mean."

"What do you mean, at it? What the hell does that mean? You mean my penis, don't you?" Agitatedly Ben pointed to the organ between his legs.

"Well, yes, I guess so." The blood rushed to her head causing her cheeks to flush.

Why can't you look at it? It's just a plain ordinary penis…nothing special. You have brothers; I know you've seen them."

"Yeah, when they were little; but it's not the same. A man's penis is a lot different."

"Sure, a little bigger, but that's about it."

"Oh, no. They're much uglier." Katie shook her head.

"How do you know if you've never seen one?"

"Well, I did in a way a long time ago. I was selling chances, and this guy opened his coat and showed me his penis. It was really disgusting. I'll never forget it. I just thought it would be better if I didn't look at it."

"That's crazy." Ben's interest—and something else—were aroused. He questioned her further. "What did it look like?"

"Well, it was purple and hairy all over." Ben laughed heartily, but stopped abruptly when he saw the pained expression on Katie's face.

"They aren't hairy all over. It might look that way when they are soft, but the hair is only around the penis, not on it. Furthermore, they definitely aren't purple. I want you to look at it." Ben kissed Katie's lips long and hard as she thought only of the need to relax. Surprisingly as he caressed her, his hand moving across her breasts through the blouse she wore, the tingling sensation she enjoyed so long ago returned. When he took her hand and placed it on the solid object between his legs forcing her to massage it, she moved only slightly and continued to rub him on her own as she let his hand slide between her legs and into her underpants, gently fingering the lips of her vagina. Keeping his lips on hers as he carried her to his bed, he placed his body over hers as his hands came down to remove her pants while she squirmed and wiggled to help him.

When he guided her hand up to his belt buckle they both tugged at it, freeing his pants and underwear with an urgent concerted effort while Katie kept her eyes tightly closed, as she had from the beginning of their lovemaking. Katie gasped for air as he swallowed her face in his mouth, and planted her hands firmly on his back as if her palms were smeared with glue while he spread her shaking legs apart. As his organ worked its way to its goal, he cried out.

"Now, Katie, now." His fingers provided a pathway for his penis, opening up the entrance to her cervix which was now very moist, as his other hand guided his hardness into her. Immediately she experienced a sudden but short-lived pain, followed quickly by a strange but pleasant feeling of being filled up. He was drowning her with his saliva, and began thrusting his body up and down against her. She was amazed; it didn't hurt this time. Before she could feel anything else, however, Ben was done and withdrew from her. After mumbling something she couldn't understand, Ben was still. As his deep blue eyes penetrated her own, he broke the silence.

"How was that? Did it hurt?"

"No...not too much." Katie was both happy and disappointed; it hadn't hurt, but it hadn't felt awesome like she had heard it should.

"See, I told you it would get better. How did you do?"

"What do you mean?"

"Did you feel anything unusual?"

"No, I'm just happy I'm not in pain." She didn't want to share her chagrin with him, pretending to be content with what happened.

"Now I want you to look at me." Katie, who was still pinned under the weight of his body, began to shake her head back and forth as Ben laughed at her. "You really have to look at it; it's not as bad as you think. Really, your fear is all a result of that dirty old man exposing his penis to you."

Ben lifted himself so he was straddling Katie with his body in full view as his fingers pried her eyes open. "Come on, chicken." Slowly she raised one eye, staring directly into his face.

"Look at it. I think it's pretty great if I do say so myself." Gradually Katie lowered both eyes to see the thing which had terrified her for so long. He was right. It wasn't purple at all. It was white, just like his skin. It definitely was not near as big as she had imagined; it was almost harmless looking. All that hair she thought covered it only surrounded it; the penis itself was bald. Embarrassed, she covered her eyes with her hands.

"It can't be that bad, Katie." Ben released his hold on her and got up to dress. He was upset.

"No, don't get mad. I just feel so dumb. It really is okay."

"You mean that?" He returned to the bed and lowered his body back down on hers, kissing her with returning passion. This time she felt an emotional intoxication beyond any she had experienced before. She assumed this was the orgasm everyone talked about.

When Ben dropped her off at home she was slightly sore, but this time the pain had been worth it. Things were looking up, or so she thought.

Ben did not talk about their future together other than to reassure her after their lovemaking that he was doing what she wanted. One day when she opened the trunk of her car to reveal some of the household items she had bought, he laughed.

"What are you buying that stuff for? You shouldn't be wasting your money on things like that." She was upset at his reaction, but all was forgotten when he pushed her into the backseat of her car and gave her one of his lustful grins. "This is the first time we've done it in your car, isn't it?"

During all the times they copulated, Katie experienced only mild sensations of pleasure; certainly nothing ecstatic, earth-shattering or mind-blowing—words Maria had used to describe orgasms. Her climax was simply a slight tingling of her innards, something she had always been able to achieve on her own in her dreams. Still the summer was one of the best ever for Katie; there was so much to look forward to. Her new job working in the school was fantastic and her car was still holding up, although barely. One thing was for certain, she didn't have to worry about getting a flat tire.

And best of all there were no new babies on the way in the Ramie household. Carrie would be three years old in November and Nan was still without child. Her emotions were steady in a pathetic kind of way. She went through the motions of getting through each day but without much enthusiasm. Still it was better than the ups and downs, and it was certainly nice to have a break from having an infant in the house.

From the day she first got it, Katie's period was like clockwork. She was surprised when it didn't arrive on schedule in August.

"Don't worry about it, Katie, it will come eventually." Ben was optimistic, but when two more weeks went by without a sign of blood even he began to panic. Katie was sure she was pregnant; her breasts hurt a lot and she felt nauseous all the time.

They sat in Ben's car for a long time just staring straight ahead, neither of them saying anything. Katie finally broke the silence.

"Ben, it could be worse."

"Oh, yeah? Tell me how." He looked directly at Katie, and she noticed he had tears in his eyes. She was totally caught off guard by the extent of his negative emotions about the reality of her being pregnant, and she immediately became defensive.

"Well, excuse me, but I thought you might be okay with this."

"Don't you realize what this is going to do to me? If anyone finds out, I'll lose my scholarship for sure. I won't be able to go to school." Ben pounded his fist against the steering wheel.

"That's ridiculous. They can't take it away from you just because I'm pregnant." Animosity began building in Katie like a volcanic eruption; she was beginning to sense she had been duped with regard to Ben's intentions.

"Oh, yes. This changes everything, believe me. My parent won't let me go to college if they know I got you pregnant. Think about it...just think about it. How are we going to do it?"

"I can work you know, it's not like I'm dying." The tone of the conversation was upsetting Katie and the nausea she felt escalated. She didn't expect him to be so adamant, so unhappy about it. It really hurt her feelings.

"What about when the baby comes? You won't be able to work then. See what I mean? You're not thinking ahead. We are in big, fat trouble."

"But I know we can work it out if we do it together." She slid her hand along the seat and gently placed it on his arm in a gesture of reassurance, but he abruptly pulled away from her touch.

"Take my word for it; everything is messed up now. I'll just die if I can't go to college. We have to think of a way to hide this until I leave for school. Yes…yes. Let me think about it. Don't say a word to anyone; just let me have some time to think about it."

For a short time Katie had felt it…the happiness associated with being loved and wanted. For the first time in her life she could actually see a light at the end of the tunnel. It was a daily hassle to fight the insecurities that still plagued her and tried to beat her down, but each day she had been coming closer to winning the battle for self-worth. Because her prospects for the future had seemed better than ever during that summer of 1964, she no longer worried so much about what was ahead of her. But now that happiness was disintegrating with each word Ben spoke. He was spoiling it all. She knew then he had never been serious about marrying her. It was all a big joke to him; just a ploy to get her to have sex with him…and now that she was pregnant, he wanted to end the game and walk away like a sore loser.

She had to remind herself this had been her game also, her master plan to ensure her passage out of an intolerable situation at home. Now seeing Ben's reaction she realized it had been wrong. Why didn't she see he wasn't serious about her and, even worse, they weren't really in love with each other after all. Suddenly Katie was back in the tunnel, and there was no light in either direction. She was trapped.

Katie grabbed her pocketbook from under the bed and searched it to make sure her money was still in it. She felt queer, like she didn't know what to do next. She was always organized with her time, knowing from one minute to the next what she was doing and what she was going to do next. This behavior was alien to her. It had been two weeks since she had agreed to keep her pregnancy a secret, but each day she felt more wretched both physically and mentally. That evening was Ben's going away party and still no one knew of their predicament.

"Katie, you know it's the best way for us to do it. I leave for college like there's nothing wrong, and after I get there I'll investigate the situation— jobs, housing, and all that stuff. Then we can make plans based on what I find out." During that phone conversation, Katie had the dry heaves so bad she could hardly stand up. The pessimist in her knew all along that he was going to leave for college without telling anyone. She also convinced herself that once he was out of town, he wouldn't make good on his promise to come back for her. But what could she do? She didn't want to tell anyone in case he was right about losing his scholarship. She was sure he would then blame her for messing up his life. In her worst moments she felt he might even deny everything; deny he was the father of her baby.

"Ben, we can't put this off too much longer. I'm already a month pregnant."

"Yeah, I know, but everything will go haywire if we let the cat out of the bag now. This way I can get settled in college before I come back for you. Really, I honestly feel this is the best way to do it. Just trust me on this."

"Personally, Ben, I think the whole plan stinks, but I'm in no position to call the shots, am I?" The lump in her throat was strangling her.

"Come on, now. Cheer up, everything will turn out okay. Hey, are you coming tonight? It should be quite a party. I think my parents got me luggage as a going away gift."

Katie didn't answer his question. She didn't like the fact that he had to ask her if she was coming. She hadn't even gotten an invitation to his party, even though weeks before she had come across a package of invitations in his kitchen and casually inquired if someone was having a party.

"Oh, didn't I tell you? My parents are planning a going-away party for me." Ben acted like a kid who just got caught with his hand in the cookie jar.

"No, you didn't. When is it?"

"Next Saturday night. You're invited, of course…your parents also."

The sarcasm was evident in her voice as Katie thanked him, and then waited for the arrival of the invitation which never came. As each day without a formal invitation passed, Katie's excitement about attending the party diminished. Now the day was finally here. It was just four hours until she was expected to show up at a going-away party for her boyfriend, and instead she was getting into her car not knowing where she was going and for what.

Later when she pulled the car into a shopping center, her hands shook against the steering wheel. She felt hemmed in, but finally was able to get herself out of the car and into the crowded store. She couldn't think properly and walked toward a sales table, searching for something but not knowing exactly what. She felt lightheaded and extremely tired as she picked through some drastically reduced men's shirts, but walked away from them after a few minutes of searching, realizing she couldn't afford to buy one even on sale.

As she walked down the main aisle of the store, she bumped into a rack of dresses. She stood staring at them intently as a thought entered her mind: she had nothing to wear to the party that night. She was already swollen and most of her clothing was uncomfortably tight. Her fingers touched the silky garments on the racks which were too expensive to even think about.

She turned to leave, but just before she exited she eyed a table on which hundreds of plastic bags were thrown. The sign read SHIFT DRESSES—$1.00. She lifted a beige plaid dress out of a bag that had a big L on it indicating it was a large, and decided it would be a perfect dress for the party. She bought it.

When Katie caught a glimpse of herself in the rearview mirror of the car on the way home, she was shocked at how bad she looked. Sometime that morning, in nervous anticipation of the party she had picked at her face, turning small blemishes into mountainous eruptions. She looked like death warmed over, and that was also exactly how she felt when she arrived home.

"Katie, where have you been? Your dad and I are almost ready to leave for Ben's party. Hurry up and get dressed."

"I'm not feeling well." Nan had already turned her attention back to polishing her nails and didn't hear her daughter's remark. Katie retreated to her bedroom where she slipped the new wrinkled shift over her aching body, turning to look at herself in the mirror. It was then she decided that she definitely was not going to the party; she couldn't go no matter what. She looked worse than she felt and that was horrendous. She threw herself on her bed and tried to make herself cry, but gave up when her throat began to hurt from the effort.

A short time later Nan opened the bedroom door and sauntered in, sitting herself down on the edge of Katie's bed. "What's the matter?"

"I'm sick; I'm not going to the party tonight."

"Are you sure? Ben will be awfully disappointed if you don't come." She reached out a freshly manicured hand and felt Katie's forehead.

"You don't feel warm. Exactly what's the matter?"

"My stomach hurts."

"I guess you're coming down with the flu; it's been going around." Watching as Nan took a long drag on the cigarette she held in her hand, Katie knew her mother was in trouble again. She sensed she was confused, not knowing what to do.

It didn't take much to throw her mother off track. Her eyes always told the story, but Katie couldn't worry about her now. She had her own problems and she knew her mother wasn't strong enough to help her. She knew if she confided in her, it would send her into a full-fledged breakdown. She had been on the edge for a long time just waiting for some catalyst, and Katie didn't want this breakdown to be her fault. Katie wished she would just take her cigarette and her red nails and leave the room.

"Well, I think your dad and I should go to the party anyway. I've been looking forward to getting out since you told us we were invited. Barbara and Jonathan are here to look after the little ones. You take care of yourself now." Before she left the room Nan planted a wet kiss on Katie's cheek, but Katie took her hand and disdainfully wiped it away.

She decided then and there it was time to kill herself...no one cared about her. She would show them. Everybody would wonder why she didn't come to the party. She knew Ben would call as soon as her parents got there, asking why she wasn't with them. She would tell him that she planned to commit suicide when he did.

And so she waited…and waited…lying in a prone position on the bed in the dark room. Waiting for some sign of concern; some visible proof of her importance in his life. He didn't call. She still couldn't cry even though it was the worst night of her life. She hated him; she hated them all.

On that night in that lonely room, Katie lost the last semblance of hope she had for happiness. During that long ordeal she experienced disbelief, self-pity, fright, hate…and finally, nothing. She had ignored it when Barbara, Amy, and Carrie had noisily come into the bedroom and listened quietly until their heavy breathing told her they were all asleep. When Nan and Jack arrived home well after midnight, Katie was still wide awake.

"Katie, are you up?" Nan slurred her words, obviously just a little tipsy. "How do you feel?"

"Not good." Katie just wanted her mother to go away and leave her alone.

"Oh, that's too bad. You missed a great party. That Ben is a real live wire."

"I really don't want to hear about it." She wished her mother would shut up, but Nan sat on the edge of Katie's bed and continued talking as if she hadn't heard her plea.

"He got such nice gifts. That boyfriend of yours sure is a party boy. Who is that blonde neighbor of his? She must be old enough to be his mother, but she sure was flirting with him. You should have been there, Katie. Well, goodnight, honey…sorry you're not feeling any better." Quickly Katie turned on her side away from Nan so that she wouldn't be able to kiss her again, just in case that was what she had in mind. As she pictured a blonde lady dancing close to Ben, Katie fell into a disturbed sleep.

During the long weeks after Ben departed for college, Katie waited patiently for his infrequent telephone calls which always left her disappointed. He wasn't making any headway toward solving their problem and most of the time was reluctant to even discuss it with her. She thought all the time about taking her own life and how she would do it, but in the end she couldn't go through with it. It was more than just about her; she didn't want to hurt the new life inside her. It was late September and Katie was now a little over a month pregnant.

As she sat on the edge of her bed Katie took a deep breath. It was almost time to pick up Ben from the train station. She chided herself for having waited so long to tell her parents, but she was afraid. The night before in a long telephone conversation, she and Ben discussed their predicament.

"We can't wait any longer, Ben! We have to tell our parents." Katie was determined to convince him they had to reveal their secret right away.

"I know. I guess I should come home this weekend. There's a train leaving for New York at five o'clock PM tomorrow evening which would put me at the station around nine thirty or so. Can you pick me up?" Without waiting for an answer from Katie, he continued.

"By the way, tell your parents about the baby before I get there."

"What do you mean? Aren't we going to tell them together?" Katie was miserable. Ben sounded so depressed like he was being forced to come home and face the music.

"No, I think it would be much better if you told your parents and I told mine."

"But wouldn't they react better if we told them together?"

"No way, Katie. It will be much simpler if we tell them separately." Before she could protest further, Ben hung up abruptly.

Katie's eager anticipation of getting everything resolved with Ben was turning into a nightmare of insecurity and doubt. Still, what could she do? More than anything else in the world she wanted to get out of the house she was living in, and this was her opportunity to do it. So what if Ben didn't like it. Her survival and now that of her baby, was what mattered most. However, in the back of her mind a disturbing thought gnawed away at her. She wondered what would have happened to their relationship if she hadn't gotten pregnant. Deep in her heart she knew the answer and it was more devastating to her than the situation she was in at present.

She sighed and lifted herself off the bed, walking slowly to the living room where Nan and Jack sat on separate chairs watching television. Clearing her throat, she stopped directly in front of Nan.

"I've got something to tell you." While she talked, Katie twisted her hands tightly together and stared down at them intently, not daring to look at her parents. A spotty, red rash appeared on her neck giving away the fact that she was a nervous wreck.

"I'm going to have a baby." She waited for some reaction, but there was none, so she continued. "Ben's coming home tonight and I have to pick him up so he can tell his parents." Relief flooded through Katie's bones like a soothing balm. It was done; she had told them. Katie lifted her head finally to face Nan and saw the dreaded familiar look on her face. She waited anxiously for some verbal response, anything to break the ice, but Nan looked through Katie with vacant eyes, her face void of expression. Jack sat quietly in his chair, rubbing his chin, and shaking his head.

Katie thought it just couldn't be possible Nan was having a breakdown right before her eyes, but she knew she had been living on the edge for a long time and it wouldn't take much—one event happening at just the right time to send her over the edge.

"I guess I better get going. It's almost time to pick up Ben." As soon as she turned to leave Katie heard her mother's weak voice.

"What are you going to do?"

"I'm not sure yet. Ben is looking into some things at school." Katie turned around to face her parents.

"When is the baby due?" Nan didn't look at Katie as she spoke these words. Her head was turned toward the picture window in the living room as she looked out at nothing, the ever-present cigarette sending out smoke streams across the room.

"In late May, I think." Katie kept her head still and moved only her eyes in the direction where Jack was sitting. His face registered no emotion and Katie felt extremely sad. Their silence dismissed her. When she walked out the door her parents were still sitting in their chairs.

The horrible, gnawing pain in the pit of her stomach was gone now as she waited alone for Ben's train. All the doubts she had still existed, only to be magnified as Ben unenthusiastically walked toward her and planted a short, cold kiss on her lips. She tasted an offensive, metallic odor on his breath when he made contact with her. His mouth was dry and his lips were cracked; it was obvious he was terrified.

"Hi, how is everything?"

"Okay, I guess." Even though she was upset by his aloofness she was glad he had come home. When he got behind the wheel of her car he slipped her hand into his, but there was panic in his expression when he turned to face her.

"You know, I'm so scared. This whole thing really stinks." He jerked his hand from hers as he started up the car. "I'm going to drive you home and take your car to my house. I might need it if my mom and dad throw me out. Did you tell your parents?"

"Yes."

"How did they take it?"

"Okay, I guess. It's hard to tell. Anyway, it doesn't matter." She couldn't help sounding curt.

"I'm glad you think so. Whew! I feel like I'm going to throw up." At that point all of the anger that had been building up inside Katie for months exploded.

"You really think this is the end of the world, don't you Ben? What happened to your optimism? Ever since you found out I was pregnant you haven't given me one reason to believe you are the least bit happy about it. I don't expect you to be jumping up and down. I know it's going to be hard. But do you have any idea how it makes me feel to see you so miserable? I really am sorry about this whole thing; it was obviously a big mistake. I thought you loved me." She stopped speaking and waited for Ben to say something, a positive word or two that would contradict some of what she had just said—but he was quiet and she knew for sure that it was true. He couldn't give her any reassurance at all.

As soon as the car pulled up to her house she reached for the handle of the door and got out quickly, unable to say goodbye. Through the open window she heard him mumble something about calling her in the morning, but she didn't turn around to acknowledge his words.

The house was dark when she let herself in, and Nan and Jack were lying motionless in bed. Jack was snoring. There was no reason why this night should be different from any other night, she thought. The mess she was in was her problem. She tiptoed into the bedroom and fell exhaustedly on the bed without removing her shoes or clothes.

The baby was crying hard, knowing it was in danger. She held it close to her as she looked around for help. She thought it was strange there was no one else in the hospital. A stabbing pain attacked her lower abdomen and liquid trickled down her legs. As she looked back she saw she was leaving a trail of blood as she ran. The blanket around the baby was also soaked with blood.

"Be quiet, be quiet. Please, sweetheart. We can't hide from them if you keep crying." Footsteps echoed through the empty corridor.

"It's them. I told you they would find us if you didn't shut up." Sliding under a table she crouched down on her knees, but the baby continued to make noise giving away their hiding place. Soon Ben's strong arms reached out for her, catching hold of her hair and dragging her out to the middle of the room. Blinded by the bright lights on the ceiling, she tried to forget the pain as the room kept spinning around. She remembered those lights from somewhere...yes, from the night the baby was born...they were the same lights; it was the room the baby was born in.

Katie cried as Ben's mother reached for the naked baby in the blood soaked blanket. She held tight to the baby with all her might. She saw Jack enter the room slowly. He winked at Ben as he said, "Give the baby to Nan; she'll take care of it." As Ben pried the baby from Katie's limp arms he examined it closely. "It looks just like her. I don't want it." Katie lunged at Ben just as he threw the baby to Nan. She began beating furiously on his chest with her fist.

"Give the baby back to me; it doesn't belong to you. Nobody wanted it but me. Why don't you all just leave us alone?" But as Katie stood frozen to the floor in shock, Nan carried the baby over to the huge open window and threw it out, savagely closing the window behind her before she ran out of the room. As Katie fell to the floor and darkness engulfed her, she heard the sounds of clapping and cheering.

It was cold, very cold. As she put her arms around her shoulders, she became aware of someone watching her. Another chill flooded through her as she opened her leaden eyelids again and saw a shadowy figure. Consciousness slowly brought with it the remembrance of all that happened and her icy hand moved slowly down her torso, fearful of what it would find when it reached its final destination. Her stomach was flat. It was true then; they had killed her baby. Darkness again appeared before her as she closed her eyes to shield herself against the pain of reality.

"Katie, Katie...wake up!" Was it the cold that made her shake so? Some outside force was prodding her and she was powerless to stop it. She struggled against the need to keep herself in the dark, halfheartedly parting her eyelids to expose herself to the threat. Instead a familiar face, a friendly figure, loomed before her.

She gagged on her words as her arm reached unsteadily upward. "Barbara, is that you? Help me, please!"

"What's the matter, Katie? You have to get up right now. Mr. and Mrs. O'Riley are on their way over." Groggily Katie watched her twelve-year-old sister excitedly walk around the small room. It was all so confusing. She wondered why they were coming again. It was over after all. She just wanted to be left alone to plan her own demise.

"Come on, Katie, you're going to get in trouble if you don't get up. What's wrong with you anyway? You look terrible." Then, oh so slowly, the pieces came together as she blinked repeatedly to get rid of the film over her eyes that made everything appear hazy. She looked at her clothes. She saw no blood on the baggy, brown dollar shift she had bought the day of Ben's going away party. She was wearing it most every day now as nothing else fit her. She realized then it had just been another ugly dream, albeit a very real one to her. It didn't happen, and disappointment enveloped her as she became aware the ordeal wasn't over. She couldn't die because her baby was still alive. What was next she wondered? What could they do to her now?

She had just enough energy to get herself out of bed and to the bathroom, where she fell against the sink and rested her head on the mirror of the medicine cabinet. She lifted her eyes slowly to see the reflection of sallow skin and dirty hair that belonged to her. She thought she couldn't feel this bad and not have something deadly. Leaning over the toilet bowl she coughed repeatedly, hoping to get rid of the lump in her throat that was making her so queasy her eyes watered and her skin turned beet red. An alarm sounded in her head warning her to lie down, giving her just enough time to make it back to her bed. She curled up on her side trying desperately, but without success, to escape into oblivion. She was aware of activity around her, but attempted to block it out. Muffled voices reached her ear and she hoped they would go away; eventually, however, they intruded.

"Are you going to get up?" It was Nan who appeared at Katie's bedside.

"I can't; I really feel awful!"

"Well, you're going to have to make an effort because a lot of people want to talk to you." Nan's voice was wooden and lacking in sympathy. Without offering to help Katie, Nan departed from the room leaving her alone to cope with a sudden surge of hate that it scared even Katie. Everyone and everything that contributed to make her life the way it was up to this point in time was the object of this animosity. Hostility was evident in her face as she entered the living room a short time later to the piteous stares of the people she now despised. It was Ben's mom who spoke first.

"Katie, you look awful. Are you okay?" Without answering Mrs. O'Riley, Katie took a vacant seat on the couch beside Ben and closed her eyes to the dizziness she suddenly experienced, swaying against the back of the sofa.

"I think she's going to faint, Ben. Do something!" In response to his mother's pronouncement Ben placed his arm around Katie, who immediately rested her head on his shoulder. Round, purple spots danced wildly in front of her eyes as she heard someone mention water. She was sweating but also felt cold as ice. Suddenly everything went black, and her head slid down Ben's chest. When she regained consciousness a few seconds later, clamminess gave way to normal perspiration on her skin as she opened her eyes to accept a sip of liquid from the cup Ben put up to her quivering lips.

"You scared us, Katie. You fainted. Are you okay now?" Again Ben's mom was doing all the talking as she continued on anxiously.

"I guess you all know why we're here?" As the room came back into focus Katie noticed Ben's mom's eyes were red and puffy. It was obvious she had been crying. Katie guessed it was a shock for her. She probably expected much more for her son than Katie, a girl from the other side of the tracks.

"We just want to make sure about everything." With that Katie looked at Ben, who turned his eyes downward so he wouldn't have to return her gaze. Katie squinted in confusion.

"Make sure about everything. What is there to make sure about?" Her voice cracked as she spoke. She felt like there were cotton balls in her mouth.

Mrs. O'Riley glanced at everyone in the room before she focused on Katie. "Well, we want to...have to...make sure you really are pregnant." At this statement Katie's mouth dropped wide open in disbelief. Again she turned to Ben...and again he avoided her.

"If you are pregnant, then we can make decisions about your future." At that Katie jerked her body away from Ben, pushing herself up until she was sitting on the very edge of the couch.

"Make decisions...what decisions? Ben and I have already discussed this. I am pregnant." Her voice quivered noticeably as she repeated herself. "I am pregnant."

"Still we think it will be best if you have a test done." Ben's mom was definitely running the show, and Katie wished someone else would say something. Totally frustrated, Katie threw her hands up in the air.

"I haven't had my period for two months." She looked around, embarrassed to be talking about it in front of the men.

"Yes, I know that, but that could be due to something else." Mrs. O'Riley shifted uncomfortably in her chair and cleared her throat as she spoke. "Isn't that right, Nan?" All eyes shifted to Katie's mom who was sitting on a folding chair, totally immobile except for her right hand which lifted up to her mouth occasionally so she could take a drag of her cigarette.

Katie wanted to scream at them. Couldn't they tell Nan was falling apart? It was obvious she didn't even hear the question. Katie was stunned at her mother's deterioration. It had only taken one lousy day. She couldn't even last one day without going to pieces. Katie knew this one definitely would be considered her fault.

Following a moment of awkward silence, Katie realized no one was going to speak in her defense.

"As I was saying, there could be something else wrong." Ben's mother was persistent. Katie was now positive Ben didn't want to believe it either...that no one wanted it to be true. It was a nightmare and it wasn't one of her dreams; it was really happening. Katie stared at them icily as she contemplated what to say, and mustering all the courage she could she proceeded.

"I would like to know why you are all acting like this is the biggest tragedy that has ever happened?" Once the words were out of her mouth Katie felt like running out of the room, but no one answered her question and more words stumbled from her lips.

"By the way Ben, thanks for your support. Not only am I pregnant with your baby and sick as a dog, but on top of that it's obvious you are just as unhappy about this as everyone else is." Even her sarcastic words couldn't bring Ben to look at her, and barely did she get the last word out of her mouth before she lost her voice. She had felt it coming with the incredible dryness that paralyzed her tongue and lips with each syllable she uttered.

"You're both so young; that's the main thing that worries us." Turning her head as she heard another voice, Katie found herself looking at Ben's father, who was staring at her with the first vestige of compassion she had seen since the meeting began. With his big hands outstretched to her Katie couldn't help but notice the hurt look in his eyes. She realized he probably thought his son's future was ruined. Katie felt as if she was in the room all by herself. She was suddenly defeated, deciding respectfully to let them have their way.

"What do you all have planned for me?" The weak but caustic voice she heard was definitely hers.

Ben's mother eagerly responded to Katie's inquiry. "Well, first we have to make sure you are pregnant. If you're not, the problem is resolved; but if you are, then we have to think of a solution."

"Wait a minute. You might as well start thinking about other solutions because I am pregnant and no test will make it any less true. Ben, say something. What are these other plans your mom is talking about?" Frantically Katie reached for Ben's arm, trying to shake him out of his trance. As she turned hopefully to face Ben, Katie held her breath as her eyes pleaded with him to let his feelings be known.

"Well, if you are pregnant, I think we should get married; but maybe we better be sure that you are because it's going to be very rough on us. I want to stay in college." His monotone voice lacking any emotion or enthusiasm proved to her what she had suspected all along—that he was trying to get out of this mess and away from her. She gave him time to say more, but he didn't.

"Well then, it's all settled." Katie addressed her next comment directly to Ben's mom. "I will go for the test." Turning quickly back to Ben, a feeling of sickness rising in her throat, she sputtered.

"Well, Ben, I guess you can go back to school now. I'm sure your parents will let you know the bad news when it comes. I really don't feel well, so please excuse me." Rising unsteadily from the couch and avoiding all of their faces, she stumbled back to bed wishing with all her heart she had the guts to kill herself right there in front of all of them.

Before work on Monday Katie arrived promptly at the office of the general practitioner recommended by Ben's mom. There Katie had her first gynecological exam. It was even more painful than the intercourse she had with Ben. The doctor had pleaded with Katie to relax so he could examine her properly. As it was he had to pry her legs apart to put them in the stirrups. It was also the first time she had blood drawn, and that made her dizzy as she hadn't eaten anything since the night before. She also left a urine sample with him.

Ben's mother called later that week with the news that the test was negative. "You're not pregnant." Relief was evident in her voice.

"How come I haven't had my period for two months? Why do my breasts hurt so much? Why am I sick all day?"

"There could be something else wrong with you, hon." Katie couldn't help but notice the air of indignation in Ben's mother's voice as if to say *I told you so.*

"I guess you already let Ben know? He must be so happy. So this is the part where everybody gets to forget about the whole thing." After what seemed like hours of silence between them, Katie continued. "I think I'm going to go to the hospital today. If I'm not pregnant, there definitely is something very wrong with me. Before you all start celebrating, maybe you should wait until the new test results come in." She hadn't meant to be so flippant, so disrespectful to her elder, but she was at the breaking point.

"I think that's a good idea. There is something wrong with you and you should find out as soon as possible what it is." With that the conversation ended.

Like an abandoned child Katie desperately needed moral support to get through the ordeal, but there was really no one in her life to give it to her. Since Katie announced her pregnancy Nan appeared on the verge of a breakdown. Her behavior was extremely erratic. Some days she acknowledged Katie's existence but only with conversation unassociated with the problem, and on other days she ignored her completely.

Jack, who didn't talk to anyone unless it was a necessity, remained consistent in his behavior toward Katie. Even under the best of circumstances there was no conversation between her and her father. The few good friends Katie had were lost when she started dating Ben, and it never occurred to her to think of imposing on them just because she was in trouble. True to form she internalized the entire matter in a completely self-destructive way. Ben's family had always been nice to her, but that was before she ruined their son's future. She couldn't really blame them; they only wanted a better life for their son.

A week passed before she received the call she had been waiting for. "Mrs. Ramie? Excuse me, Miss Ramie?"

"Yes, this is she."

"I'm calling with the results of your pregnancy test. It was positive. Also your blood work looks good, but you should begin prenatal care as soon as possible. Good luck to you!" Katie wasn't one bit surprised. Her first reaction was to pick up the phone and call Ben, but she hadn't heard from him since he went back to school after the fiasco of a meeting with their parents. The news would have to wait until he called her; if he ever did. His call came a week later.

"Hi, Katie, how are you?" He sounded far away. She thought she heard a lot of partying noise in the background.

"Most of the time I'm pretty miserable, but that's to be expected I guess."

"My mom told me you didn't believe the test results."

"No, I didn't Ben. I went to the clinic at Northside to have them done again. This time the test came out positive. I got the results in the mail this morning in case anyone would like to have it verified in writing." A period of uncomfortable silence followed Katie's acrid remark.

"Well then, that settles it. I guess I should come home this weekend so we can talk about everything?"

"There really is nothing to talk about!" As much as an addict needs drugs Katie needed reassurance, needed to be convinced of her worth. "I think you made it perfectly clear you would like to forget that I exist." Katie heard a female in the background calling to Ben.

"That's nonsense, Katie. I'm coming home this weekend." After he said goodbye she hung up the phone dejectedly, feeling unwanted and unloved. She thought it served her right for thinking this would be her way out. She should have known it would go the way everything else in her life had gone. How could she have been so stupid as to have thought she was going to find happiness?

That Friday night as she sat on the hardback chair in the small, dark office of the church rectory, Katie tried to keep her thoughts from wandering as the priest spoke.

"You both made a grave mistake. I think you realize that now. Being brought up in the Catholic faith as you both were, I am surprised you didn't consider the teachings of the church in your decision."

Contempt engulfed Katie like a flame as the situation brought back the hateful memories of parochial school. Sister St. Charles' face appeared before her, chastising her for her wrongdoings. It seemed all the religious people she ever knew were happiest when they were in a position of castigating people. Bringing herself back to the present she heard the end of the priest's conversation.

"...and now the situation is complicated further by the fact that a child is on the way." Shaking his head he continued. "The bans of marriage will be announced at mass next weekend and I will schedule the service for the third Saturday in October. In the meantime I would like to see you both again, say next Friday evening?"

"Ah...Father, I really don't think I can make it next Friday." As Ben mumbled a halfhearted objection Katie noticed he seemed as unsettled by this man as she was. "I wasn't planning to come back home until the wedding. The trip from school is four hours and I've missed a lot of classes." Ben began to perspire as he rushed on nervously with the conversation. "I play football and the school pays for my tuition, you know...well, the coach is getting pretty upset with me."

With raised eyebrows the priest glared at Ben, causing him to back down. "I guess I could make it home if you feel it's important. I was just worried about my grades and all."

The man of God tapped his pencil against the appointment book he was writing in and glanced quickly from Katie to Ben, haughtiness emitting from his every movement. "Yes, I think it is very important. Don't you, Ben?"

"Yes, Father." Meekly, Ben lowered his head.

Like a turtle that hides in its shell at impending danger Nan was protecting herself from the impact of Katie's pregnancy by retreating into her other world. She was deteriorating with each passing day and gradually losing control over her life again. This deterioration had started long before Katie's announcement. She had stopped taking her pills months before. Every once in a while she would pop one or two antidepressants when she felt the demons returning; they were now all around her since she found out she was going to be a grandmother.

Meanwhile Katie wallowed in self-pity, rejecting vehemently all attempts by people to help her.

"Hi, Katie, this is your cousin Paula. Listen, mom just told me you were getting married in a couple of weeks and I called to offer you the use of my wedding dress."

"Oh, that's so sweet of you Paula, but I don't think so." She thought she didn't deserve to wear a nice wedding gown after the terrible thing she had done.

Even Ben's mom and dad had rallied once they realized Katie was indeed pregnant and it was inevitable she and Ben would be married, but Katie couldn't appreciate their help because she was too blinded by old wounds, too far gone to forgive and forget.

"You have to decide on what you're going to wear, Katie. It's getting close." Still in shock at the unexpected call, Katie let Ben's mom carry the conversation. "If you want we can look at dresses today."

"No thanks, it's really okay. I have a couple of dresses in my closet I can wear." She wondered why she was lying to her; she didn't have a thing to wear. She didn't even want to think about the wedding.

"No, Katie, I insist. I'll pick you up around noon today. See you then." Before Katie could object, she hung up the phone.

Later as they made their way to the store, Ben's mom inquired. "Has your mom or dad mentioned anything about a reception after the ceremony? Nothing big, maybe just the family?"

"No, they haven't said anything about the wedding at all. I guess there won't be anything. My mom's in real bad shape, and I'm sure she will be in the hospital before the wedding takes place." Hearing Ben's mom gasp, Katie instantly regretted telling her, but she knew she would find out eventually anyway.

"Is she that bad? I had no idea. Well, I guess I'd better start thinking about something. Ben's grandmother will be coming from the city, so I'll arrange for a reception at our house." Katie winced, hating the fact that Ben's parents were making all the preparations for the wedding; it made her feel worse than ever. She wanted them to stop being so nice to her. She didn't deserve it.

Katie's future mother-in-law loved shopping, and her enthusiasm showed as she went through the racks of dresses. "Oh, this is a pretty one, don't you think?" Holding up the off-white knit dress for Katie to see, she pushed her toward the dressing room. "I think this one will be perfect. Let's see if it fits."

As she undressed, she thought it wasn't right that Ben's parents should be buying her wedding dress. She wished her parents were as enthusiastic about the marriage and could afford to help her out. She'd come through for them many times when they were in trouble by watching the children, but where were they when she needed them? A familiar feeling of enmity surged through her as she thought about them.

Alone in the dressing room she looked at herself in the mirror, feeling her slightly swollen belly which had already succeeded in ruining her waistline. For the first time since becoming pregnant Katie thought about the physical thing that was happening to her. A real live human being with limbs and eyes was growing inside her. Shivering from the strange excitement she felt, Katie lifted the dress over her head.

In the car on the way home, morning sickness—actually for Katie it was all day sickness—began to creep up on her as she listened to Ben's mom's enthusiastic conversation. "I think we made a good choice for the dress, don't you?"

"Uh-huh." It was all Katie could say. If she opened her mouth again, she would throw up for sure.

"What time did you say you had to babysit?"

"Gee whiz, I almost forgot…four o'clock. Am I late?"

"No, I'll get you there in plenty of time." She had no doubt she would reach her destination promptly, as Ben's mom was a very speedy driver. Putting her head back on the seat, Katie thought about the babysitting job. She shouldn't have taken it, but she needed the money. She had to start buying things and now she needed a pair of cream shoes to go with her new dress. She had some old black pumps but they wouldn't do. She should have gotten a black dress to go with them—goodness knows it would have been more fitting for the occasion.

The car accelerated as Mrs. O'Riley spoke.

"It's almost four o'clock now, I'd better take you right to your job. You'll have to show me where they live."

But as soon as the O'Riley car turned the corner to Katie's street, she knew something was up. Was that Aunt Madge's car? *No*, she thought. She must be imagining things. But what were all those cars doing in front of the house where she was supposed to be babysitting? *Oh, God, no*, she thought. *I hope they didn't plan anything for me.* But when Candy Lalor opened the door to reveal a room full of her friends and relatives, she was indeed shocked. Flustered she let the hostess lead her to a chair that was set up specifically for her in the middle of the room.

As she joined the group, her arms pumping with excitement, Mrs. O'Riley threw Katie a devious grin. "How did I do? You didn't suspect anything, did you?"

"No, not until I saw all of the cars. I can't believe you did this for me. Thank you so much." She wished she could cry for them. She knew people liked to see tears; it seemed like you appreciated things more if you cried. But she couldn't.

There were so many gifts to open that her face hurt from smiling in acknowledgement of them—a toaster, blender, pots and pans, dishes, silverware, lingerie sets including a beautiful white silk number for her wedding night, and dozens of other household items. She needed them all.

The gift from Ben's parent's was the most generous of all. They gave them a stereo system. Katie grinned widely at Ben's mom, wishing her own mother was more like her.

Searching the faces in the crowded room Katie realized what her heart already told her—Nan was not there. The stereo was the last gift she opened, and she was painfully aware she had not received a gift from her parents. Embarrassed by all the fuss and with a huge lump in her throat, Katie made a sincere effort to thank everyone.

"I really don't deserve this beautiful shower. You're all so kind, and I thank you from the bottom of my heart. It's just too much!"

After refreshments were served the party broke up, and Jonathan was summoned to help Katie carry her treasures home. On the way back he confided in her.

"Mom's having another nervous breakdown." Jonathan's statement was made with the utmost confidence. "I'll tell you, she almost botched up your party. If it was up to her, she would have invited the whole world and then forgot the date and time. I swear you're so lucky Candy and Ann took over. They know what she's like. It sure would have been embarrassing having all those people show up and her not ready for them. Why, she couldn't even boil water to make a cup of tea today."

"You mean it was mom's idea to have the shower."

"Well, I guess you could say she started the idea."

"I don't believe it." It was all so confusing. She didn't get it, but then she never had. She prayed to God for help even though she knew she didn't deserve it.

"Is dad home, Jonathan?"

"Are you kidding? As usual he left for work when it was time; didn't say a thing to any of us. Barbara and I spent all day in the house making sure she didn't do anything...you know!"

"I guess she will be in the hospital before I get married?"

"You better hope so, Katie, or else it's going to be a real mess."

She breathed a sigh of relief when she saw Nan sleeping on the couch and went into the bedroom where Jonathan had placed all her gifts, shoving them under her bed and Carrie's crib. She then went out into the kitchen to relieve Jonathan and Barbara and began preparing dinner for everyone. The kids were restless from being in the house all day, and it was after nine before she got them settled down and into bed.

Nan slept until about eight that night. After she woke up Katie made her a cup of tea and a grilled cheese sandwich, and Nan sat quietly at the table for hours smoking and nibbling at her food. She was definitely in the depressed stage of her illness. Katie knew this was the calm before the storm. Soon the mania would start...and the voices, too. When she heard the lock turn in the front door around midnight, Katie left her mother's side where she had been sitting for hours. No words passed between Katie and her father. She collapsed on her bed deep in thought about what was happening to her life. After what seemed like hours she fell into a restless sleep.

The next morning she got up for work and slipped quietly out of the house. Jack was sleeping beside Nan. She couldn't worry about them; they were going to have to take care of themselves this time. She wasn't well herself. She prayed nothing would happen to the kids.

As she drove to work Katie wondered how long Nan's catatonic behavior would last this time. However, it was really her own feelings that worried her more than anything else as she was sinking lower and lower. Life just didn't seem to be worth the effort. It was always one problem after another. Then there was that dream she was repeatedly having.

"Here she is, Mrs. O'Riley. Isn't she beautiful? You can have her for a half hour. Here's her bottle. Take good care of her." As soon as the nurse left the room the baby bottle in Katie's hand began to shake violently as she held her baby. Her little girl looked exactly like her dead brother Kevin. She shocked Katie when she opened her tiny mouth to talk.

"Why didn't you help me, Katie? I called to you. Why did you run away from me?" The baby cried and turned away from Katie in disgust.

She couldn't take it anymore. She got up from the bed and slowly and calmly walked over to the window in the hospital room, opening it up with her free hand. She released her arm from around the baby and it slid down along her skin, but no matter how hard Katie tried to shake the baby from her arm she couldn't get rid of it…it stuck to her like glue.

She actually broke out in a cold sweat as she reminisced about the horrible dream. She was more and more convinced she had seen Nan lift Kevin and carry him toward the window and that she might have even ignored his pleas for help while she ran for her own life. Since becoming pregnant herself she also thought more about the possibility that she was capable of the same deadly behavior as her mother. Dwelling on it constantly only caused the ugly nightmare to occur more frequently. Now Katie worried she could do the same thing to her precious baby that her mother had done to Kevin and Marty. The thought was destroying what little sanity she had left.

Because she was emotionally and physically exhausted, Katie found it difficult to keep up with her work, and confided her pregnancy to her supervisor who was glad to hear there was a legitimate reason for her decreased productivity.

"You're a very efficient and hard-working person, Katie, and I'm sure as soon as the morning sickness goes away you will return to your normal self. I hope you will come back to work for us after the baby is born. We would hate to lose you!"

She honestly didn't know what was going to happen to her at this point. She hoped she wouldn't have to disappoint her boss. She felt bad about hurting so many people already. Also, because of all the stress her face broke out with acne and she had a permanent rash on her neck.

After work she forced her lifeless body into the car and with mounting desolation began the journey home. *If only things were different*, she thought.

She had to face it...nothing was going to change. No one really cared about her. She was now positive that no one ever did. As long as she was a good girl and kept up her grades, watched the kids, didn't complain, didn't cause any trouble then everything was okay. But now that she was in trouble, they didn't want to be bothered with her. She realized she was losing control and she was frightened, diverting her attention to her surroundings. Her thoughts were disjointed.

The neighborhood was getting so run down. Why hadn't Ben called her? He wanted to back out, she was sure of it. He hadn't really asked her to marry him and hadn't said he loved her since well before she got pregnant. She was glad she didn't have to walk the streets of her neighborhood anymore. Or maybe that's exactly what she should do—it might be a good way to end it all. She wondered if Ben would even show up at the ceremony. She felt so sorry for the kids. Poor Barbara and Jonathan, they were going through the same thing she went through...and Amy, George, Sammy, and Carrie—she wondered what was in store for them. She gritted her teeth at the anger she felt from deep within her gut as she recalled running frantically along the dark streets by herself.

Katie parked the car in front of the house. She had to stop this, had to calm down, couldn't go on like this...it was driving her crazy.

Before she even opened the car door she could sense it. There was something about the unnatural stillness around the house. Of course she had been wrong before—many times—when she got off the school bus on a gray day just like this one to the eerie quietness, waiting at the front door for a long time before getting the courage to open it. She prayed she was mistaken this time also. She needed to be wrong because she knew it wasn't like those other times when she was able to remain outside herself—always removed, always in control.

"My God, what happened in here?" Her body was frozen at the front door as she whimpered to herself. "What happened? What happened to my stuff?"

It caught her eye first—the white negligee lying in a heap in the middle of the room. She tripped over the broken toaster in her path as she collapsed on the floor next to her cherished gown. She slid her doddering hands under the bundle and picked up the remains of the once beautiful article of clothing. It had been torn and cut into hundreds of small pieces. Even the lace trim had been ripped from the severed sleeves and collar and shredded into nothingness.

"Who could have done this?" Shaking her head in disbelief, her eyes focused on the rest of the room. Catching the light from the living room window, the toaster flashed its dented frame for Katie's tired eyes to see. It must have been thrown or stepped on. Little bits of fabric from the other negligees were scattered throughout the ruins of her kitchen utensils, broken plates, dented pots and pans, bent silverware, torn tablecloths and sheets, and the badly cracked blender. Appalled, Katie reached for the electric can opener her godmother had given to her. It looked as if it had escaped the massacre until she examined it more closely. The cord had been severed.

She was now too numb to deal with any more of the destruction and avoided looking into the stereo box which was perched awkwardly on the arm of the living room couch. She was still holding the can opener when she walked into the kitchen to find Jack and Nan sitting placidly at the table. While Jack stirred his coffee nervously, his chin resting on his chest, Nan sat with her back to Katie.

They knew she was in the kitchen, and she knew they weren't going to say anything. Katie began to talk, nervously at first.

"I don't know why this was done to my stuff, but I'll never forgive you for this. I haven't done anything to deserve this kind of treatment." With a sudden surge of mettle she continued.

"You know, living with you both has been hell. Do you even realize that? And you!" She pointed her finger at Jack. "You haven't helped me one time in my whole life either by your words or actions. You're like a …a nothing!"

He didn't react.

"And you!" She turned her accusing finger to her mother, moving across the room so Nan could see her clearly. "Why, you're a weak, selfish person who gets sick every time something goes wrong. Do you know what you two are together? You're the lousiest excuse for parents that ever walked the face of the earth. Thanks for the going-away present. I really didn't expect much more from the both of you than this!" Katie stomped out of the room, but not before she threw the can opener across the kitchen floor.

Once inside the bedroom Katie received much needed consolation from Barbara, who had been eavesdropping on the one-sided conversation. "Honestly, Katie, I tried to stop her but she was like a wild animal. Dad should have brought her to the hospital days ago. Instead he just stood there watching her. I'm so sorry, Katie. It isn't fair." She reached into her bureau drawer and pulled out two white tea towels, handing them proudly to Katie. "Here, I hid these for you so she couldn't destroy them."

"Thank you, Barbara." Katie hugged her beaming little sister briefly and covered her face with the tea towels as she sat on the bed, her head pounding, thinking about everything for a long time. She eventually threw herself across the bed and drifted off to sleep, but before she did, she decided there was only one solution to her problems.

Sometime later Katie bolted upright in bed with a feeling of being trapped. When she realized it was the middle of the night, she didn't think she could possibly go back to sleep with everything going on inside her. There was so much confusion. She was certain Ben didn't want to marry her. He might go through with it, but only out of duress. She couldn't stay with Nan and Jack another day, not after what happened with her shower gifts. She had to do it; it was the only way out.

She began rocking back and forth in the dark room as if in a trance, repeating the phrase over and over to herself...she had to do it; it was the only way out. Suddenly the tenseness left her body, and she was exhausted. She returned to a reclining position on the bed. This time a feeling of warmth surged through her as she fell into unconsciousness.

Katie rubbed at her eyes to rid them of the haziness that hung over everything. She stretched fiercely and turned quickly away to avoid the face that loomed in front of her. The lips on the face were moving but the words were garbled. So acute was the weight in her limbs that it was all she could do to lift her body off of the bed. She could only think of one thing.

Moving statue-like from the bedroom, she noticed as she left it three, maybe four, fuzzy figures watching her departure. Through the dense fog she mechanically found the bathroom, and after closing the door leaned her stiff body against the wall, using it as a brace to slide down to the floor. She remained in a crouched position with her head against her knees until someone knocked on the door.

"Come on, Katie. Are you going to take all day in there? I have to get ready for school." Jonathan lowered his voice as he continued. "You better come out, now. Mom's acting real strange again this morning and everyone's scared."

But the words he uttered didn't make any sense to his sister. She didn't hear his pleas at all. She was focused on a single thing, and her mind couldn't comprehend anything else that was going on around her. Motivated by only one thought, she lifted her body from the floor and splashed some water on her face. She caught a glimpse of herself in the mirror, stared for a moment in amazement, and then quickly turned away unable to take a second look. Something she saw in the reflection frightened her to death—it was her eyes.

When she departed from the bathroom she was vaguely aware of the obscurity of everything around her, but it didn't upset her anymore. Dim figures in her path seemed to quickly disappear, and she heard the faint sound of a cry coming from the distance. The bedroom door slammed fiercely behind her and she jumped, startled at the unexpected noise, not realizing she had made it herself.

Grabbing pugnaciously at the few things that belonged to her in the small, crowded closet, she soon became exasperated in her search for one thing in particular, throwing all the clothes she had in her hand on the floor and kicking at them violently as if obsessed. Moving quickly to the dresser drawer she flung it open and snatched up all of the contents, tossing them wildly on the bed until a familiar pattern caught her eye. Folded almost to handkerchief size was the sleeveless plaid shift she was looking for, the one she had planned to wear to Ben's party.

She slipped quickly into the dress, tying the sash much too tightly around her swollen waist. She ignored the mess she had made in the room as she searched turbulently for her pocketbook, forgetting it was in its usual hiding place behind the bureau. The frayed black strap finally caught her eye, and after she slipped into a pair of old, black shoes she was satisfied that she was ready to go. She was no longer tense, unhappy or frightened because her plan, the one that would end her grief, encompassed her mind and body.

When she entered the hallway she caught sight of the boy's bedroom door closing rapidly, but things seemed clearer now and she felt very much in control. Katie walked hastily to the kitchen where Nan was sitting at the table smoking a cigarette and picking at the ashes which fell on the plastic table cloth. Katie reached for a glass and filled it with water, gulping the whole thing down quickly. She avoided looking at her mother as she spoke.

"Do you want to go for a ride?" A pain shot through Katie's chest causing her to hyperventilate as she waited for an answer, because everything depended on getting her mother out of the house. Still avoiding Nan's face Katie breathlessly continued. "Maybe we could go see Aunt Bev?" Katie crossed her fingers as she waited for Nan's response.

In squeaky syllables that made Katie flinch Nan finally spoke. "That would be nice. I've been trying to get her on the phone. The Blessed Mother asked me to give her a message."

"Okay, I'll take you there. Hurry up and get ready." As a wave of nausea overcame her, Katie backed into one of the kitchen chairs.

Ignoring her daughter's clumsiness Nan sluggishly got up from the table, but stopped abruptly when she was almost out of the kitchen and turned to Katie, looking confused as she talked. "But we'll never get to California in your car. Everyone says you're lucky to make it down the block in that thing!"

"No, I didn't say Aunt Wanda...I said Aunt Bev. Remember she lives in the city." Katie had to get her mother to her sister's apartment in the city; it was a critical part of the plan. "It won't take long to get there."

"Okay, but I will need to call Wanda from Bev's house because I have to get that message to her today or the Blessed Mother will be very upset with me." As she stared directly into Katie's face Nan's grin disappeared, and her hand went immediately to her throat clutching it tightly. For a split second, a feeling so terrifying, so alarming, passed between the two of them as they exchanged glances, that it caused them both to back away from each other in disoriented movements.

When she was alone in the kitchen waiting for Nan to get ready for their trip, Katie concentrated anxiously on the plan. The ending was clear, but that was all. Dumbfounded she leaned her weary head on her hands as she tried in frustration to fill in the missing links. The house was deathly quiet.

Inside the small bedroom six children huddled in fright. The two older ones were keeping the younger ones silent. Their usual protector against the evil that loomed when Nan was ill was Katie, but on this particular morning they were keenly aware something was very different. There were two ene-mies roaming the house, and they knew they had to avoid contact with either one of them. Their dad had long since left for his own refuge, having agreed to work another double shift.

Back in the kitchen Katie stealthily opened the cutlery drawer and with-drew the implement she needed, shoving it precariously into the pocket of her shift. When Nan appeared at the entrance to the kitchen eager to start their journey, Katie was so deep in thought she was unaware of her mother's return.

"I'm ready to go now." At the sound of Nan's shrill voice Katie bolted quickly from her place by the drawer.

As both women left the house, a multitude of little heads appeared at the living room window anxiously watching their departure.

When she was settled behind the wheel of her car, Katie shook her head in a vain attempt to clear it of that solitary thought. In her mind a dozen roads crossed over each other and led to a big apartment building, a place she had only been to a few times before. Hundreds of open windows appeared before her eyes.

Still in a stupor Katie silently stared ahead, concentrating hard on the hazy objects on the road and following the bright green signs to New York City. In the midtown tunnel a feeling of panic gripped at her when she could-n't see the opening, couldn't see any light. She didn't want to be trapped in a tunnel. She had to get to that building or her plan would fail. The sight of so much concrete made her feel hemmed in, claustrophobic, and her hands turned chalk white as they tightened around the wheel. But minutes later a wide, evil smile crossed her face as the car emerged noisily from the tunnel.

Once dumped into the city Katie winged her way through the maze of urban roads like a homing pigeon, looking for landmarks that would bring her closer to that all-important building. The streets were busy with activity, and Katie fought hard to maintain control over the blurred vision which plagued her.

As she approached a familiar intersection the structure she was searching for loomed large before her, looking dirty in the grayness of the city streets. The light turned red, and she impatiently stopped the car to let hordes of people cross to the other side. They all seemed to be walking in slow motion. Katie closed her eyes, feeling helpless against the tricks her senses were play-ing on her. She decided she couldn't go through with the plan; it wasn't going to work. But just as quickly changed her mind...she had to do it. It would be the best thing for everyone.

Nan sat quietly beside Katie contemplating all the things she had to say to her sister. She was on pins and needles at the thought of the visit. Leaning her head back against the car seat she breathed a sigh of relief, knowing it wouldn't be long before she had someone to talk to, someone who would really listen to her.

It was sheer luck that allowed Katie to find a parking space directly across from her aunt's apartment, for she couldn't have driven another block. As she attempted to parallel park, she misjudged the room available and scraped the side of the automobile in front of her with the fender of her car as she pulled into the space. A passerby shouted to Katie, but she didn't hear him or realize what she had done. She was sweating profusely even though it was a cool October day. She wished it was over. She was sure when it was done that everything would be great. She chastised herself for not thinking of it sooner before everything got out of control.

As they climbed the stairs to Bev's apartment Katie carefully checked the surroundings, her senses keenly honed to the abnormal preoccupation of her brain. An undercover agent couldn't have taken in all of the things Katie saw while walking up the five flights of stairs. She memorized the placement of every window and door on each level, the number of apartments, the color of the walls, and the number of steps. Her eyes were in constant motion taking it all in, and everything was now vividly clear. The fog had lifted.

When they knocked on Bev's door she answered it with annoyed surprise. "You should have called me, Nan. What the hell are you doing here?" Even in her inebriated state Bev could tell there was something wrong with her sister.

"Oh, oh. I see we have a little problem here again." At first hesitating and then with much trepidation Bev reluctantly let her sister and niece into the apartment. As she staggered down the hall to her living room she said a quick prayer to the Almighty to keep her safe.

Nan was completely oblivious of the fact that her sister was drunk. She was immersed in her own selfish thoughts.

When they were settled in the living room Bev slurred her words as she asked her guests if they wanted a drink. She didn't wait for an answer as she stumbled across the room, tripping over a magazine rack to get to a table where several bottles of liquor sat.

"I was just getting ready to pour myself one. You know what they say— one a day is good for you. My, you girls sure surprised me. I hate surprises you know." As she turned to face her niece for the first time the glass Bev was holding in her hand dropped to the floor, smashing into a hundred little pieces.

"Good God, Katie, you look terrible. Are you okay? What the hell is going on with you two?" Ignoring the dangerous fragments at her feet, Bev reached for another glass. She really needed a drink badly.

Nan was totally oblivious of the scene taking place before her as she embarked on an animated conversation with her sister. "Bev, I have always done my best to be a good wife and mother and you know how hard that is. You understand, don't you? Jack doesn't talk to me at all and I'm convinced he's the reason why I'm so unhappy, but I'm not going to let him do it to me again. Do you know who I talked to last night?"

Again she continued on without waiting for answers to her questions...she really didn't care about them anyway. "I talked to the Blessed Mother. She told me I had nothing to worry about, and I would soon be going on a trip. I know exactly what she meant. That's why I have to call Wanda to make the arrangements as soon as possible. I'm so...."

With a wave of her hand Bev cut Nan off. The liquored state she was in gave her the boldness to stop her sister's haranguing in midstream. She couldn't recall how many times she had been awakened in the middle of the night to hear Nan whining on the other end of the line about the injustices in her life. Many times she wanted to slam the phone down in her ear, but chickened out because of the guilt she would most surely feel. In her mind her sister was a spoiled woman who was lucky her husband hadn't divorced her the first time she was declared legally insane. Many guys, including Bev's own husband, walked away from their wives and children with a lot less provocation than Jack had. Now Bev sensed there was something more seriously wrong here than just another one of Nan's pain-in-the-ass nervous breakdowns.

"Katie, Katie...yoo-hoo. Can you hear me?" Even shouting at the top of her lungs Bev couldn't seem to get her attention, and so she turned to Nan.

"What's going on here? You seem to be the one with the big mouth. What's wrong with Katie?" Nan lifted her shoulders in an exaggerated shrug as she scanned Katie, but quickly deflected her gaze back to Bev as she spoke.

"I needed to get out of the house. Jack is always working. He never has the time to take me anywhere. I really don't know what I'm going to do about...."

"How the hell she drove here is beyond me!" Bev continued to stare in awe at Katie, ignoring Nan's senseless chatter. "She looks catatonic!" Bev was becoming more and more uncomfortable by the minute, and she nervously gulped down her drink as she tried to think of a way to get them out of her apartment.

"Katie's been very bad. She's part of my problem. She's pregnant. I had to punish her. She knows she didn't really deserve those gifts."

Feeling like she was at the movies watching a horror show, Bev listened in stunned silence to Nan's revelations. She got up again and grabbed a bottle of booze filling her empty glass to the brim with whiskey, but when she turned to go back to her seat and glanced at Katie once again it was as if she was seeing a completely different person than the one who looked comatose just minutes before.

"Don't worry, I won't be a problem to you much longer." Katie stared directly at Nan as she spoke haltingly. She was wearing a macabre smile on her once emotionless face.

It was at that point Bev decided she had to get rid of them both. She knew some of the crazy things Nan did during her breakdowns, and she didn't want to get involved with any of it. Why, she already felt goofy enough herself, and they had only been in the house for a few minutes. It didn't surprise her at all that Katie looked so out of it after living with Nan for all those years. She felt sorry for Jack and the kids, but she felt sorrier for herself at that moment.

"Oh, by the way Bev, I want you to be the first to know. I'm pregnant again." Staring directly at Katie as she announced her news, Nan smiled viciously. It was difficult to gage if she was actually telling the truth.

"Jesus Christ, Nan. How could you let that happen again? You know what having a baby does to you, and Carrie is at a good age now. What is she, three or four?" Bev was beyond being polite and said what was on her mind, but her insolence fell on deaf ears.

Katie sat motionless on her aunt's uncomfortable chair completely dumbstruck after her mother's pronouncement. She was seven years old again and back in the kitchen of that dreadful apartment so far up from the ground, the one they lived in after the big reunion.

"Mommy's pregnant. Mommy's pregnant." She was a pathetic figure skipping around the living room as she continued to sing. "Mommy's going to have a baby to throw out the window. Mommy is a murderer. Mommy is a murderer."

Horror struck, Bev watched the scene unfolding in front of her. She lumbered from her chair and caught Katie by the hand, leading her to the door. Katie wondered who the person with the big face was. Her mouth was huge, and she could see all the way down to her throat. Where was she taking her?

"Nan, come on. Katie needs help. You must leave and go home right now." Reluctantly Nan walked slowly out the door, joining Katie in the hall. Bev started to close her door even before Nan was totally out of the apartment, and as she ran back to her bottle of booze, she felt only relief at having succeeded in getting them out of the house. They were both nuts, and she didn't feel it was her responsibility to deal with them. How they managed was of no concern to her. She gulped down another drink in short order.

The big-faced lady was gone. A door slammed hard and Katie backed into the wall. As beads of perspiration formed on her forehead again she studied the familiar hallway. She thought she was alone and trembled violently. "No, no, that's not the plan. No, no." Her agonized cries echoed through the building.

"Katie, Katie." From somewhere out of her line of vision came her mother's voice. "I want to go home. Please take me home."

As Katie's eyes made contact with her mother standing at the top of the stairs, she was suddenly ecstatic. Nan began to cry, false, weeping noises which reminded Katie of all the hateful times she had forced herself to comfort her with lies, words said in desperation to appease the monster. Katie was feeling very tranquil now as she shouted to Nan.

"How many times did you comfort me, bitch? Where were you when I needed help growing up?" Katie's life appeared before her like a well orchestrated slide show and she could see it all clearly now—the reasons for her unhappiness, for every dark day in her life—but no more. As she approached the pitiful, sobbing creature standing across from her, Katie suddenly felt like she was in the funhouse at an amusement park. Nan's distorted face appeared before her alternatively changing from wide to long, like a piece of elastic.

"Mommy's pregnant. Mommy's having a baby to kill. Mommy's...." Katie chanted. But all other thoughts were erased from her memory when she saw something that made her realize everything was now right for the culmination of her plan. She stopped tormenting Nan as quickly as she had started.

Nan avoided the gaze of her oldest child as she backed down the steps one at a time holding the banister with both hands. Afraid, disoriented, and confused, she cried out. "They will be coming for me soon. They always come to help me, to give me a shot. Where are they?" She was on the verge of hysteria and actually began shedding genuine tears. "Help me, help me. I'm not strong. I'm not to blame. He is. If it wasn't for him everything would be okay."

It wasn't as difficult as Katie thought it would be.

In a state of panic, Nan removed both of her hands from the railing to protect herself against Katie as she inched closer to her. She tripped down the last step of the fourth floor landing, stumbling wildly toward the open window. In a flash Katie was on top of her, placing both of her hands across Nan's heaving chest and administering a firm push. It was just what was needed to send Nan tumbling over the ledge into the alley below.

She stood motionless against the window. She didn't look out. She knew what was down there. She had seen it a thousand times before. She hummed to herself in relieved happiness, a huge smile erupting on her face. In the background the sounds of sirens drew closer, reminding her of the day they came to her rescue so many years ago.

Her smile faded slowly when she remembered there was something else she had to do. Groping in her pocket until she felt the sharpness of the object she sought, Katie pulled out the familiar knife and held it close to her. "My friend, you thought I'd forgotten you...now you're going to help me get rid of all my problems forever." As she clumsily continued to finger the knife, Katie was unaware she had run out of time. The big boots caught her eyes first—black and very familiar-looking. She had seen them before a long time ago in reality, and many, many times in her dreams.

"Give me the knife, sweetheart. You're cut." He was huge, this man kneeling before her.

"Oh, no, you can't have this...I need it. You don't understand. I'm not finished with it." She held on tightly; blood was now flowing from her hands. Suddenly she was slapped across the face, just like she was so long ago by the evil grandmother. The assault jarred her and allowed the perpetrator to confiscate the knife.

"Sorry, little lady. I had to do that for your own good." But as she snuggled against him breathing in the smell of leather, she felt safe. He was taking her away from the evil in the house. Just before he left the building with Katie in his arms, a police officer stopped him.

"The woman in the alley is dead; looks like a fall. What about her?'

Shrugging, the burly man shifted the bundle in his arms. "I don't know. Other than a few cuts on her hand, she seems fine."

And with that he carried her out into the world where she was free to be insane.